D0494223

Edexcel A2 Biology

Ann Fullick

STUDENTS' BOOK

This book also includes

Active Book

A PEARSON COMPANY

CONTENTS

Unit 4 The natural environment and species survival

TOPIC 5
On the wild side

TOPIC 6
Infection, immunity and forensics

Ayaan Jaber
YR 13 – Ayesha
community education

Unit 5 Exercise, energy and coordination

TOPIC 7
Run for your life

TOPIC 8
Grey matter

How to use this book

This book contains a number of great features that will help you find your way around your A2 Biology course and support your learning.

Introductory pages

Each topic has two introductory pages to help you identify how the main text is arranged to cover all that you need to learn. The left-hand page gives a brief summary of the topic, linking the content to three key areas of How Science Works: *What are the theories? What is the evidence? What are the implications?*

The right-hand page of the introduction consists of a topic map that shows you how all the required content of the Edexcel specification for that topic is covered in the chapters, and how that content all interlinks. Links to other topics are also shown, including where previous knowledge is built on within the topic.

Main text

The main part of the book covers all you need to learn for your course. The text is supported by many diagrams and photographs that will help you understand the concepts you need to learn.

Key terms in the text are shown in bold type. These terms are defined in the interactive glossary that can be found on the ActiveBooK CD-ROM using the Glossary tab.

Introductory pages

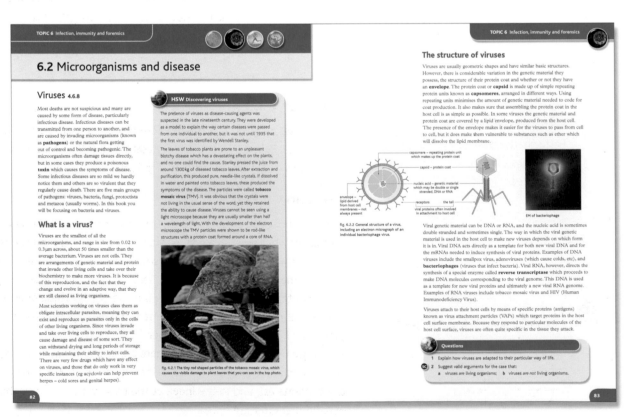

Main text

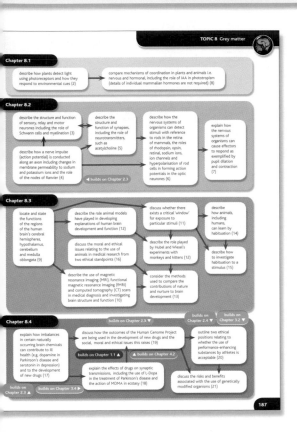

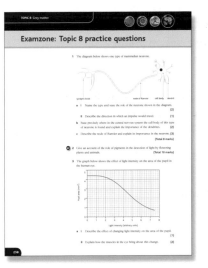

Examzone page

Examzone pages

At the end of each topic you will find two pages of exam questions from past papers. You can use these questions to test how fully you have understood the topic, as well as to help you practise for your exams.

HSW boxes

How Science Works is a key feature of your course. The many HSW boxes within the text will help you cover all the new aspects of How Science Works that you need. These include how scientists investigate ideas and develop theories, how to evaluate data and the design of studies to test their validity and reliability, and how science affects the real world including informing decisions that need to be taken by individuals and society.

Practical boxes

Your course contains a number of core practicals that you may be tested on. These boxes indicate links to core practical work. Your teacher will give you opportunities to cover these investigations.

Question boxes

At the end of each section of text you will find a box containing questions that cover what you have just learnt. You can use these questions to help you check whether you have understood what you have just read, and whether there is anything that you need to look at again. Some question boxes contain stretch and challenge questions **SC**. These questions help you practise different types of assessment and offer opportunities to link what you know from other topics together.

The contents list shows you that there are two units and four topics in the book, matching the Edexcel A2 specification for biology. Page numbering in the contents list, and in the index at the back of the book, will help you find what you are looking for.

How to use your ActiveBook

The ActiveBook is an electronic copy of the book, which you can use on a compatible computer. The CD-ROM will only play while the disc is in the computer. The ActiveBook has these features:

Find Resources

Click on this tab to see menus which list all the electronic files on the ActiveBook.

Student Book tab

Click this tab at the top of the screen to access the electronic version of the book.

Interactive view

Click this button to see all the icons on the page that link to electronic files, such as documents and spreadsheets. You have access to all of the features that are useful for you to use at home on your own. If you don't want to see these links you can return to **Book view**.

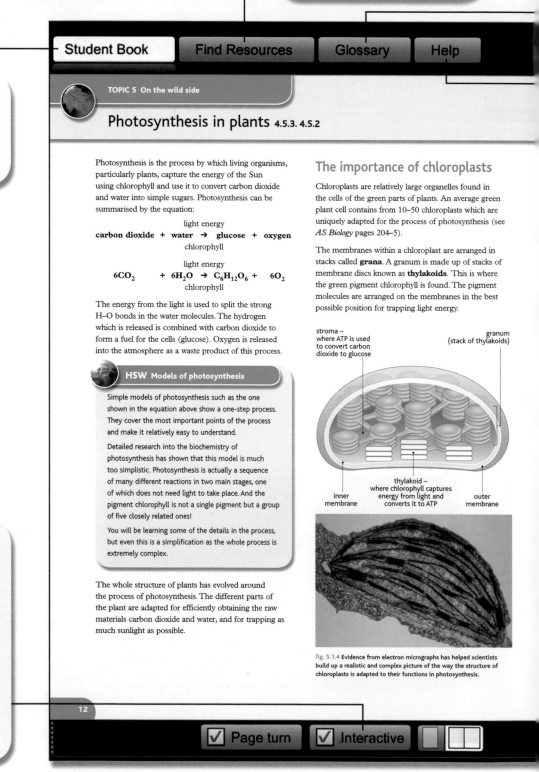

| Student Book | Find Resources | Glossary | Help |

TOPIC 5 On the wild side

Photosynthesis in plants 4.5.3, 4.5.2

Photosynthesis is the process by which living organisms, particularly plants, capture the energy of the Sun using chlorophyll and use it to convert carbon dioxide and water into simple sugars. Photosynthesis can be summarised by the equation:

$$\textbf{carbon dioxide} + \textbf{water} \xrightarrow[\text{chlorophyll}]{\text{light energy}} \textbf{glucose} + \textbf{oxygen}$$

$$6CO_2 + 6H_2O \xrightarrow[\text{chlorophyll}]{\text{light energy}} C_6H_{12}O_6 + 6O_2$$

The energy from the light is used to split the strong H–O bonds in the water molecules. The hydrogen which is released is combined with carbon dioxide to form a fuel for the cells (glucose). Oxygen is released into the atmosphere as a waste product of this process.

HSW Models of photosynthesis

Simple models of photosynthesis such as the one shown in the equation above show a one-step process. They cover the most important points of the process and make it relatively easy to understand.

Detailed research into the biochemistry of photosynthesis has shown that this model is much too simplistic. Photosynthesis is actually a sequence of many different reactions in two main stages, one of which does not need light to take place. And the pigment chlorophyll is not a single pigment but a group of five closely related ones!

You will be learning some of the details in the process, but even this is a simplification as the whole process is extremely complex.

The whole structure of plants has evolved around the process of photosynthesis. The different parts of the plant are adapted for efficiently obtaining the raw materials carbon dioxide and water, and for trapping as much sunlight as possible.

The importance of chloroplasts

Chloroplasts are relatively large organelles found in the cells of the green parts of plants. An average green plant cell contains from 10–50 chloroplasts which are uniquely adapted for the process of photosynthesis (see *AS Biology* pages 204–5).

The membranes within a chloroplast are arranged in stacks called **grana**. A granum is made up of stacks of membrane discs known as **thylakoids**. This is where the green pigment chlorophyll is found. The pigment molecules are arranged on the membranes in the best possible position for trapping light energy.

stroma – where ATP is used to convert carbon dioxide to glucose

granum (stack of thylakoids)

thylakoid – where chlorophyll captures energy from light and converts it to ATP

inner membrane

outer membrane

fig. 5.1.4 Evidence from electron micrographs has helped scientists build up a realistic and complex picture of the way the structure of chloroplasts is adapted to their functions in photosynthesis.

✓ Page turn   ✓ Interactive

Glossary

Click this tab to see all of the key words and what they mean. Click 'play' to listen to someone read them out to help you pronounce them.

Help

Click on this tab at any time to search for help on how to use the ActiveBook.

Evidence from electron micrographs also shows that the granal membranes are covered in particles which seem to be involved in ATP synthesis (see page 139).

These membrane stacks are surrounded by a matrix called the **stroma**. The stroma contains all the enzymes needed to complete the process of photosynthesis and produce glucose. This can then be used in cellular respiration, converted to starch for storage or used as an intermediate for the synthesis of other organic compounds such as amino acids and lipids.

Chlorophyll

The other major adaptation of the chloroplasts is the light-capturing, photosynthetic pigment chlorophyll. 'Chlorophyll' is actually a group of five closely related pigments. These include **chlorophyll *a*** (blue-green), **chlorophyll *b*** (yellow-green), the **carotenoids** (orange carotene and yellow xanthophyll) along with a grey pigment phaeophytin which is a breakdown product of the others. Chlorophyll *a* is found in all photosynthesing plants and is the most abundant of the five. The other pigments are found in varying proportions, and it is these differences which give the leaves of plants their almost infinite variety of shades of green.

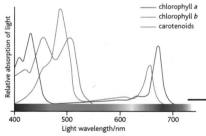

fig. 5.1.5 **The different photosynthetic pigments absorb light and capture its energy at a variety of different wavelengths, making more of the light available for use by the plant.**

Each of the pigments absorbs and captures light from particular areas of the spectrum. As a result, far more of the energy from the light falling on the plant can be used than if only one pigment was involved.

HSW Simple evidence for the different photosynthetic pigments

Plants look green. If you extract the pigments from a plant by grinding up leaves with acetone and filtering, the filtrate looks green. So how can you show that there are five different pigments? The answer is paper chromatography. With a suitable solvent the pigments travel up the paper at different speeds and are readily separated.

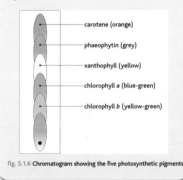

carotene (orange)

phaeophytin (grey)

xanthophyll (yellow)

chlorophyll *a* (blue-green)

chlorophyll *b* (yellow-green)

fig. 5.1.6 **Chromatogram showing the five photosynthetic pigments.**

There are two distinct chlorophyll complexes known as **photosystem I** (**PSI**) and **photosystem II** (**PSII**). Each system contains a different combination of chlorophyll pigments and so absorbs light in a slightly different area of the spectrum (wavelength 700 nm for PSI and 680 nm for PSII). The different photosystems have been identified as different-sized particles attached to the membranes in the chloroplasts in electron micrographs. PSI particles are mainly on the intergranal lamellae, while PSII particles are on the grana themselves. They have different functions in photosynthesis as you will see.

Key words

Click on any of the words in **bold** to see a box with the word and what it means. Click 'play' to listen to someone read it out for you to help you pronounce it.

Questions

1 a Chloroplasts are not present in all plant cells – why not?
   b Summarise the adaptations of chloroplasts for their role in photosynthesis.

2 Using the data in fig. 5.1.5, explain why plant leaves usually appear green.

Zoom feature

Just click on a section of the page and it will magnify so that you can read it easily on screen. This also means that you can look closely at photos and diagrams.

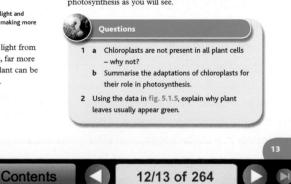

13

Topic 5   On the wild side

This topic deals with ecosystems, including the capture of energy through photosynthesis and its transfer between trophic levels. Many other factors affect the distribution and abundance of species, and changes in these factors as a result of global warming have great implications for all life on Earth including the effect on evolution and speciation.

What are the theories?

Photosynthesis is a complex process that captures most of the energy that is then transferred through ecosystems. This topic looks at the reactions of photosynthesis and how efficiently this energy is then transferred between trophic levels. The carbon cycle is described, as preparation for the discussion on global warming.

This topic also looks at the many abiotic and biotic factors that affect the distribution and abundance of organisms. Climate change as a result of global warming will change some of these factors, and computer modelling makes it possible to predict what some of the effects could be. The effect on evolution and speciation will be more difficult to predict. However, new data from the analysis of DNA and proteomes supports the accepted scientific theory of evolution.

What is the evidence?

Although there is a lot of evidence supporting the idea that human activity is causing global warming, this is still a hotly debated topic. You will be looking at some of the evidence, to assess its reliability, and exploring why the debate continues. You will explore some of the predictions made by modelling the effects of climate change on organisms. There will also be opportunities to carry out your own investigations on the factors affecting the distribution and abundance of species, and on the effect of temperature on the development of organisms.

What are the implications?

The debate over the human contribution to global warming has highlighted the way different groups respond to evidence. Although debate is central to the scientific process, decision-makers in governments need certainty in order to provide the pressure needed to persuade society and industry to accept uncomfortable change. This also raises ethical questions, since although a global response is needed, different countries have different needs. Responding to global warming in the same way may affect some countries more than others.

The map opposite shows you all the knowledge and skills you need to have by the end of this topic. The colour in each box shows which chapter they are covered in and the numbers refer to the Edexcel specification.

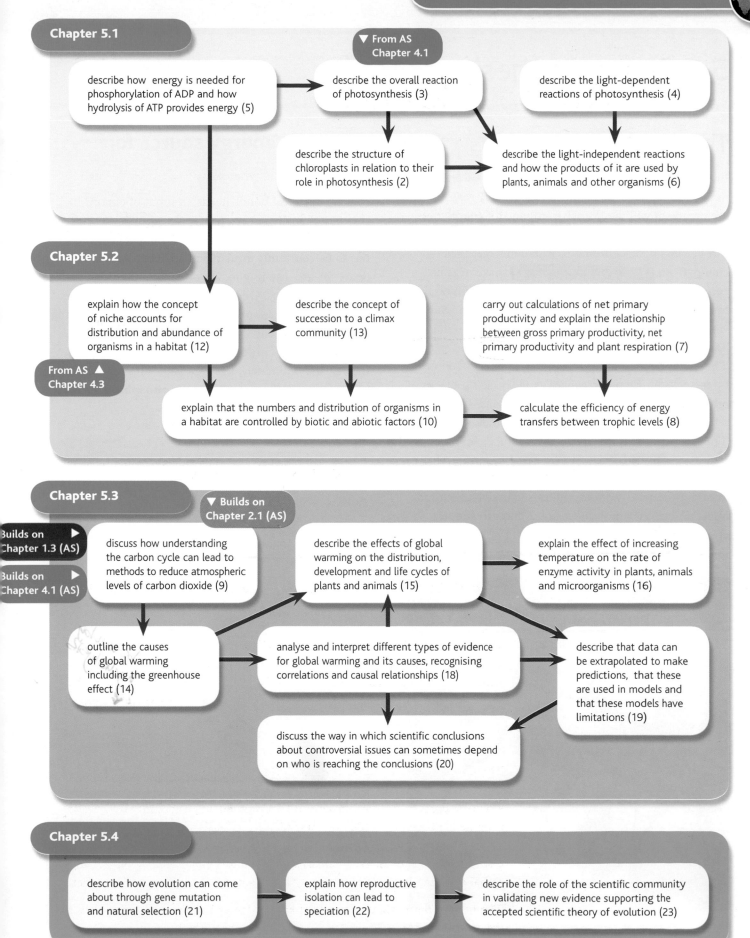

Chapter 5.1

describe how energy is needed for phosphorylation of ADP and how hydrolysis of ATP provides energy (5)

▼ From AS Chapter 4.1

describe the overall reaction of photosynthesis (3)

describe the light-dependent reactions of photosynthesis (4)

describe the structure of chloroplasts in relation to their role in photosynthesis (2)

describe the light-independent reactions and how the products of it are used by plants, animals and other organisms (6)

Chapter 5.2

explain how the concept of niche accounts for distribution and abundance of organisms in a habitat (12)

describe the concept of succession to a climax community (13)

carry out calculations of net primary productivity and explain the relationship between gross primary productivity, net primary productivity and plant respiration (7)

From AS ▲ Chapter 4.3

explain that the numbers and distribution of organisms in a habitat are controlled by biotic and abiotic factors (10)

calculate the efficiency of energy transfers between trophic levels (8)

Chapter 5.3

▼ Builds on Chapter 2.1 (AS)

Builds on ► Chapter 1.3 (AS)

Builds on ► Chapter 4.1 (AS)

discuss how understanding the carbon cycle can lead to methods to reduce atmospheric levels of carbon dioxide (9)

describe the effects of global warming on the distribution, development and life cycles of plants and animals (15)

explain the effect of increasing temperature on the rate of enzyme activity in plants, animals and microorganisms (16)

outline the causes of global warming including the greenhouse effect (14)

analyse and interpret different types of evidence for global warming and its causes, recognising correlations and causal relationships (18)

describe that data can be extrapolated to make predictions, that these are used in models and that these models have limitations (19)

discuss the way in which scientific conclusions about controversial issues can sometimes depend on who is reaching the conclusions (20)

Chapter 5.4

describe how evolution can come about through gene mutation and natural selection (21)

explain how reproductive isolation can lead to speciation (22)

describe the role of the scientific community in validating new evidence supporting the accepted scientific theory of evolution (23)

5.1 Photosynthesis

The need for energy 4.5.5

Energy is the currency of life. If the supply of energy to the cells of a living organism fails for any reason, the organism will die. Massive amounts of energy continually flow through the biosphere and organisms can be classified according to where they get their energy from. **Autotrophic** organisms make organic compounds from carbon dioxide. Most of them do this by **photosynthesis** – they trap energy from the Sun which is transferred into the chemical energy in the bonds of organic molecules such as glucose and starch. These compounds are then used as an energy source by the cells of the plant, as well as the building blocks of other important molecules such as proteins. There are a few autotrophic bacteria that are not photosynthetic. They use energy from chemical reactions to synthesise their food. **Heterotrophic** organisms generally eat plants or other animals which have eaten plants. They use the products of photosynthesis indirectly, both for making necessary molecules and as fuels to supply energy for a wide variety of activities. The Sun is thus the ultimate source of energy for almost all organisms.

fig. 5.1.1 **The ability of plants to trap and use the light energy from the Sun in the process of photosynthesis underpins almost all life on Earth.**

ATP – the energy source for the cell

Making chemical bonds needs an input of energy. In the cells of any living organism, chemical bonds are constantly being broken and made. So in a cell, energy has to be constantly available in an accessible form, ready for use instantly in any one of a multitude of different reactions. One molecule is believed to be the universal energy supplier in cells. It is found in all living organisms in exactly the same form. Anything that interferes with its production or breakdown is fatal to the cell and, ultimately, the organism. This remarkable compound is called **adenosine triphosphate**, or **ATP** (see *AS Biology* page 108).

(a)

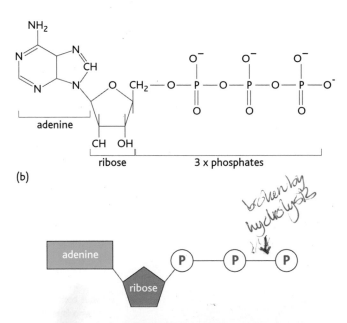

(b)

fig. 5.1.2 **ATP is a nucleotide with three phosphate groups attached. It is the chemical energy stored in the phosphate bonds, particularly the last one, which is made available to cells to use in synthesising or breaking bonds. (a) Structural formula of ATP (some hydrogen atoms have been omitted for simplicity, (b) simplified diagram of an ATP molecule.**

Figure 5.1.2 shows the structure of ATP. When energy is needed, the third phosphate bond can be broken by a hydrolysis reaction. This is catalysed by the enzyme ATPase. The result of this hydrolysis is **adenosine diphosphate** (**ADP**) and a free inorganic phosphate group (**P$_i$**) and energy. About 34kJ of energy is released per mole of ATP hydrolysed. Some of this energy is lost as heat and wasted, but the rest is used for any energy-requiring biological activity in the cell such as active transport (see *AS Biology* page 108) or muscle contraction (see pages 148–9).

The breakdown of ATP into ADP and phosphate is a reversible reaction. ATP can be synthesised from ADP and a phosphate group in a reaction which requires an input of energy (34kJ per mole of ATP produced) and the action of the same enzyme, ATPase (see **fig. 5.1.3**). The energy needed to drive the synthesis of ATP usually comes from catabolic (breakdown) reactions or **reduction/oxidation** (**redox**) reactions. As a result, the ATP molecule provides an immediate supply of energy, ready for use when needed.

Figure 5.1.3 shows the cycle between ADP and ATP.

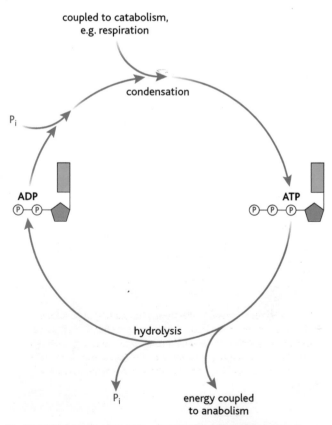

fig. 5.1.3 The energy released in catabolic (breakdown) reactions is used to drive the production of ATP. ATP acts as a store of energy which is released as needed for cell functions, releasing ADP and inorganic phosphate which can be resynthesised into ATP.

Making ATP – the electron transport chain

There are two main ways in which ATP is formed from ADP and inorganic phosphate in the cell. One is using energy released from the catabolic reactions which take place – for example in cellular respiration. However, the main way in which ATP is synthesised is by the removal of hydrogen atoms from several of the intermediates in a metabolic pathway.

When two hydrogen atoms are removed from a compound, they are picked up by a **hydrogen carrier** or **acceptor**. The acceptor therefore becomes **reduced**. Electrons from the hydrogen atoms are then passed along a series of carriers known as an **electron transport chain** (also called electron transfer chain). The components of the chain are reduced when they receive the electrons, and oxidised again when they pass them on. These **redox** reactions each release a small amount of energy which is used to drive the synthesis of a molecule of ATP. In this way the energy is readily available for use when it is needed in the cell. You will be learning more about the production of ATP later (Chapter 7.1).

Questions

1 Some people describe photosynthesis as the most important reaction in living organisms. Why might it deserve this title – and why not?

2 ATP is regarded as the universal energy supply molecule.

   a How is it fitted for this role in the cells?

   b What type of evidence would you look for to confirm this statement?

Photosynthesis in plants 4.5.3. 4.5.2

Photosynthesis is the process by which living organisms, particularly plants, capture the energy of the Sun using chlorophyll and use it to convert carbon dioxide and water into simple sugars. Photosynthesis can be summarised by the equation:

$$\text{carbon dioxide} + \text{water} \xrightarrow[\text{chlorophyll}]{\text{light energy}} \text{glucose} + \text{oxygen}$$

$$6CO_2 + 6H_2O \xrightarrow[\text{chlorophyll}]{\text{light energy}} C_6H_{12}O_6 + 6O_2$$

The energy from the light is used to split the strong H–O bonds in the water molecules. The hydrogen which is released is combined with carbon dioxide to form a fuel for the cells (glucose). Oxygen is released into the atmosphere as a waste product of this process.

HSW Models of photosynthesis

Simple models of photosynthesis such as the one shown in the equation above show a one-step process. They cover the most important points of the process and make it relatively easy to understand.

Detailed research into the biochemistry of photosynthesis has shown that this model is much too simplistic. Photosynthesis is actually a sequence of many different reactions in two main stages, one of which does not need light to take place. And the pigment chlorophyll is not a single pigment but a group of five closely related ones!

You will be learning some of the details in the process, but even this is a simplification as the whole process is extremely complex.

The whole structure of plants has evolved around the process of photosynthesis. The different parts of the plant are adapted for efficiently obtaining the raw materials carbon dioxide and water, and for trapping as much sunlight as possible.

The importance of chloroplasts

Chloroplasts are relatively large organelles found in the cells of the green parts of plants. An average green plant cell contains from 10–50 chloroplasts which are uniquely adapted for the process of photosynthesis (see *AS Biology* pages 204–5).

The membranes within a chloroplast are arranged in stacks called **grana**. A granum is made up of stacks of membrane discs known as **thylakoids**. This is where the green pigment chlorophyll is found. The pigment molecules are arranged on the membranes in the best possible position for trapping light energy.

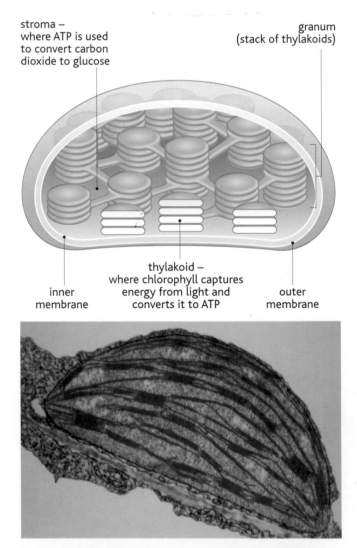

stroma – where ATP is used to convert carbon dioxide to glucose

granum (stack of thylakoids)

thylakoid – where chlorophyll captures energy from light and converts it to ATP

inner membrane

outer membrane

fig. 5.1.4 Evidence from electron micrographs has helped scientists build up a realistic and complex picture of the way the structure of chloroplasts is adapted to their functions in photosynthesis.

Evidence from electron micrographs also shows that the granal membranes are covered in particles which seem to be involved in ATP synthesis (see page 139).

These membrane stacks are surrounded by a matrix called the **stroma**. The stroma contains all the enzymes needed to complete the process of photosynthesis and produce glucose. This can then be used in cellular respiration, converted to starch for storage or used as an intermediate for the synthesis of other organic compounds such as amino acids and lipids.

Chlorophyll

The other major adaptation of the chloroplasts is the light-capturing, photosynthetic pigment chlorophyll. 'Chlorophyll' is actually a group of five closely related pigments. These include **chlorophyll *a*** (blue-green), **chlorophyll *b*** (yellow-green), the **carotenoids** (orange carotene and yellow xanthophyll) along with a grey pigment phaeophytin which is a breakdown product of the others. Chlorophyll *a* is found in all photosynthesing plants and is the most abundant of the five. The other pigments are found in varying proportions, and it is these differences which give the leaves of plants their almost infinite variety of shades of green.

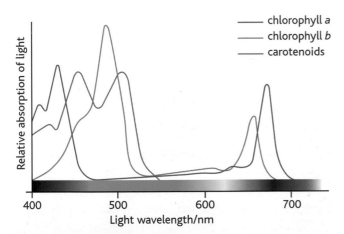

fig. 5.1.5 The different photosynthetic pigments absorb light and capture its energy at a variety of different wavelengths, making more of the light available for use by the plant.

Each of the pigments absorbs and captures light from particular areas of the spectrum. As a result, far more of the energy from the light falling on the plant can be used than if only one pigment was involved.

HSW Simple evidence for the different photosynthetic pigments

Plants look green. If you extract the pigments from a plant by grinding up leaves with acetone and filtering, the filtrate looks green. So how can you show that there are five different pigments? The answer is paper chromatography. With a suitable solvent the pigments travel up the paper at different speeds and are readily separated.

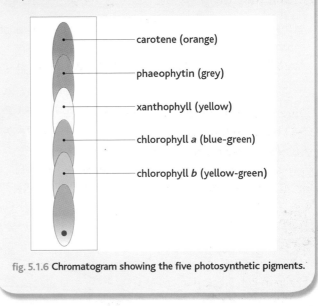

fig. 5.1.6 **Chromatogram showing the five photosynthetic pigments.**

There are two distinct chlorophyll complexes known as **photosystem I** (**PSI**) and **photosystem II** (**PSII**). Each system contains a different combination of chlorophyll pigments and so absorbs light in a slightly different area of the spectrum (wavelength 700 nm for PSI and 680 nm for PSII). The different photosystems have been identified as different-sized particles attached to the membranes in the chloroplasts in electron micrographs. PSI particles are mainly on the intergranal lamellae, while PSII particles are on the grana themselves. They have different functions in photosynthesis as you will see.

Questions

1 a Chloroplasts are not present in all plant cells – why not?

  b Summarise the adaptations of chloroplasts for their role in photosynthesis.

2 Using the data in **fig. 5.1.5**, explain why plant leaves usually appear green.

The biochemistry of photosynthesis 4.5.4, 4.5.6

Photosynthesis is a two-stage process involving a complex series of reactions. The reactions in the first stage only occur in light, while those of the second stage occur independently of light. The **light-dependent** reactions produce materials which are then used in the **light-independent** stages. The whole process takes place all the time during the hours of daylight. However, the light-independent reactions can also continue when it is dark.

HSW Evidence for two stages of photosynthesis

There are several strands of evidence for the two stages of photosynthesis.

1 Light-dependent chemical reactions get the energy they need from light. They do not use heat energy, so temperature should not affect the rate of the reaction. However, when the rate of photosynthesis is investigated experimentally, temperature has a clear effect (see **fig. 5.1.7**). Initially photochemical (light-dependent) reactions are limiting the rate of the overall process and so temperature has no effect. But once there is plenty of light available, the process seems to be limited by different, temperature-sensitive reactions. This suggests there are two distinct phases to photosynthesis, one dependent on light and the other controlled by temperature-sensitive enzymes (see *AS Biology* pages 84–9).

2 A plant which is given alternating periods of dark and light forms more carbohydrate than a plant in continuous light. The best explanation is that the light-dependent reactions produce a chemical which feeds into the light-independent stage. The light-independent stage cannot keep up and so in continuous light this product builds up. As the concentration rises, it inhibits the enzymes controlling the light-independent reactions for making carbohydrates. A period of darkness ensures that all of the light stage products are converted into carbohydrate without the concentration getting too high. This system is very efficient in a natural environment with periods of light and dark (day and night).

More recent techniques have allowed regions of the chloroplast to be isolated. The reactions occurring on the grana have been shown to depend on the presence of light but those of the stroma do not.

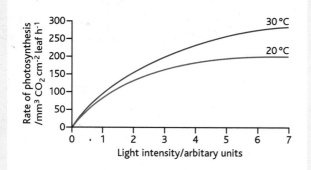

fig. 5.1.7 **The effect of temperature on the rate of photosynthesis suggests that two different processes are involved.**

The light-dependent stage of photosynthesis

The light-dependent stage of photosynthesis takes place on the thylakoid membranes of the chloroplasts. It has two main functions. One is to produce ATP, which supplies the energy needed for the synthesis of carbohydrates. The other is to split water molecules in a **photochemical** reaction, providing hydrogen ions to reduce carbon dioxide and produce carbohydrates.

Light is a form of electromagnetic radiation and the smallest unit of light energy is a photon. When a photon of light hits a chlorophyll molecule, the energy is transferred to the electrons of that molecule. The electrons are excited – they are raised to higher energy levels. If an electron is raised to a sufficiently high energy level it will leave the chlorophyll molecule completely. The excited electron can be picked up by an electron acceptor (carrier molecule). This in turn results in the synthesis of ATP by one of two processes – **cyclic** and **non-cyclic photophosphorylation**.

In both cases ATP is formed as the excited electron is passed along an electron transport chain.

The electron transport chain is a model that can be used in different cellular processes to describe the sequence of reactions by which living organisms make ATP. It can be imagined as a series of downwards steps. Each step is a different carrier molecule, and represents an energy level. As electrons move along the chain, they lose energy which can be used to drive the synthesis of ATP from ADP and inorganic phosphate. Details of electron transport chains are covered in Topic 7; see pages 138–141).

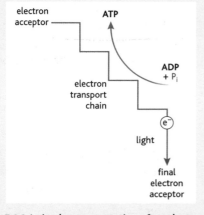

fig. 5.1.8 **A simple representation of an electron transport chain. The carriers may vary but the principles are the same wherever they are found.**

Cyclic photophosphorylation

Cyclic photophosphorylation involves only PSI and drives the production of ATP. When light hits a chlorophyll molecule in PSI, a light-excited electron leaves the molecule. It is taken up by an electron acceptor and passed directly along an electron transport chain to produce ATP. When an electron returns to the chlorophyll molecule in PSI, it can then be excited in the same way again.

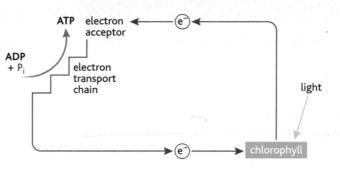

fig. 5.1.9 **Cyclic photophosphorylation.**

Non-cyclic photophosphorylation

Non-cyclic photophosphorylation involves both PSI and PSII. It splits water molecules to provide reducing power to make carbohydrates. At the same time it results in the production of more ATP.

Water always dissociates spontaneously into hydrogen (H^+) ions and hydroxide (OH^-) ions. As a result there are always plenty of these ions present in the cell, including in the interior of the chloroplasts (**fig. 5.1.10**).

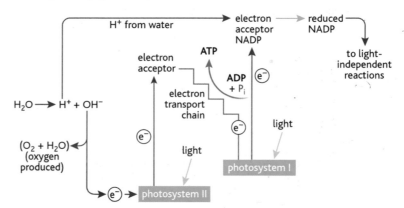

fig. 5.1.10 **Non-cyclic photophosphorylation: one electron leaves a chlorophyll molecule in PSI and moves into the light-independent stage of the process. A different electron is returned to PSI from PSII by an electron transport chain, driving the production of more ATP as it does so.**

In light conditions, photons are constantly hitting chlorophyll molecules in both PSI and PSII, exciting the electrons. In non-cyclic photophosphorylation an excited electron from PSI is picked up by an **electron acceptor**, in this case **nicotinamide adenine dinucleotide phosphate** (**NADP**). The NADP takes up a hydrogen ion from the dissociated water at the same time to form reduced NADP. This reduced NADP is then used as a source of reducing power in the light-independent reactions of photosynthesis to make glucose.

At the same time an excited electron from PSII is picked up by another electron acceptor and passes along an electron transport chain until it reaches PSI. This drives the synthesis of a molecule of ATP, and PSI receives an electron to replace the one that was lost to the light-independent reactions.

Now the chlorophyll molecule in PSII is short of an electron and unstable. The original electron cannot be returned to the chlorophyll because it has continued on to PSI. So an electron has to be found from somewhere to restore the chlorophyll to its original state. This electron comes from the splitting of water – a process known as **photolysis** as it depends on light (see **fig. 5.1.10**).

Photosynthesis is a reaction that occurs millions of times in every chloroplast. This means many hydrogen ions are removed by NADP, and many hydroxide ions are 'left behind'. The hydroxide ions react together to form oxygen and water. As a result of the reaction electrons are freed and taken up by chlorophyll.

$$4OH^- - 4e^- \text{ (lost to chlorophyll)} \rightarrow O_2 + 2H_2O$$

Once each PSII is chlorophyll molecule has received an electron it is restored to its original state, ready to be excited again when hit by a photon of light. Four chlorophyll molecules regain electrons in the production of one molecule of oxygen.

This clever piece of biochemistry was worked out by Robert Hill and Fay Bendall at Cambridge and is often referred to as the Z scheme, though nowadays the Z is usually turned round so it looks like an N!

The light-independent stage of photosynthesis

The light-independent stage of photosynthesis uses the reducing power (reduced NADP) and energy-supplying ATP produced by the light-dependent stage. This stage consists of a series of reactions known as the **Calvin cycle** which take place in the stroma of the chloroplast. A series of small steps results in the reduction of carbon dioxide from the air to bring about the synthesis of carbohydrates. Each stage of the cycle is controlled by enzymes (see **fig. 5.1.11**).

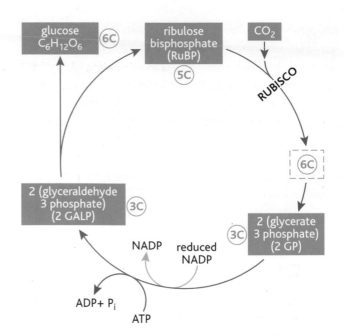

fig. 5.1.11 The Calvin cycle: here the products of the light-dependent stage of photosynthesis are used in a continuous cycle to fix carbon dioxide. The end result is new carbohydrates.

In the first step, carbon dioxide from the air combines with the 5-carbon compound **ribulose bisphosphate (RuBP)**, making it part of the photosynthetic reactions. The carbon dioxide is said to be fixed. The enzyme **ribulose bisphosphate carboxylase/oxygenase** (usually known as **RUBISCO**) is necessary for this vital step. Research has shown that RUBISCO is the rate-limiting enzyme in the process of photosynthesis. It makes up about 30% of the total protein of a leaf so this enzyme is probably one of the most common proteins on Earth.

The result of the reaction between RuBP and carbon dioxide is, in theory, a 6-carbon compound. Scientists are convinced that this theoretical compound exists but it is highly unstable and no one has been able to isolate it. It immediately splits to give two molecules of **glycerate 3-phosphate** (**GP**), a 3-carbon compound. GP is then reduced (hydrogen is added) to form **glyceraldehyde 3-phosphate** (**GALP**), a 3-carbon sugar. The hydrogen for this reduction comes from reduced NADP and the energy required from ATP, both produced in the light-dependent stage.

Much of the 3-carbon GALP passes through a series of steps to replace the ribulose bisphosphate needed in the first step of the cycle. However, some of it is synthesised into the 6-carbon simple sugar glucose.

The glucose produced during photosynthesis is used as a fuel for respiration in the plant. It is converted into double sugars such as sucrose for transport round the plant and into polysaccharides such as starch for energy storage and cellulose for structural support (see *AS Biology* pages 38–9). Glucose is needed as a building block for amino acids (combined with nitrates from the soil), and for nucleic acids with the addition of phosphates. The products of photosynthesis are also used to produce lipids – in fact many compounds needed by the plant originate from photosynthesis.

The reactions of the Calvin cycle take place both in the light and in the dark. They only stop in the dark when the products of the light reaction run out, leaving no reduced NADP or ATP available in the chloroplasts.

HSW Melvin Calvin and his cycle

Melvin Calvin worked at the University of California with a team of scientists from many different disciplines – one of the first people to mix biologists, chemists and physicists on a single project! He came up with a method for investigating the reactions that occur in photosynthesis, which sounds incredibly simple, but no one had thought of it before. He produced a thin, transparent vessel known as a 'lollipop'. Into this was placed a suspension of photosynthetic protoctists called *Chlorella* which were supplied with radioactively labelled ^{14}C. Light was shone through the suspension of organisms so they could photosynthesise.

The experiment was repeated, with the *Chlorella* being killed at intervals ranging from a few seconds to a few minutes after the start of photosynthesis. This stopped all enzyme-controlled reactions immediately. The radioactive compounds formed were then extracted, separated by paper chromatography and identified. In this way the biochemical pathway which we now call the Calvin cycle was built up.

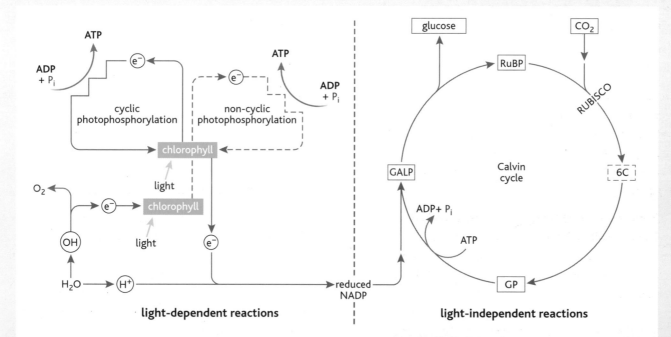

fig. 5.1.12 The full process of photosynthesis, which occurs continuously in plants when they are exposed to light.

Questions

1 Make a table to compare what happens in cyclic and non-cyclic photophosphorylation.

2 Calvin cycle reactions are also known as the light-independent reactions of photosynthesis. Explain why this name is appropriate yet in some ways inaccurate.

3 In GCSE Biology you learnt about limiting factors in photosynthesis. Light and carbon dioxide levels as well as temperature affect the rate at which photosynthesis takes place. Using what you have just learnt, explain why these three factors limit the rate of photosynthesis.

5.2 How ecosystems work

What is ecology? 4.5.12

Your study of adaptation, biodiversity and endemism in *AS Biology* will have shown you that real ecology is a long way from the emotive picture of the 'environment' often portrayed in the media. The word ecology comes from the Greek '*oikos*' meaning 'house'. It is the study of the interactions that determine the distribution and abundance of organisms within a particular environment. Put simply, ecology is the study of living things in their home environment.

What is an ecosystem?

An **ecosystem** is a life-supporting environment. It includes all of the living organisms which interact together, the nutrients that cycle through the system, and the physical and chemical environment in which the organisms are living. An ecosystem consists of a network of habitats and the communities of organisms associated with them.

fig. 5.2.1 There are many ecosystems in the biosphere, from the Arctic wastes to lush tropical forests, from underground caves to the vast oceans.

Useful terms

Like any other area of scientific study, ecology has its own very specific terms. Some of these are reminders from your AS level studies. Others will be important in this part of your course.

- A **habitat** is the place where an organism lives, such as a stream, a tropical rainforest or a sand dune. You can think of the habitat of an organism as its address. Many organisms live only in a small part of a habitat – a single fig on a tree or between the palps of a water shrimp for example. Such habitats are referred to as **microhabitats**.

- A **population** is a group of organisms of the same species, living and breeding together in a habitat. The three-spined sticklebacks in a particular pond or the skin mites in your mattress are examples.

- A **community** is all the populations of the different species of organisms living in a habitat at any one time. For example, in a habitat such as a rock pool the community consists of populations of different seaweeds, sea anemones, shrimps, small fish such as gobies, crabs and other species. More details may be given in the name, such as the soil community, or the animal community in the soil.

- The ecological **niche** of an organism is difficult to define. It can best be described as the role of the organism in the community, its way of life. If the habitat is the address of the organism, the niche describes its profession. It can be broken down into specific elements, for example the food niche or the **habitat niche**. Several organisms can share the same habitat, occupying different niches. So for example, the food niche occupied by a fox in a woodland is the top predator, squirrels occupy the large tree-dwelling herbivore niche, and rabbits fill the large ground and burrow-living herbivore niche.

- **Abiotic factors** are the non-living elements of the habitat of an organism. They include those related to the climate, such as the amount of sunlight (solar energy input), temperature extremes and rainfall, and those related to the soil (edaphic factors), including the drainage and the pH. In aquatic habitats the oxygen availability in the water is very important. Abiotic factors have a big effect on the success of an organism in a particular habitat.

- **Biotic factors** are the living elements of a habitat which affect the ability of a group of organisms to survive there. For example, the presence of suitable prey species will affect the numbers of predators in a habitat.

Biomes – the major ecosystems

The **biosphere** could be considered as the largest ecosystem on Earth. However it is so large that it is very difficult to study it as a whole. So it is divided into smaller parts distinguished by their similar climates and plant communities. These major ecosystems or **biomes** are shown in **fig. 5.2.3**. Biomes are generally subdivided into smaller ecosystems for ease of study.

fig. 5.2.2 Within a diverse habitat such as a tropical rainforest different populations of organisms live interdependently as part of a complex community.

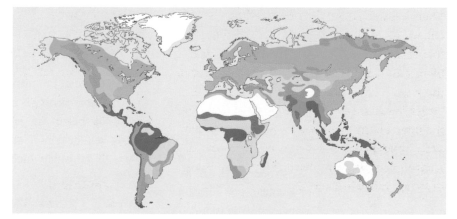

5.2.3 Map of the world showing the major land biomes (key in table below).

Colour	Name of biome	Description of biome	Level of biodiversity
	Tropical rainforest	High humidity (rain all year), warm and plenty of sunlight	Very high
	Tropical seasonal forest	Drier than tropical rainforest, warm, sunny	High
	Savannah	Dry tropical grassland	Medium
	Tropical woodland	Wetter than savannah, grassland with thornwoods, bushes and trees	More than savannah
	Desert	Very little rainfall, often extremes of temperature between day and night	Very low
	Temperate grassland	Warm dry temperate areas, e.g. prairies, steppes and pampas	Medium
	Temperate shrublands	Hot dry summers and cool wet winters	Medium
	Temperate forests	Warm moist regions, including deciduous and conifers	Less than tropical rainforest
	Taiga	Evergreen forests in cold subarctic and subalpine regions	Low
	Tundra	Very cold, arctic and high mountain regions	Very low

Questions

1 How does the habitat of an organism differ from its niche? Give examples to illustrate your answer.

2 Choose three of the major biomes of the Earth:

   a Find out about the range of temperatures experienced, the rainfall, etc. in the biome.

   b Find out about two plants and two animals found in these biomes with their adaptations for the conditions.

   c Using the table above, link the water availability and the temperatures in the biomes you have chosen to the level of biodiversity found.

How ecosystems evolve 4.5.13

The major biomes of the Earth have developed over thousands or even millions of years from original bare rock into the ecosystems of today. This has been brought about by **succession**, a process by which communities of animals and plants colonise an area and then over time are replaced by other, usually more varied, communities.

Primary succession

Primary succession occurs from the starting point of an empty inorganic surface, such as bare rock or a sand dune. This type of succession can be seen after the eruption of a volcano or landslide, or after the emergence of a new volcanic island. The first plants are **opportunists** or **pioneer species** such as lichens, algae and mosses. These organisms can penetrate the rock surface, helping to break it into grains, and trapping organic material that will break down to form humus. The inorganic rock grains and the organic **humus** are the start of the formation of soil.

fig. 5.2.4 The bare rock of the island of Surtsey, which emerged as a result of a volcanic eruption in 1967, gave scientists an ideal opportunity to study primary succession.

Once there is soil, other species such as grasses and ferns can establish root systems. The action of their roots and the humus they form when they die and decay add to the soil. As the soil layer develops, more water and nutrients are retained and become available for plant roots, so that less hardy species can survive. Gradually larger plants can be supported and the diversity of species increases. As plant biodiversity increases, so the diversity of animals that can be supported also increases. Eventually a **climax community** is reached, where the biodiversity and range of species are generally constant. A climax community is self-sustaining and usually the most productive group of organisms which that environment can support. Primary succession must have been of prime importance in the formation of the biosphere but today it is found in only a few places, such as the island of Surtsey.

HSW Developing ideas of climax community

In 1916 F.E. Clements proposed the idea that climate is the major factor in determining the make-up of the climax community in a particular place. He said that for any given climate, there was only one possible climax community, and that this should be known as the **climatic climax community**. This view has been modified over time as scientists learn more about ecosystems and recognise that many factors interact to determine any given climax (see later in this chapter). So a climatic climax community is now defined as one that remains generally constant over time.

In the modern landscape there are many examples of another type of climax community. These are constant and self-sustaining but they are not truly natural. Humans have changed the landscape, such as by clearing woodland and grazing domestic animals, and this has changed the ultimate climax community. A final community which is partly the result of human intervention is known as a **plagioclimax**. Examples include chalk grassland and lowland heaths. Probably all of the modern British countryside consists of plagioclimax communities rather than climactic climaxes. But if the limiting factors are removed – if people move away, for example – a climatic climax community will eventually develop.

Secondary succession

Secondary succession is the evolution of an ecosystem from existing soil that is clear of vegetation. It occurs as rivers shift their courses, after fires and floods, and after disturbances caused by humans. The sequence of events is very similar to that seen in primary succession, but because the soil is already formed and contains seeds, roots and soil organisms, the numbers of plants and animals present right from the beginning of the succession are much higher. Simply digging a patch of earth and leaving it is sufficient to observe the beginnings of a secondary succession.

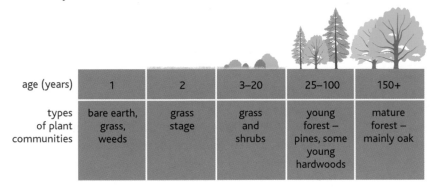

age (years)	1	2	3–20	25–100	150+
types of plant communities	bare earth, grass, weeds	grass stage	grass and shrubs	young forest – pines, some young hardwoods	mature forest – mainly oak

fig. 5.2.5 The stages of a secondary succession from bare earth to oak woodland. The timescale is very approximate!

The time it takes to go from an area of bare earth to a climax community varies enormously. It depends on many different factors, including temperature, rainfall levels and the underlying fertility of the soil. However, a succession of different types of plants and animals is always seen. The climax community formed will depend not only on the climatic factors, but also on the plants and animals that are either within or are able to colonise the area. This can mean that a secondary climax community differs from the original primary climax community, as we see when virgin rainforest is cut down and the area left to regenerate naturally.

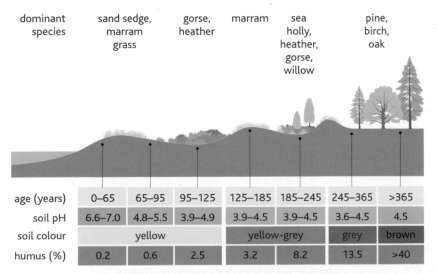

dominant species	sand sedge, marram grass	gorse, heather	marram	sea holly, heather, gorse, willow	pine, birch, oak

age (years)	0–65	65–95	95–125	125–185	185–245	245–365	>365
soil pH	6.6–7.0	4.8–5.5	3.9–4.9	3.9–4.5	3.9–4.5	3.6–4.5	4.5
soil colour		yellow			yellow-grey	grey	brown
humus (%)	0.2	0.6	2.5	3.2	8.2	13.5	>40

fig. 5.2.7 The gradual edaphic change from sand to a more mature soil, the maturing topography and the differences in the plants and animals making up the communities populating each habitat, can readily be observed on the sand dunes at Gibraltar Point.

fig 5.2.6 Human intervention inevitably affects biodiversity – the forest that regenerated here in Manu, Peru contained very different species from the one that was originally cut down.

Observing succession is not always easy, because it is a process which occurs over a long time. Sand dunes can help overcome this problem because they can show a complete record of the stages of the succession. For example, at Gibraltar Point on the east coast of England the oldest dunes, those furthest from the sea, are in the late stages of the succession. Nearest to the sea are the youngest, newly formed dunes which are in the very earliest stages of colonisation (see **fig. 5.2.7**).

Studying an ecosystem

Figure 5.2.8 is the result of a practical study of an ecosystem. Techniques such as taking a transect can be used to study the topography of an area – that is the shape, height and depth of the land surface. Quadrats can be used to give valid and reliable measures of the numbers and types of plants. These data help to build up a picture of the different plant communities in the area. The animal communities can be investigated by many methods, including quadrats, nets, pitfall traps and taking soil samples. The abiotic factors which affect a habitat, such as rainfall and temperature, and edaphic features, such as the soil type and pH, are also measured and recorded to give as much information as possible about the ecology of the area. You will be learning how to carry out many of these techniques as part of your field work.

fig. 5.2.8 **Studying the ecology of an ecosystem involves active work in the field.**

HSW The Surtsey Research Society

On 14 November 1963 off the coast of Iceland a volcanic eruption burst through the surface of the sea. The column of steam and ash could be seen for miles and the hot magma cooled rapidly to form a new island. By 1967 when the eruptions finally stopped the island covered 2.7 km², a huge area of bare volcanic rock.

While the island was forming, a group of researchers got together, determined to make the most of the rare opportunity to observe the primary succession of completely new land. The Surtsey Research Society has had an overview of all the research carried out on the island since then. The colonisation and succession sequences of the island have been carefully recorded and photographed. Access to the island has been carefully controlled and no tourism has been allowed, so the succession of plant and animal life has been as natural as possible.

There have been a number of fascinating discoveries, some of which show that earlier predictions about primary succession don't always occur and may vary depending on availability of organisms to colonise. Moulds, bacteria and fungi quickly became established. Somewhat surprisingly, several species of flowering plants – sea rocket, sea lyme grass, oyster plant and sea sandwort – were also found growing on the island between 1965 and 1967, before mosses and lichens appeared. Scientists found seeds for these plants washed up on the shore and germinated some of them, confirming the hypothesis that new land is often colonised by seeds carried in water.

For several years the flowering plants all died during the winter and recolonisation had to take place each spring. Then in 1968–9 sea sandwort overwintered for the first

time and in 1971 the first flowers appeared on Surtsey – a turning point for the succession. By 1975 there was a constant community of plants, but relatively little biodiversity, and this continued for the next 10 years.

In the early 1980s birds, including fulmars, guillemots, kittiwakes and gulls, arrived on the island and breeding colonies were established. The birds increased the nutrient levels of the soil with their droppings, the plant populations flourished and many new species appeared. In 10 years the number of higher plant species more than doubled, from 21 to 44. The evidence suggested that the seeds of the new species were carried in by the birds. For example, a far greater diversity of plant life is seen around the gull colonies than elsewhere on the island.

Scientists think that the number of plant species on Surtsey will reach a peak in the next few decades. Then, as the island is gradually affected by erosion and some of the early pioneer species die out, the eventual climax community may have only around 10 different species in it, similar to other islands in the area.

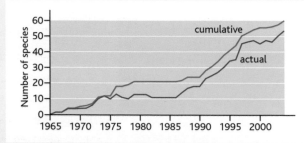

fig. 5.2.9 **Graph showing the increase in biodiversity of plants on Surtsey with the passage of time. Cumulative – total number of species ever observed; actual – number of species at time of observation.**

fig. 5.2.10 Ecological succession in action on the island of Surtsey.

Questions

1 What is meant by the term ecological succession?

2 What is meant by a climax community and do such communities always look the same?

3 Describe the difference between primary and secondary succession.

 4 Use the data in fig. 5.2.9 to answer these questions.

   a Explain the shape of the curve showing the actual number of species on Surtsey in terms of the natural succession.

   b Why is there a difference between the actual and cumulative number of plant species observed on Surtsey?

   c If the island develops as the scientists predict, how would you expect these curves to develop over the next 20 years?

The effect of abiotic factors 4.5.10

One aspect of ecology is to try to understand why and how different factors affect living organisms and determine the distribution of organisms in a particular habitat. The community of organisms in a habitat is controlled by both abiotic (non-living) and biotic (living) factors. The interaction of these factors results in different ecological niches which change as the factors change. Understanding the abiotic and biotic factors that affect living organisms can help us predict the effect of changes on an ecosystem.

Abiotic factors can vary a great deal within a habitat to produce **microclimates**. These provide different niches and so determine the distribution and abundance of different populations within the habitat. For example, logs may be placed for seating on a grass area. Although the area will be largely dry and well lit, under a log it will be damp and shady, allowing very different organisms to grow and thrive compared with those in the grassy areas.

Light

The amount of light in a habitat – the solar energy input – has a direct effect on the numbers of organisms found there. Plants are dependent on light for photosynthesis. Any plant populations which are going to thrive in habitats with low light levels must be able to cope with this factor. For example, some plants reproduce early to avoid the shade caused by larger plants (**fig. 5.2.11**). Other plants are able to photosynthesise and reproduce successfully in low light levels, often by having extra chlorophyll or a different mix of chlorophyll pigments which are sensitive to lower light levels. This allows these plants to thrive in a niche (shady woodland floor dweller) where other plants would die (see **fig. 5.2.12**).

Animals are affected by light levels indirectly as a result of the distribution of food plants. Seasonal light changes can also affect reproductive patterns and, without the cues from changing light levels, many aspects of animal behaviour would be lost (see pages 238–9).

fig. 5.2.11 Bluebells produce leaves early in the year and photosynthesise in spite of the low temperatures. They flower as the insects which pollinate them appear in late spring before dying back to become dormant through the shady summer months.

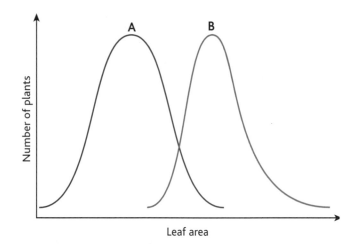

fig. 5.2.12 Some plants cope with a shady situation by growing larger leaves. Graph A shows the range of leaf area in a nettle population grown in the open. Graph B shows that the leaves of nettles grown in the shade have on average a considerably larger area and are less likely to show the full range of sizes of the normal distribution curve.

Temperature

For any particular organism, there is a range of temperatures within which it can grow and successfully reproduce. Above or below that range reproduction does not occur even if the organism survives. It is the extremes of temperature which determine where an organism can live, not the average.

The temperature of the environment particularly affects the rate of enzyme-controlled reactions in plants and ectothermic animals (whose body temperature is mainly determined by heat exchange with the environment). In some areas of the world the daytime temperatures can be so high that they exceed the temperature at which endotherms can normally control their body temperatures. Many animals have evolved behaviours and physiological features which enable them to cope. Organisms without these adaptations do not survive.

Wind and water currents

Wind has a direct effect on organisms in a habitat. Wind increases water and heat loss from the body and so adds to the environmental stress an organism has to cope with. Fewer species can survive in areas with strong prevailing winds while occasional gales and hurricanes can devastate populations. Whole woodlands may be destroyed and the communities of plant and animal life within them lost (see **fig. 5.2.13**).

fig. 5.2.13 The damage seen here was caused by very high winds which swept across the south of the UK in the autumn of 1987. Within 20 years, recovery was almost complete.

In water currents, organisms have to flow with the current, be strong swimmers or be able to hang on tight and resist the force of the water. Currents are most damaging to populations when the strength increases suddenly, such as when flooding occurs.

Water availability

In a terrestrial environment the availability of water is affected by several factors including the amount of precipitation, the rate of evaporation and edaphic factors such as the rate of loss by drainage through the soil. Water is vital for living organisms, so where the supply is limited it will cause severe problems. If the water stress becomes too severe the organisms will die unless, like camels and cacti, they have special adaptations to enable them to survive and reproduce. Equally, an increase in the availability of water can lead to a huge change in a habitat and to a massive increase in population size of some organisms. For example in deserts, after a little rain has fallen the seeds of many desert plants germinate, grow and flower in a very short space of time, in the phenomenon known as the 'flowering of the desert'. This in turn provides a food bonanza for insects and other animals which normally just manage to survive in the harsh conditions, so there is a population explosion all round!

fig. 5.2.14 The effect of water availability on a habitat is clearly illustrated by some of the plants that live in the extremely hostile environment of the desert.

Oxygen availability

Oxygen can be in short supply in both water and the soil. When water is cold, or fast flowing, sufficient oxygen dissolves in it to support life. If the temperature of the water rises, or it becomes still and stagnant, then the oxygen content will drop, making it a much more difficult habitat and often affecting the survival of populations within it. Soil is also usually a well-aerated habitat. The spaces between the soil particles contain air so there is plenty of oxygen for the respiration of plant roots. In waterlogged soil the air spaces are filled with water and the plant roots may be deprived of oxygen. The plants may die as a result. However, some plants, like mangroves, have special adaptations such as aerial roots which allow them to thrive in waterlogged conditions.

Edaphic factors: soil structure and mineral content

The structure of the soil on which organisms live and grow can affect the various populations associated with it. Sand has a loose, shifting structure that allows very little to grow on it. Plant populations that are linked by massive root and rhizome networks, such as marram grass, can and do survive. They not only reproduce successfully but also bind the sand together, which makes it more suited for colonisation by other species. Not only does marram have an extensive branching root network, but it is also well adapted to survive the physiological drought conditions which occur on the seashore. The leaves curl round on themselves with the stomata on the inside, creating a microenvironment which reduces water loss. Marram grass fills the sandy, salt-resistant, dune-binding niche perfectly.

Soils that contain a high proportion of sand are light, easily worked and easily warmed. However, they are also very easily drained. Water passes through them rapidly, carrying with it minerals which may be needed by plants. This **leaching** of minerals reduces the population density of plants that can grow in the soil. Conversely, it is difficult for water to drain through soils that are made up predominantly of tiny clay particles. This means they are heavy, take longer to warm up, are hard to work and are easily waterlogged. Mineral leaching is not a problem in soil of this type, but the populations which it will support are still limited. The ideal soil, **loam**, has particles of a wide range of sizes. It is heavier and less prone to leaching than sandy soils, yet easier to warm and work than clay. Different types of plants have evolved to grow well in the different soil types – and none of them thrives in different soils.

fig. 5.2.15 The edaphic features of different types of soils produce different growing conditions which support very different plants. For example, the bog asphodel on the left only grows in damp, acid soils whereas the horseshoe vetch on the right is found only in freely draining chalk and limestone soils.

HSW Conflict between nature and need

When we farm, we remove the crop before the plants die and decompose, and break the natural cycle that returns minerals to the soil. Over time, soil mineral concentrations will decrease with monocultures (where one crop is grown over a large area). This can happen rapidly for those minerals that the crop particularly takes up. The problem may be minimised by crop rotation, where different crops are grown in different fields in rotation, altering the mineral demands made on the soil each year.

Farmers can also apply fertilisers to increase mineral concentrations again, but this causes problems. Using artificial fertilisers over many years can still lead to loss of fertility, so increasing amounts of expensive chemicals are needed. They also interact with other minerals in the soil so that the soil loses its crumbly structure, which affects how well the plants grow on it, as well as the organisms that live in it. Using natural fertilisers such as farmyard manure can supply the required minerals in a slow release form as the manure decays and keep the structure of the soil, but it is more difficult to apply the right quantities for the crop.

Science and practical experience provide evidence of the impact of different farming methods and suggest ways in which land can be sustainably managed. But each way has cost and ethical implications. Science cannot decide which is the best way; that is for each society to choose and choice will depend on the needs of the people making that choice.

fig. 5.2.16 Intensive modern agriculture using artificial fertilisers increases crop production but has long-term implications for soil health. Is this the best way to produce food?

Questions

1 a What are abiotic factors? Give some examples.

   b Why do abiotic factors have such a major impact on the distribution of all organisms in a habitat?

2 Abiotic factors interact to make up the conditions of a particular habitat. Describe an example of the way in which the impact of one abiotic factor may be influenced by another.

3 Choose one abiotic factor and investigate organisms which are adapted to survive in the extremes of these conditions, e.g. temperature – adaptations of plants and animals to very high and very low temperature; water currents – animals and plants that are adapted to very fast flowing currents and to still, stagnant water.

Biotic factors 4.5.10

Biotic factors are all of the living elements in a habitat, such as predators, parasites and disease-causing organisms.

Predation

It is easy to see how predators can affect the abundance of their prey species. Horses grazing a field must reduce the reproduction of the grass by eating the potentially flower-forming parts and a fox family must reduce the numbers of the local rabbit population.

A mathematical model that describes the relationships between predator and prey populations predicts that the populations will oscillate in a repeating cycle. The reasoning underlying this model is straightforward. As a prey population increases there is more food for the predators and so, after an interval, the predator population grows too. The predators will increase to the point where they are eating more prey than are replaced by reproduction, so the numbers of prey will fall. This will reduce the food supply of the predators, so they will not produce as many offspring, and so their numbers will fall as well, allowing the abundance of prey to increase again and so on (see **fig. 5.2.17**).

The situation in a natural habitat is always more complex than the model. For example, other research shows that the hare population follows a similar pattern even in areas where there are no lynxes. The hares are responding to cycles in their food which appear to be related to climatic variations and changes in insect pest populations. This is why it is important to study all the factors in an ecosystem. You will be looking at this in more detail on the following spreads.

Finding a mate

Reproduction is a powerful driving force and the likelihood of finding a mate, or achieving pollination, will help to determine the organisms which are found in any habitat. So if a single seed is dispersed to a new area, germinates, grows and survives, that species of plant is unlikely to become a permanent resident unless other plants of the same species also grow in the area, or the plant can reproduce successfully asexually. Similarly a single individual of any animal species in an area does not mean that the species lives in the habitat. There must be males and females so mates can be found. Availability of mates has a big effect on the abundance of any type of animal in an area.

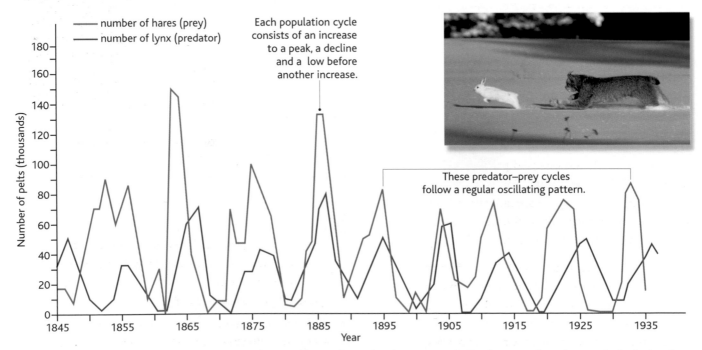

fig. 5.2.17 The graph shows the fluctuations in the populations of lynx and snowshoe hares in Canada. The data come from the records of pelts kept by the Hudson's Bay Company in Canada.

Territory

Many species of animals show clear territorial behaviour. A territory is an area held and defended by an animal or group of animals against other organisms which may be of the same or different species. Territories have different functions in different animals but they are almost always used in some way to make sure that a breeding pair has sufficient resources to raise young. The type and size of territory will help to determine which species live in a particular community. You will be looking at territories in more detail when you look at the role of competition in determining the distribution of animals living in a habitat.

fig. 5.2.18 **Gannets have small breeding territories because they feed out at sea, but without one a bird cannot nest and reproduce.**

Parasitism and disease

Parasitism and disease are biotic factors which can have a devastating effect on individuals. Diseased animals will be weakened and often do not reproduce successfully. Sick predators cannot hunt well, and diseased prey animals are more likely to be caught. Some diseases are very infectious and can be spread without direct contact, such as avian (bird) flu, which can be spread in the faeces of an infected bird.

Parasites affect their hosts usually by feeding off the living body of their host and so weakening it. Occasionally they can wipe out whole populations. For example, Dutch elm disease is a parasitic fungus spread by elm bark beetles which has destroyed most of the mature elm trees in the UK.

Parasites and infectious diseases spread more rapidly when there is a high population density, as individuals are in much closer proximity to each other. If almost all of the organisms in an area are the same species, an infectious disease or parasite can have a devastating impact as it will affect most of the individuals directly or indirectly. In a community with greater biodiversity, although the effect on any infected individual will be as great, the effect of a disease or parasite on the whole community will be much less. Many species will be unaffected and there will be plenty of alternative food options.

HSW Facial tumours in Tasmanian devils

Devil Facial Tumour Disease affects and kills only Tasmanian devils. In an infected individual malignant tumours develop around the face that spread and kill it within about 6 months. This one disease could change the face of the Tasmanian ecosystem for ever. Originally scientists suspected a virus was involved. Now it appears that this devastating biotic factor arose through a mutation in a single Tasmanian devil, probably in the mid-1990s, which reduced the number of chromosomes from 14 to 13. Tissue from all the tumours investigated has been shown to have this same mutation. Tasmanian devils bite and savage each other when they feed or mate, and bits of the deadly tumours are passed on through bites on the face. The impact on the devil population has been huge – numbers are down from around 150 000 to under 50 000. But now that scientists understand how the disease is transmitted there is some hope that a programme of vaccinations might be developed in time to save the species.

fig. 5.2.19 **The facial tumours which affect Tasmanian devils kill them by making it impossible to eat and drink.**

Questions

SC 1 Animals mark out and defend their territories in a number of ways. Find out how three different animals mark and protect their territories, including at least one species of bird and one mammal.

2 Why is disease likely to have a greater effect on an ecosystem with little biodiversity than on a more diverse community?

Population ecology 4.5.10

When scientists are considering the ecology of an area and the impact of changes on the populations of living organisms it is difficult to distinguish clearly between the biotic and abiotic factors which shape an ecosystem, as they are frequently interlinked. And it is rare that one factor works alone – in a natural habitat the factors determining distribution and abundance of organisms are always complex. The box shows one example of why it is important to study all the factors in an ecosystem.

HSW Investigating factors affecting the population cycles of snowshoe hares

Charles Krebs and his team at the University of British Columbia investigated snowshoe hare populations in Yukon Territory, Canada. Their hypothesis was that both food supply and predation interact to affect the hare population and give rise to the pattern of the lynx/hare abundance. They chose nine 1 km^2 areas of undisturbed forest and measured the abundance of hares over 11 years (the average lifetime of a hare). In two of the areas extra food was supplied to the hares all year round. Another two areas were fenced off with mesh that let hares through but not lynxes – extra food was provided in one of these areas but not the other. In two more areas the soil was fertilised to increase the food quality. The remaining three areas were untouched and left as controls. The data collected (see Figure 5.2.20), show that both food and predation affect the abundance of hares.

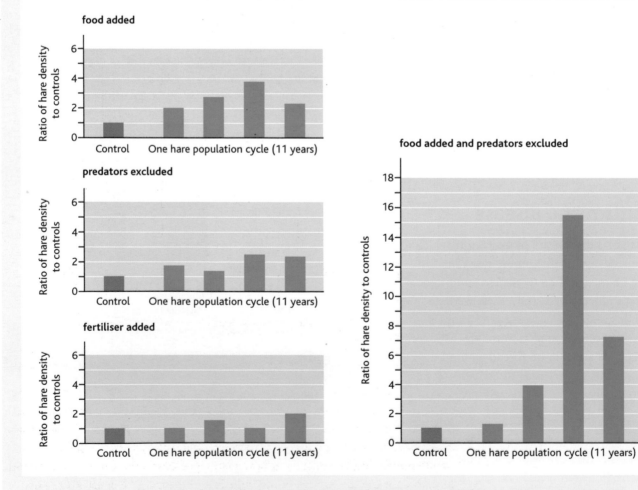

fig. 5.2.20 Results of investigations into factors affecting snowshoe hare populations in Canada. Population censuses were carried out at intervals through the 10 year cycle. The results of four of these censuses are shown here.

HSW Thinking outside the box!

Scientists often have to think 'outside the box' to explain their observations. A regular census of breeding birds in a woodland in southern England showed major changes in the populations of the breeding birds between 1950 and 1980 (see fig. 5.2.21). The woodpigeon population almost doubled quite suddenly between 1965 and 1970, but garden warblers disappeared altogether from the wood in 1971. The breeding blue tit population also increased fairly steadily. The biggest change in the habitat of Eastern Wood itself was that regular felling stopped, so there were more mature and dead trees. Had the increase in pigeons caused the drop in garden warblers, or had the end of felling caused the changes in bird populations? While there appeared to be correlation between these events, it did not seem enough to explain the changes in the bird populations. Scientists were looking at correlations – but felt they needed to look again to find the real causes of the changes.

It turned out that changes in biotic and abiotic factors far beyond the wood itself were affecting the bird populations. During the late 1960s many farmers across the south of England started growing oilseed rape, and rape fields provide pigeons with an abundant supply of food through the winter. Many more pigeons survived to breed in the woodland due to a biotic factor beyond the wood.

Garden warblers were affected by abiotic factors thousands of miles away in West Africa. These small birds migrate to Africa for the winter. Lack of rain meant severe drought in their overwintering grounds, so the numbers surviving and making it back to the UK to breed fell dramatically. Only the blue tits were affected by changes in the woodland habitat. The increase in old and dead trees meant an increase in the small holes that blue tits nest in, so the population increased.

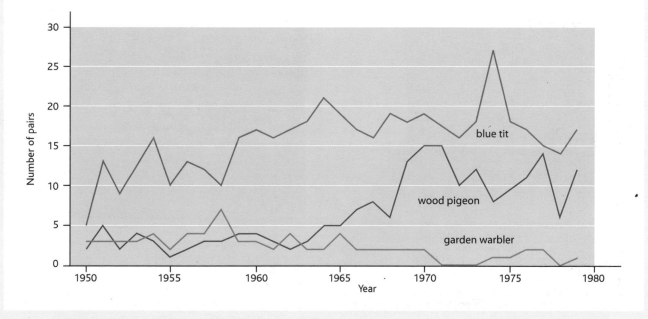
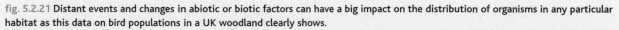

fig. 5.2.21 Distant events and changes in abiotic or biotic factors can have a big impact on the distribution of organisms in any particular habitat as this data on bird populations in a UK woodland clearly shows.

The factors that affect the number of organisms occupying a particular niche – whether biotic or abiotic – may be density dependent or density independent. The effect of density-independent factors is the same regardless of population size. For example, extremes of temperature will usually have the same effect on all individuals irrespective of how many individuals there are. These factors tend to limit the *distribution* of individuals and therefore of species. One of the effects of climate change as a result of global warming is the change in distribution of species as temperature extremes change.

The impact of a density-dependent factor will depend on how many organisms there are in a specific area. For example disease and parasitism are factors that are strongly density dependent – the more individuals there are in a given area, the more likely it is that the disease or parasite can be transmitted between individuals. Breeding success in territorial animals and birds is usually density dependent also, as individuals without territories are unlikely to breed. Only the strongest individuals will be able to hold territories when space is a limited resource. Density-dependent factors are important in limiting the *abundance* of species.

fig. 5.2.22 **Male tigers mark their territory to warn other males in the area that they will fight for that space. They do this by scratching trees and also by squirting urine.**

Many factors can be both. For example, the amount of water present in an area where there are relatively few plants is completely independent of the number of living things. It is affected by the amount of rainfall, the amount of sunshine and the type of soil, for example. However, in a densely overgrown area, the amount of water taken up by plants in transpiration will have a big impact on the water available in the soil and therefore it may be a density-limited resource.

Competition

Competition often results between individuals for density-dependent factors, and this can determine the size and the density of a population. Competition occurs when two organisms are competing for the same resource which is in limited supply. The competition may be for abiotic resources such as sunlight, minerals or food, or for biotic resources – territories, nest sites or mates. The competition for mates, for example, has led to sexual selection, which you studied in *AS Biology* (pages 242–3) and to the evolution of sexual dimorphism, where the males and females of the species look very different.

fig. 5.2.23 **In the rutting season the competition between stags for the females can be very direct indeed.**

Intraspecific competition is competition for a limited resource between members of the same population or species (see HSW box). For example, meerkats are small mammals that live in family groups, and both males and females will defend their territory against other groups of meerkats wanting to forage there. The territory provides the food they need for their growing young, and so is the limiting resource.

As a result of intraspecific competition, some individuals may not survive, or may not reproduce, and so population growth slows. In contrast, if resources are sufficiently plentiful there is little or no competition and the numbers of individuals will increase as fast as possible.

HSW Understanding intraspecific competition in Puerto Rican frogs

Eleutherodactylus coqui is a species of frog that lives In the tropical rainforests of Puerto Rico. These frogs feed on insects and are active at night, hiding during the day to avoid predators. They lay eggs in moist spots and the male guards them until tiny froglets hatch out. There is plenty of food – enough to support a larger population of frogs than exists. Scientists set about to discover the limiting resource.

They investigated the idea that competition for space might be a factor limiting the population size by dividing the study area into 100 m² plots. In some areas the frogs were provided with many small bamboo shelters while in others the habitat was left unchanged. All of the shelters in the test plots were rapidly occupied and the population density increased accordingly, while the population density of the frogs in the control plots remained the same. This confirmed the original hypothesis.

fig. 5.2.24 Coqui frogs got their name from sound they make – ko-KEE. The ko marks the territory and the kee attracts females!

Interspecific competition occurs when different species within a community compete for the same resources. Competition will reduce the abundance of the competing species. If there is a greater density of one species or it has a faster reproduction rate, then competing species may become extinct in that area. For example, years ago sailors released goats on Abingdon Island, which is part of the Galapagos Archipelago. Goats are relatively large, fast-breeding mammals, with appetites to match. Since their introduction, the growing goat population has consumed huge numbers of the island's plants, including the ones which the giant tortoises ate. The reptiles could not compete effectively because they reproduce much more slowly, and in the 1960s they became extinct on Abingdon. Isabela Island, which supports a higher proportion of **endemic** Galapagos species than any other, faces the same problem. Local scientists are working to eradicate the goats and remove the introduced competition.

fig. 5.2.25 On Isabela Island many endemic species – including the giant tortoises – are threatened by competition from goats.

Questions

1 Explain the difference between intraspecific and interspecific competition and how they affect the distribution and abundance of organisms in a habitat.

SC 2 Use data from fig. 5.2.20 to answer these questions

 a Describe the impact of the different experimental conditions on the density of the hare population.

 b Suggest an explanation for the difference between the effect of simply adding food or removing predators compared with the enclosures where both food was added and predators excluded.

 c Suggest an explanation for the hare population dipping towards the end of the population cycle and back this up with evidence if possible. Why do you think the population where the grass was fertilised does not show this dip?

SC 3 Explain how density-independent factors and density-dependent factors affect the distribution and abundance of organisms.

Energy transfer in ecosystems 4.5.1, 4.5.8

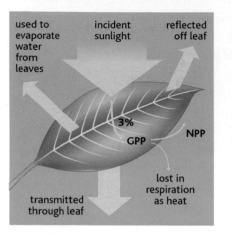

fig. 5.2.26 **Most of the solar input energy that reaches a leaf is not available for producing new plant tissue (GPP).**

Energy within an organism can be used to produce more body tissue, that is to increase its **biomass**. Since the source of energy in most ecosystems is the Sun, the rate at which producers convert the Sun's energy into organic material will determine the flow of energy within those ecosystems.

Only a very small percentage of the solar energy input from the Sun is actually transferred into plant material (see **fig. 5.2.26**). Figures vary, but between 1 and 3% is generally accepted. **Gross primary productivity** (**GPP**) (sometimes more simply called gross primary production) in plants is the rate at which energy is incorporated into the plants. It may be measured in units of biomass/area/time, such as simple $gm^{-2}\,year^{-1}$ or gC (grams of carbon assimilated) $m^{-2}\,year^{-1}$. It may also be measured in units of energy, e.g. $kcal\,m^{-2}\,year^{-1}$. Plants use up to 25% of this accumulated energy for their own metabolic needs. Most importantly they respire, breaking down glucose to release energy in the form of ATP for use in metabolic processes. The rest of the energy is stored in their body tissues. This stored energy is known as the **net primary productivity** (**NPP**).

NPP = GPP – plant respiration

The NPP of different ecosystems has been estimated. This productivity will depend on all the abiotic factors and biotic factors that affect plant growth within the ecosystem. For example, graph B shows clearly the importance of the availability of water within an ecosystem, as well as warmth. Latitude is another key factor because the solar energy input within a specific area is lower at latitudes nearer the pole than closer to the equator (see **fig. 5.2.27**).

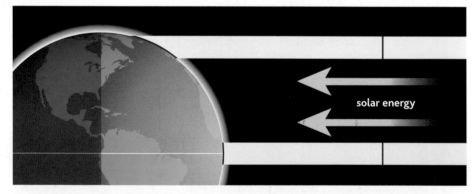

fig. 5.2.27 **The solar energy input on a square metre of the Earth's surface is greater at the equator than near the pole because the curvature of the Earth means the energy is spread out over a larger area of the surface at the poles.**

If you combine the NPP of each type of ecosystem with the area of the Earth's surface it covers, you can see how much each type contributes to the overall NPP of the Earth (see **fig. 5.2.28**). For example, tropical rainforests cover only about 5% of the Earth's surface but yield over 30% of the global NPP. The oceans contribute a similar proportion to the global NPP but only because they are so vast.

The human population of the world is growing at a very rapid rate and even at its current level humans are consuming up to 40% of the NPP of the planet.

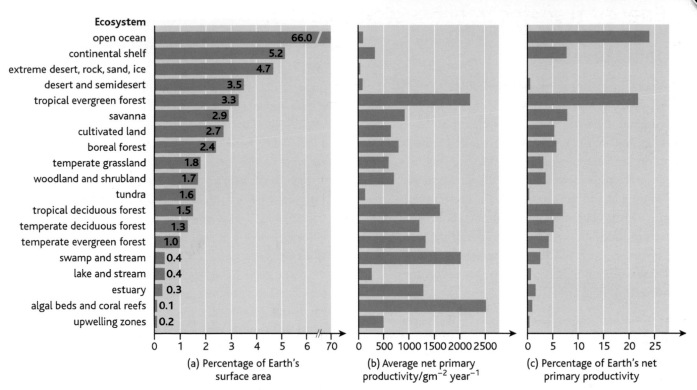

fig. 5.2.28 **Different ecosystems contribute different amounts to the NPP of the Earth.**

HSW Building models of energy flow

In the 1920s Charles Elton, a young Oxford biologist, began to study the relationships between the animals on Bear Island (off the northern coast of Norway) and their scarce food resources. The main carnivores were arctic foxes, which ate birds such as sandpipers and ptarmigan. The birds ate the leaves and berries of plants or, in some cases, ate insects which fed on the plants. Elton called these feeding interactions a **food chain** and proposed a general model to explain energy flow through a community. Each link in the food chain represents a specific **trophic** (or feeding) **level** (see **fig. 5.2.29**).

Your studies of food chains will have shown how limited

this idea is, and that the interrelationships between organisms in an ecosystem are better described by a **food web**. You may also have realised that in parallel with this grazing food chain are the **decomposers**, microorganisms such as bacteria and fungi that break down the remains of animals and plants and return the mineral nutrients to the soil. In terms of energy flow, these may be eaten by other animals when scavenging and so link back to the grazing chain, or may die and be broken down by other decomposers.

Although a food chain is a highly simplified model, it has helped us to develop an understanding of energy flow through ecosystems.

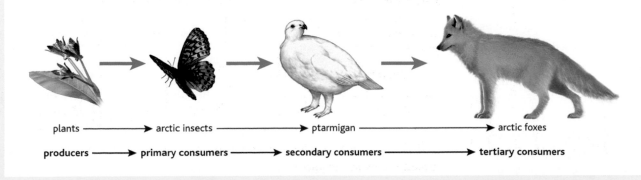

fig. 5.2.29 **A food chain such as this is the simplest representation of the feeding relationships and energy flow within an ecosystem.**

Energy transfer to higher trophic levels

The energy in plant material is available to herbivores, but relatively little of it ends up as new animal material. Some of the energy is never assimilated but is lost as undigested and therefore unused material in the faeces. Much of the assimilated energy is used to drive respiration and is then lost to the atmosphere as heat energy. Some is lost as chemical energy in metabolic waste products and heat energy in the urine of the animal (see **fig. 5.2.30**). The energy used to make new animal biomass is known as **secondary production**.

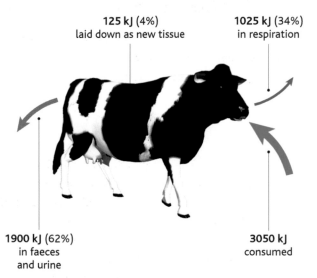

125 kJ (4%)
laid down as new tissue

1025 kJ (34%)
in respiration

1900 kJ (62%)
in faeces
and urine

3050 kJ
consumed

fig. 5.2.30 **The fate of energy in the food eaten by a primary consumer. Similar losses will occur in other consumer trophic levels.**

Similar energy losses occur between animal trophic levels, herbivores to primary carnivores, and so on up the food chain. The proportion of energy used to make biomass compared with the energy available to an organism in the trophic level below is a measure of the efficiency of energy transfer. This measure is often quoted as being around 10%, but it varies greatly. Studies have shown it as low as 0.1% for some small herbivorous mammals and as great as 80% for some microorganisms. It is most commonly between about 2 and 24%. The causes of such wide variation depend on many factors, including the effort required to find food, the digestibility of the food and the metabolic rate of the organism.

HSW How reliable are the figures?

In 1942, an American ecologist, R.L. Lindeman, published the results of his study of energy transfers in an ecosystem at Lake Mendota in Minnesota in the journal *Ecology*. His results showed the following: producers 0.4%, primary consumers 8.7%, secondary consumers 5.5%, tertiary consumers 13.0%. Lindeman was the first person to attempt to calculate trophic efficiencies and he suggested that trophic efficiency might increase as you go up the trophic levels. This became known as his 'law of trophic efficiency' which is often misquoted as saying that the efficiency of energy transfer between any trophic level and the next is about 10%. Lindeman died before the paper was published, and since then there have been many studies on energy transfer efficiency. These provide such wide-ranging values that neither Lindeman's original proposal, nor the generalised version, can be considered reasonable.

Consider the assumptions made in calculating the energy in the organisms of an entire ecosystem. Not only do you need to be certain that you have identified all the most abundant species in the ecosystem, you also need to know how many there are, what an average body size is, how much energy that body size represents, and so on. Also at what time of year do you make the measurements? In temperate regions there is likely to be more energy in plant and animal bodies during the summer, and more in decomposers during the winter. What effect might this have on your estimates? And how do you calculate the rate of energy transfer into a trophic level (and all the organisms that represents) over a whole year?

The values that are quoted from studies are the mean values from the calculations and usually have large standard errors (a statistical way of showing how close the mean is to the real value – small is close, large means not very reliable). This is not surprising given the many assumptions that are made during their calculation.

So far we have considered only the grazing food chain. For any trophic level, up to 99% of the energy may pass directly to the decomposers, and this will vary depending on factors such as temperature, water availability and, particularly in temperate zones, which season, such as after leaf fall. Figure 5.2.31 shows the results of one study that attempted to assess the energy transfers throughout a whole ecosystem.

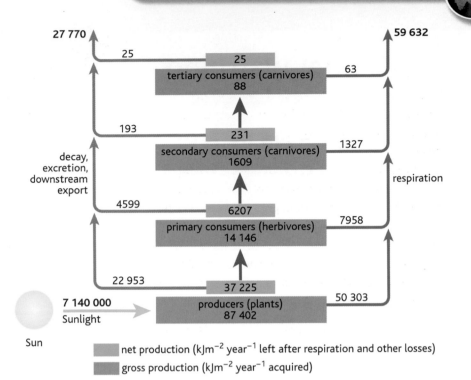

net production (kJm^{-2} year^{-1} left after respiration and other losses)

gross production (kJm^{-2} year^{-1} acquired)

fig. 5.2.31 The complex energy interactions between different energy levels in the river at Silver Springs, Colorado as measured by E.P. Odum in 1957.

Energy transfer and food chain length

As you have seen, relatively little of the solar energy falling on the Earth is used to produce plant material, and increasingly small amounts of that energy are passed from one trophic level to the next in a food chain. One of the main effects of the relatively inefficient transfer of energy through food chains and webs is to limit the number of trophic levels. At higher trophic levels, the organisms usually need to range over larger distances, so, by the fourth or fifth trophic level, it could take more energy to get food and a mate than is needed for growth and reproduction. Some scientists suggest this explains the longer food chains in ecosystems in tropical regions that receive higher solar inputs than nearer the poles. However, the complexity of food webs in tropical systems makes it difficult to judge what is a food chain exactly and therefore the accuracy of this idea.

Questions

1 a Which type of ecosystem is most productive compared with its percentage of the area of the Earth?

   b Which type of ecosystem is least productive based on the same comparison?

   c Why is primary production in the open oceans so important?

2 a Calculate the efficiency of the energy transfers between the trophic levels in the ecosystem shown at Silver Springs (to 1dp).

   b Calculate the average energy transfer for this system.

3 Look at fig. 5.2.31.

   a Suggest why Odum's diagram shows only trophic levels and not the individual species in the food web. Give as many reasons as you can.

   b What assumptions would Odum needed to have made in order to create this diagram?

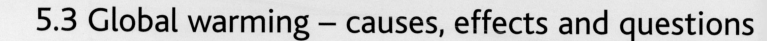

5.3 Global warming – causes, effects and questions

The carbon cycle in nature 4.5.9, 4.5.14

The inefficient transfer of energy between organisms is not a problem as there is a constant supply of fresh energy from the Sun. However, the same is not true for the other ingredients of life, such as water, and minerals, such as carbon and nitrogen. Complex cycles have evolved which ensure that the chemical constituents of life are continually cycled through ecosystems. These cycles involve a biotic phase, where the inorganic ions are incorporated in the tissues of living things, and an abiotic phase, where the inorganic ions are returned to the non-living part of the ecosystem.

The carbon cycle

As you saw in your AS course, carbon is fundamental to the formation of the complex organic molecules, such as carbohydrates, proteins, fats and nucleic acids, which are the building blocks of life. There is a massive pool of carbon in the carbon dioxide present in the atmosphere and dissolved in the water of rivers, lakes and oceans. This carbon dioxide is absorbed and the carbon incorporated into complex compounds in plants during photosynthesis. The carbon then passes to animals through food chains. The carbon dioxide is continually returned to the atmosphere or water in the process of respiration.

The interactions of the carbon cycle can best be summarised in a diagram such as **fig. 5.3.1**. You will be looking at the microorganisms involved in the carbon cycle in more detail on page 91.

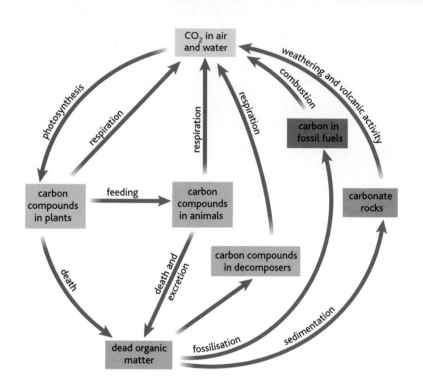

fig. 5.3.1 **The carbon cycle in nature.**

Carbon sinks

Figure 5.3.1 shows that there are massive abiotic and biotic **carbon sinks** in nature. These are reservoirs where carbon is removed from the atmosphere and 'locked up' in organic or inorganic compounds. In the biotic part of the system carbon is removed from the atmosphere by photosynthesis and stored in the bodies of living organisms. Soil also contains masses of organic, carbon-rich material in the form of humus. In the abiotic part of the system, rocks such as limestone and chalk, and fossil fuels such as coal, oil and natural gas, hold vast stores of carbon.

The oceans also act as massive reservoirs of carbon dioxide and contain around 50 times more dissolved inorganic carbon than is present in the atmosphere. The carbon dioxide is in continual exchange at the air–water surface. Carbon dioxide dissolved in the water is taken up in photosynthesis by the phytoplankton that live in the surface waters of the oceans. Large amounts of carbon are also stored in the calcium carbonate shells produced by many different marine organisms and in coral reefs. By lowering the concentration of dissolved carbon dioxide they make it possible for more carbon dioxide from the air to be absorbed by the water.

The Atlantic Ocean is a particularly important ocean sink, absorbing up to 23% of human-produced carbon each year. The Southern Ocean covers a much bigger area but only contains 9% of the total carbon. The differences are due to a variety of factors, including water temperature and ocean currents in the Northern (Atlantic) Ocean which move carbon-rich water downwards and bring more water up from the depths to absorb more carbon.

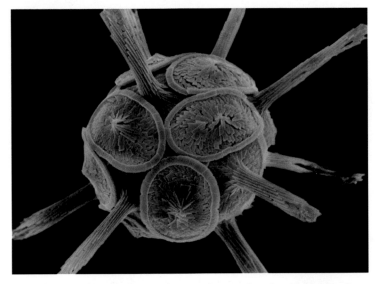

fig. 5.3.2 **Over half of all photosynthesis each year takes place in microscopic phytoplankton in the oceans.**

The quantity of carbon stored in the different carbon sinks is measured in petagrams: 1 petagram is 10^{15} g or 1 billion tonnes. So for example, around 110 petagrams of carbon are removed each year from the atmosphere into the bodies of living organisms by photosynthesis. About 50 petagrams are returned to the atmosphere by the respiration of living organisms, and another 60 petagrams become part of the process of decomposition. The carbon becomes part of the organic material in the soil – the soil sink – before eventually being released back to the atmosphere as carbon dioxide.

Left to itself the carbon cycle is self-regulating – the amounts of carbon released in respiration and other natural processes and absorbed in photosynthesis remain in balance so that atmospheric carbon dioxide levels remain relatively steady.

The human influence?

Until the last few hundred years, humans were probably fairly carbon-neutral. However the evidence is building that the enormous increase in the production of carbon dioxide by people since the Industrial Revolution in the eighteenth and nineteenth centuries, coupled with the development of the internal combustion engine and its use in cars from the nineteenth century onwards is now threatening the balance of the carbon cycle. Scientists are collecting evidence that the level of carbon dioxide in the atmosphere is increasing and many predict that this could have major effects on climate, geology and the distribution of organisms.

As we look at some of these effects below, an understanding of the carbon cycle will help you consider models of ways in which atmospheric carbon dioxide levels may be reduced.

Questions

SC 1 Given that combustion is a natural process, explain how humans are destabilising the natural carbon cycle.

2 In table 5.3.1 the amounts in many of the different carbon sinks are shown as ranges. Suggest reasons why the quantities in the different sinks have changed over time.

Sink	Amount in petagrams
Atmosphere	From 578 (in 1700) to 766 (in 1999)
Soil organic matter	1 500–1 600
Ocean	38 000–40 000
Marine sediments and sedimentary rocks	66 000 000–100 000 000
Terrestrial plants	540–610
Fossil fuel deposits	4 000

Table 5.3.1 Estimated major stores of carbon on the Earth.

Greenhouse gases 4.5.14

Carbon dioxide is one of the 'greenhouse gases'; others include methane and water vapour. These gases have a very important role in the atmosphere, without which life on Earth as we know it would not be possible.

Greenhouse gases reduce heat loss from the surface of the Earth in a way that is similar to how glass panels reduce heat loss from a greenhouse. This is known as the **greenhouse effect**. When radiation from the Sun reaches the Earth, some is reflected back into space by the atmosphere and by the surface of the Earth and some is absorbed by the atmosphere. The key wavelength is infrared, the radiation that we feel as heat. Infrared radiation that reaches the Earth's surface is of a fairly short wavelength. This is absorbed by the surface of the Earth and then radiated from the surface at a longer wavelength. Some of this radiation is absorbed and reradiated back to the Earth's surface by greenhouse gas molecules in the atmosphere. This maintains the temperature at the surface of the Earth at a higher level which, fortunately for us and most of the organisms that live on Earth, is suitable for life. Without greenhouse gases in the atmosphere, the surface of Earth could look more like that of Mars.

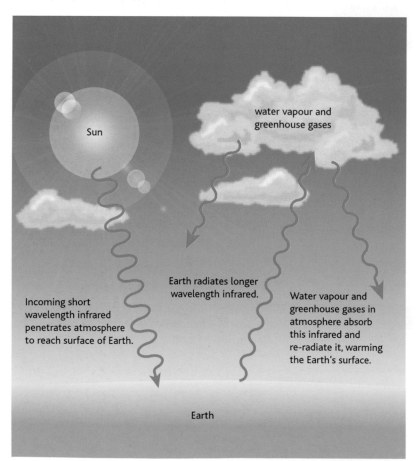

Incoming short wavelength infrared penetrates atmosphere to reach surface of Earth.

Earth radiates longer wavelength infrared.

water vapour and greenhouse gases

Water vapour and greenhouse gases in atmosphere absorb this infrared and re-radiate it, warming the Earth's surface.

Sun

Earth

fig. 5.3.3 **The greenhouse effect.**

The role of methane

Methane is a potent greenhouse gas, and over a period of 20 years has a 72 times greater effect on warming the atmosphere than carbon dioxide. However, much less of it is produced than CO_2. Its main sources are from the decay of organic material by some kinds of bacteria, particularly in wet conditions, and from the digestion of ruminant herbivores, such as deer and cows. It naturally breaks down high in the atmosphere in a series of reactions that eventually form carbon dioxide and water molecules.

Methane levels have risen by about 150% since 1750 for several reasons. Rice paddy fields are waterlogged during much of the time the rice is growing. Bacteria in this waterlogged soil release methane as they grow. Levels of rice production have been increasing steadily to feed the ever-increasing world population, and so more methane is produced. In addition, as the human population grows, so do the numbers of animals that we depend on for food, including cattle. So the amount of methane released from their digestion increases too. Scientists have calculated that up to 60% of the methane in the atmosphere now is produced as a result of human activity in some way.

Greenhouse gas	Percentage estimated contribution
Water vapour	36–70
Carbon dioxide	9–26
Methane	4–9
Ozone	3–7

Table 5.3.2 **The estimated contributions of the main greenhouse gases to the greenhouse effect. The variation depends on the amount of water vapour present and the concentrations of other greenhouse gases.**

HSW Managing methane, changing cows!

Cows belch a lot – and every time they burp they release methane gas. Estimates of the amount of methane produced per cow per day vary from 100 to 700 dm³. This varies depending on factors such as the breed of cow, the type of food eaten and whether the cow is giving milk. There are an estimated 1.2 billion cows in the world so a lot of methane is being produced. The IPCC (the Intergovernmental Panel on Climate Change) estimate that 16% of the methane produced as a result of human activities comes from livestock, and dairy cows produce the most.

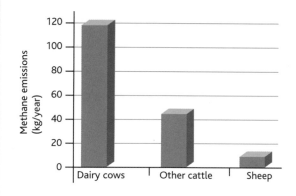

fig. 5.3.4 **Annual methane emissions from North American dairy cows, other cattle and sheep.**

A number of research teams have set out to breed or engineer new strains of grass which can be digested more easily by cows, reducing methane emissions. And an Irish research team looked at whether changing the way cows are farmed could reduce overall methane emissions. Older cows produce more milk, but less methane per pint. By keeping cows alive, healthy and giving milk for longer, the average methane emissions of the entire herd can be reduced (see **fig. 5.3.5**).

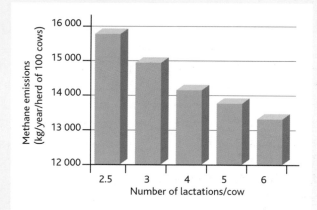

fig. 5.3.5 **This graph shows that a herd of 100 older cows – who have had five or six calves and therefore five or six lactation cycles – produce a lot less methane than a herd of younger cows who have had fewer calves.**

Adding concentrates to the diet also reduces methane emissions per cow, because the concentrates are easier to digest and help prolong the cow's working life. However, generating the electricity needed in the manufacture of the concentrates produces carbon dioxide, so a balance needs to be struck.

Current evidence suggests that with a combination of good husbandry, careful breeding and possible genetic engineering of food plants people may be able to drink milk, eat beef – and reduce the production of methane at the same time.

Questions

1 There is one very simple way of reducing the methane emissions from cattle. What is it and why do you think it is not widely suggested?

SC 2 The term 'greenhouse effect' is widely used to suggest something negative. Why is this an inaccurate use of the term?

Looking at the evidence 4.5.18

The UK Met Office has daily weather records going back to 1869, but written evidence from diaries and ships' logs go back over 100 years more. Recent weather records suggest that the Earth's surface temperature is increasing. In 1998 the IPCC gathered together a lot of data to produce this graph of temperature in the Northern Hemisphere (see **fig. 5.3.6**).

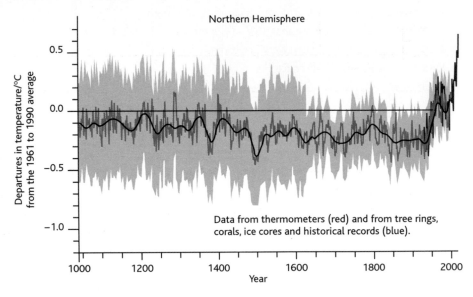

fig. 5.3.6 The IPCC 'hockey stick graph' published in 2001 uses data from a variety of sources to show how the temperature has changed over centuries. The term 'hockey stick' comes from the shape of the graph. Note that the grey is the error on each measurement, i.e. the range in which the real value is thought to lie, so we cannot actually be too accurate!

You can see that we have data of measured temperatures only since the mid-1800s. Further temperatures are inferred from other data that can give an indication of the temperature but not an exact value. These other sources of data are called temperature **proxies**, and the **error lines** shown in grey on the graph indicate how accurate these values are thought to be. The black line indicates the **mean** values. Temperature proxies include tree rings, corals, ice cores and peat bog data.

Frozen isotopes

One widely used source of temperature proxies comes from Antarctic and Greenland ice cores. Scientists drill deep down into the ice and then analyse the air trapped in the different layers. This provides a record which goes back thousands of years. The precision of analysis of the air samples from the core ice is given as 0.2 ppm. Records of the oxygen isotopes in melted ice (the proportions of O^{18} to O^{16}) reflect the air temperature at the time the ice layer was laid down and so give scientists data on the air temperature. Atmospheric carbon dioxide levels can also be measured.

The results of the analysis of air from ice cores for over 300 000 years is shown in **fig. 5.3.7**. It appears that about 140 000 years ago the surface of the Earth was about 6 °C cooler than it is today and the Earth was in an Ice Age. On the other hand, about 120 000 years ago the climate was 1–2 °C warmer than it is now. These warm periods are known as **interglacials** and since then we have had another ice age and some more warming.

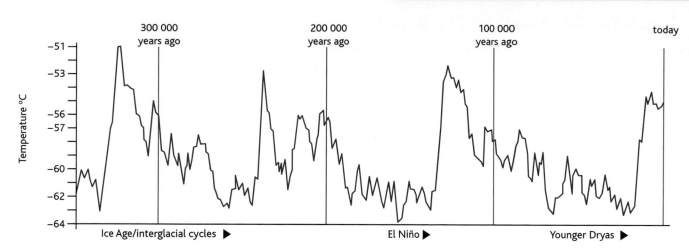

fig. 5.3.7 **Data from ice cores show how the temperature of the Earth has fluctuated over time.**

Dendrochronology

Another temperature proxy is dendrochronology or, more precisely, dendroclimatology. Dendrochronology is the dating of past events using tree ring growth. Trees increase in width as they get older by cell division of one particular layer in their trunks. When there is plenty of moisture and trees are growing quickly, such as early summer in temperate regions, these new cells are large. As conditions get more difficult, the new cells produced are smaller. Eventually growth stops for the year until the next spring. It is the contrast between the small cells at the end of one year and the large ones produced the next spring which give the appearance of rings. So by counting the rings, it is possible to find an approximate age for a tree or piece of timber. It is always approximate, because if conditions vary a lot during the year, a tree will produce more than one growth ring.

Dendroclimatology is the study of what dendrochronology can tell us about the climate in the past. The problem with evidence from dendrochronology is that growth in trees is dependent on many factors, including amount of sunshine, temperature, carbon dioxide levels and amount of rainfall. This is a relatively new science, but one which scientists hope will be very useful in the future as they refine their techniques and discover ways to determine which factors have affected the growth of tree in the past. One way to check the reliability of the data is by comparing results from different places (fig. 5.3.8). If the rings are similar then the climate was changing generally, not just in a small area. However, this does not solve the problem of what wider rings mean – better climate possibly, but does that mean warmer, wetter, sunnier, more carbon dioxide, or even some combination of these?

Many people have questioned the validity of using tree-ring data to determine past temperature conditions and this has undermined some of the findings on climate change. Data from coral reefs can be used to confirm the evidence from trees, as the proportions of different isotopes taken up by the coral vary as the sea temperatures change and this gives another valuable proxy record of climate change.

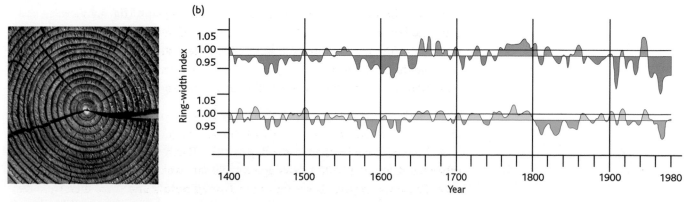

fig. 5.3.8 (a) **Tree rings can age a tree – and much more. (b) Graphs of two trees of the same species but growing 200 km apart show very similar patterns, suggesting the changes affecting them happened over a large area.**

Another source of data for a temperature proxy comes from peat bogs. Peat bogs are made of partly decomposed plant material, mainly *Sphagnum* mosses. The peat is very acidic, cool and anaerobic, which prevents bacteria from decomposing organic material. As a result, pollen grains, moss spores and even plant tissues are preserved in peat. By sampling cores of peat, we can look back in time at the plants and mosses growing in and around that area from hundreds and even thousands of years ago. As the types of plants that can grow in an area are affected by climate, the pollen/moss record can give a clear reflection of how the climate has changed with time. For example, cotton grass and some species of *Sphagnum* moss indicate cool wet conditions, while other species of *Sphagnum* and species of *Polytrichum* moss reflect a period of drier conditions in the bog. Pollen blown in from around the area adds to the picture. So pollen from horse-chestnut trees indicates warmer conditions, whereas pollen from birch trees shows that it was cooler.

Peat growth rate depends on the prevailing conditions and varies widely. So evidence from undisturbed peat bogs (and lake sediments), like that collected by Dmitri Mauquoy and his team from Aberdeen University (see **fig. 5.3.9.**), can

give a clear and unbroken record of the climate, and has resulted in a continuous record from about 7500 BP which gives clear evidence of periods of warming and cooling.

fig. 5.3.9 **Dmitri Mauquoy and colleague from Aberdeen University extracting a core from a peat bog. One metre of peat like this is a record of at least a thousand years of life in and around the peat bog, so analysis of the findings isn't easy.**

Increasing data reliability

Both dendrochronology and peat bog dating are used to confirm radiocarbon dating in a process known as **wiggle matching**. For example, wood of known ages from ancient trees, or samples of peat bog where the age is known from evidence of flood, etc. are dated from radiocarbon measurements and the results

compared to give a form of **calibration**. This gives scientists clear reference points which they can use to determine the accuracy of their estimations of age, making the data considerably more reliable.

Data like these were used to produce the IPCC graph you saw in **fig. 5.3.6**. In 2008 scientists recalculated the figures using more than 1200 temperature proxy records, going back 1300 years without using tree-ring data, and used two different statistical methods. They found that the hockey stick graph (**fig. 5.3.6**) was valid whichever statistical method was used and whether tree-ring data were included or not.

Evidence for increasing levels of carbon dioxide

Scientists have found evidence for the increasing levels of carbon dioxide in the atmosphere in many different ways. Some of the most famous evidence comes from what is known as the Mauna Loa curve, a series of readings taken at regular intervals at the Mauna Loa

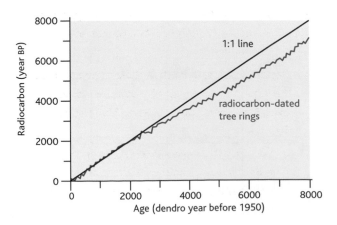

fig. 5.3.10 **The accuracy of radiocarbon dating and dendrochronology can be seen using wiggle matching graphs such as this one.**

observatory on Hawaii. The air is sampled continuously at the top of four 7-metre tall towers and an hourly average of carbon dioxide concentration is taken (along with a number of other readings). The air in the area is relatively free from local pollutants and scientists believe it is representative of the air in the Northern Hemisphere. Measurements started in 1958 and the monitoring methods and instruments used have remained very similar throughout that time. The records show that the level of atmospheric carbon dioxide has increased from 315.98 ppmv (parts per million by volume of dry air) in 1959 to 381.74 in 2006. The annual fluctuations in the levels of carbon dioxide seem to be the result of seasonal differences in the fixation of carbon dioxide by plants, as in temperate regions plants lose their leaves in winter and take up less carbon dioxide.

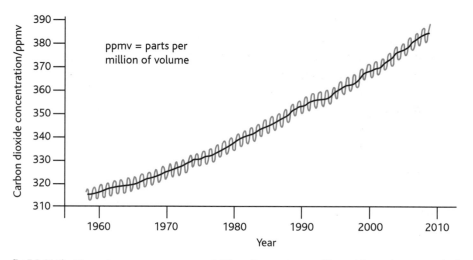

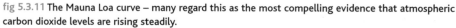

fig 5.3.11 The Mauna Loa curve – many regard this as the most compelling evidence that atmospheric carbon dioxide levels are rising steadily.

Ice core data also show clear changes in carbon dioxide concentration. **Figure 5.3.12** shows data taken from the Law Dome ice cores – particularly pure and undisturbed ice in the Antarctic. The shape of the curve is reminiscent of the temperature curve.

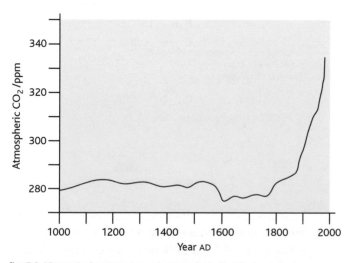

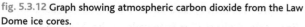

fig. 5.3.12 Graph showing atmospheric carbon dioxide from the Law Dome ice cores.

Questions

1 What is the overall percentage increase in atmospheric carbon dioxide from 1959 to 2006 based on the Muana Loa data?

2 Why is the data from Muana Loa regarded as reliable?

3 What can the data from the Law Dome ice cores tell us that the Mauna Loa data cannot and how reliable is the data?

4 Some people use these data alone to demonstrate the impact of human activity on carbon dioxide levels in the atmosphere. Why is this a misuse of the data?

5 a Why was the original 'hockey stick' graph produced by the IPCC in 1998 challenged?

   b How has the 2008 update helped to reassure many doubters?

The global warming debate 4.5.18

A lot of evidence from many studies now suggests a clear **correlation** between the increase in temperature and carbon dioxide levels. However, one problem is that the correlation is so close (see **fig. 5.3.13**) that it is difficult to know whether increases in greenhouse gases are *causing* the increase in temperatures – or whether the rise in greenhouse gases is the *result* of rising temperatures.

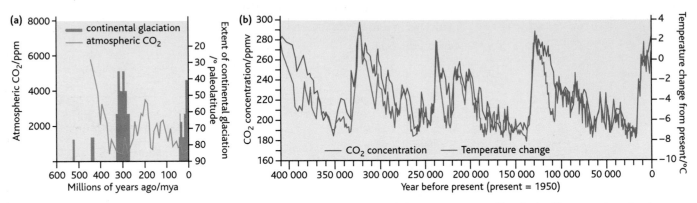

fig. 5.3.13 (a) The pattern of atmospheric carbon dioxide concentration and continental glaciation over several hundred million years from data in gases trapped in the Antarctic and Greenland icecaps. (b) Data from ice cores from Vostok (in the Antarctic) showing carbon dioxide content of the air trapped in the ice cores and the air temperature change relative to modern temperature based on measurements of the isotopic composition of the gases.

To say that there is a **causal relationship** we need some mechanism that explains how one factor changes the other. From our understanding of the greenhouse effect and because of the timing, a logical step is to consider that humans are responsible. Since the Industrial Revolution we have burnt increasing quantities of fossil fuels for energy and for transport, and more recently to generate electricity, and all this produces carbon dioxide. However, some scientists have proposed a mechanism where solar activity affects cloud formation and therefore surface temperature. **Figure 5.3.14** seems to show a much closer correlation between solar activity and atmospheric temperature than it does between carbon dioxide concentrations and temperature. However, the IPCC reached the conclusion that the sum of these activities over the past 50 years would most likely have produced cooling rather than warming.

All these arguments are based on data that require detailed interpretation and the use of computer modelling to model a very complex system. So *proving* a causal link is almost impossible. However, increasing numbers of studies, on different aspects of global warming such as polar ice melting and climate change in different regions of the world, using different computer models, are suggesting that it is the increase in atmospheric carbon dioxide that is increasing surface temperature, and that human carbon dioxide emissions are responsible for at least some of the current warming. The IPCC believe there is sufficient evidence now to state this is a causal link. However, it will almost certainly turn out that global warming is multifactorial, with many different inputs, not just carbon dioxide levels.

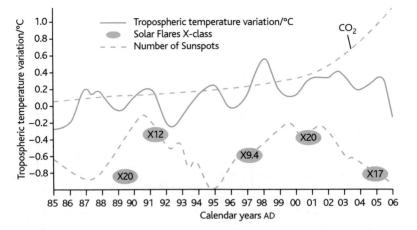

fig. 5.3.14 The relationship between solar activity (sunspots and flares), temperatures high in the atmosphere and carbon dioxide levels from 1980 to 2006.

HSW Communicating with the public

In 2007 the IPCC looked at data and models of climate change presented by scientists from all around the world. They saw that **anthropogenic** (produced by people) carbon dioxide levels increased by 80% between 1970 and 2004, mainly due to the use of fossil fuels. The IPCC finally decided that the balance of the evidence shows a 90% probability that human activities resulting in the build up of greenhouse gases are at least partly responsible for the observed increase in global temperatures. In their 2007 report they state that there is *very high confidence* that the net effect of human activities since 1750 has been one of global warming.

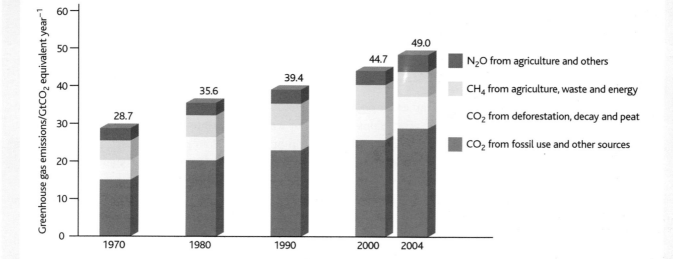

fig. 5.3.15 **The emissions of different greenhouse gases have increased over the past 40 years or so.**

The IPCC use language carefully designed to indicate how strongly the evidence backs up the hypothesis. They have decided that it is *very likely* that human activities have contributed to the rise in sea level in the second half of the twenty-first century, but only *likely* that they have also influenced the changes in wind and weather patterns that have been observed. And it is *more likely than not* that human activities have influenced the risk of heat waves and droughts since the 1970s.

At the moment climate changes and environmental damage are occurring far faster than anyone imagined. In fact the IPCC have decided that the evidence means that there are likely to be some irreversible impacts on the environment from the warming seen already.

Questions

1 In fig. 5.3.13 how do the different data in graph (a) and graph (b) support the theory that carbon dioxide levels and the temperature at the Earth's surface are linked? How reliable is the data?

2 Using fig. 5.3.15 calculate the percentage increase in carbon dioxide from fossil fuel use and compare it with the overall percentage increase in greenhouse gases from all sources.

3 a Look at fig. 5.3.14 showing solar activity and find out more about the evidence put forward for the 'solar flare' theory of global warming. What are the main strengths and weaknesses of this line of evidence?

 b Compare the correlation between solar activity and atmospheric temperatures with the correlation between carbon dioxide levels and temperature as seen in fig. 5.3.13 graph (b) and any others you may find. Discuss the validity of the data and the strength of the correlations as a basis for the feasibility of any causal relationships.

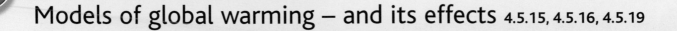

Models of global warming – and its effects 4.5.15, 4.5.16, 4.5.19

In order to investigate the relationship between carbon dioxide and Earth's temperature in the past, scientists have developed huge computer models. These models have taken years to develop and are still being refined as new research shows how different factors interact. There are many factors to consider, such as rates of photosynthesis across the world, rates of carbon dioxide production by natural causes, the exchange of carbon dioxide between the atmosphere and oceans and the effect of changing temperature on all of these. Scientists hope that by making models that fit the data from the past as accurately as possible, they will then give us reasonable tools for predicting the future.

Predicting the future

We can **extrapolate** the data on greenhouse gases and use them in models to make predictions about what will happen to temperature in the future. These extrapolations can be used in other models to predict the long-term effects of increased temperature on the environment. These models can be very useful. For example, some of the predictions shown in **fig. 5.3.16** are being used by the IPCC to help plan international responses to the problems of rising carbon dioxide levels and global warming. But there are many limitations because not only is it impossible to tell the exact impact of carbon dioxide on global warming, it is also impossible to predict the impact of global warming on particular aspects of the world climate. In addition, extrapolations from past data cannot take into account unknown factors in the future, including how current trends in use of resources and technologies may change. So, assuming that the models are reasonably accurate, and assuming that the predictions of temperature in the future based on carbon dioxide emissions are realistic, what effect might this have?

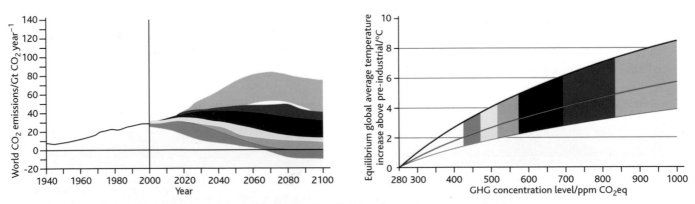

fig. 5.3.16 The lines of the left-hand graph predict possible global carbon dioxide emissions in gigatonnes of carbon dioxide per year. These results are fed into other models that predict the average global temperature compared with pre-industrial levels (shown in the graph on the right). As you can see there are large margins of error!

Risk of flooding

In 2002, 500 billion tonnes of ice broke away from the Antarctic peninsula and eventually melted into the sea. Antarctic temperatures have increased by an average of 2.5 °C in the past 50 years – faster than anywhere else on the Earth. Many scientists believe that the thinning of the ice is a clear indication of global warming.

The Antarctic ice contains around 70% of the world's fresh water. In the Arctic the sea ice has been retreating by about 2.7% each decade since 1978 and many glaciers are also retreating at a rate of about 50 m a year. As the ice melts, the volume of water in the seas and oceans of the world will increase, causing sea levels to rise. And as the water gets warmer, its volume increases, resulting in an even bigger impact on sea levels. The implications for human life as sea levels rise are immense – around 100 million people live less than 1 metre above current sea levels. For example in the UK large areas of the east coast could be lost for good, and the Netherlands might disappear completely!

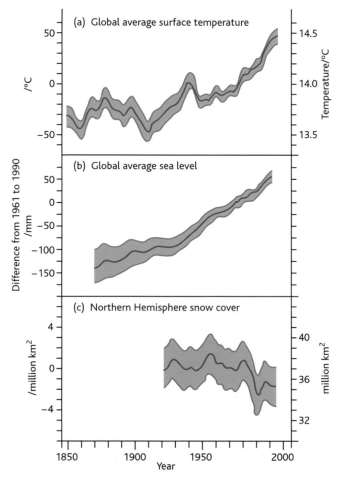

fig. 5.3.17 The correlation between rising temperatures, melting snow and rising sea water can be clearly seen in these IPCC graphs.

Climate change

Rising temperatures affect weather and rainfall patterns. It is impossible to link any one weather event to global warming, but statistical evidence suggests that there is an increase in extreme weather events linked to the rise in global temperatures.

Rainfall patterns are complex but they also seem to be changing. For example, if the current trend of low rainfall continues in Africa, it has been predicted that by the year 2020 between 75 and 250 million people will be short of water for their crops and to drink. In contrast, in some areas rainfall has been both higher than average and extremely heavy, leading to flooding, which causes devastation and carries away the vital topsoil. An international group of scientists have taken monthly recorded rainfall from around the world from 1925 to 1999 and compared what really happened to various computer models. They found that many of the changes corresponded to those expected if global warming was a factor.

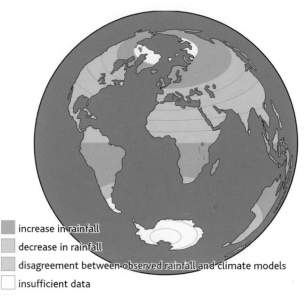

increase in rainfall

decrease in rainfall

disagreement between observed rainfall and climate models

insufficient data

fig. 5.3.18 This diagram, published in the journal *Nature*, shows how measured rainfall corresponds to climate change models.

The effect on organisms

Temperature has an effect on enzyme activity which in turn affects the whole organism. A 10 °C increase in temperature will double the rate of an enzyme-controlled reaction (see *AS Biology* page 88). However, there is an **optimum temperature** for many enzyme-controlled reactions and if the temperature increases beyond that point the enzyme starts to **denature** and the reaction rate falls. As a result, increasing temperature could have different effects on processes, including the rate of growth and reproduction. If plants grow faster they will take up more carbon dioxide and may therefore reduce atmospheric carbon dioxide levels. In other places, temperature may exceed the optimum for some enzymes, and organisms there will die.

Temperature and brine shrimp development

It is possible to model the effect of increasing temperature on the development of living organisms in the laboratory. There are many different experimental procedures which you can use, such as the germination of seeds, the growth rate of young seedlings, or the hatching rate of brine shrimps. You will need to plan the temperature differences you use and control the temperatures of your investigations very carefully.

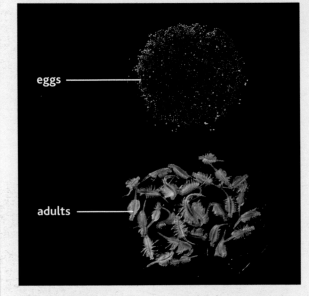

eggs

adults

fig. 5.3.19 You can model the effect of global warming on tiny invertebrates like these brine shrimp.

The majority of plant and animal species are found in the tropics. Many have very little tolerance for change because conditions in the tropics tend to vary very little throughout the year. Experimental data suggest that a change of just a couple of degrees could be fatal to many species. The insects which are so vital as pollinators of the many flowering plants are particularly vulnerable. And if they go, so do the plants and then the animals which feed on the plants… .

In higher latitudes, seasonal cycles affect life cycles. Global warming appears to be affecting the onset of the seasons, affecting both life cycles and the distribution of species. Warmer temperatures mean that plants grow and flower earlier. Insects such as moths and butterflies become active earlier in the warmth, and the plant food they need for their caterpillars is available. Some birds can adapt to these changes. For example, the breeding cycle of the great tits in Wytham Woods near Oxford in the UK has moved forward, triggered by the same temperature changes that mean the winter moth larvae that form the main food supply for the baby birds are also around on the leaves. The UK tits lay eggs about 2 weeks earlier now than they did 47 years ago. However, great tit populations in the Netherlands are not doing so well. The breeding time is getting earlier every year – but the caterpillars are emerging even earlier so the birds are missing the peak population, and raising fewer chicks.

For some animal species breeding earlier in the year may mean they can fit more than one breeding cycle in, so those populations will increase. Changes in temperature could have an even more drastic effect on some organisms. For example, the embryos of some reptiles are sensitive to temperature as they develop. Male crocodiles develop only if the eggs are incubated at 32–33 °C. If the eggs are cooler or warmer, females develop. If global warming means only female crocodiles, it could be the end of a species that has survived virtually unchanged for millions of years.

Changes in species distribution

A change in climate could affect the range of many different organisms. For example, alpine plants in mountainous parts of the UK are becoming rarer. Because most animals can move more easily than plants, they can often survive change more easily. So as areas become warmer, some animals may be able to extend their ranges northwards while becoming extinct at the southern end. Others may be able to colonise a bigger area. In a study by Parmesan *et al.* in 1999, of 35 species of non-migratory European butterflies, the ranges of 63% of the species had shifted northwards by between 35 and 240 km in the past 100 years and only 3% (one species) had shifted south. The shift in butterfly populations paralleled a 0.8 °C warming over Europe during this time.

If organisms involved in the spread of disease are affected, patterns of world health could change as well. The World Health Organization (WHO) has warned that global warming could be responsible for a major increase in insect-borne diseases in Britain and Europe. The prediction is that by 2100 conditions could be ideal for disease-carrying organisms such as mosquitoes, ticks and rats. The WHO are urging countries to make plans so that preventative measures can be put in place as the climate changes.

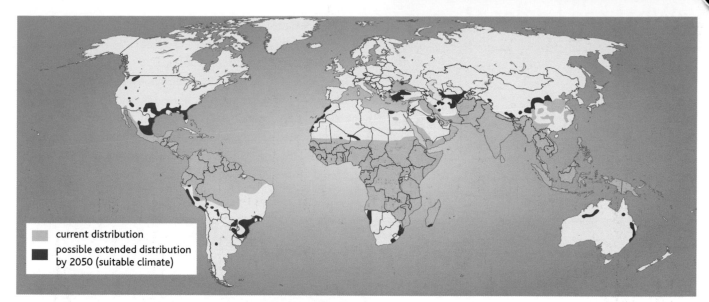

fig. 5.3.20 **The current distribution of the** *Anopheles* **mosquito – and so malaria – could change if one of the more pessimistic models of global warming proves accurate.**

Figure 5.3.21 summarises what the IPCC thought in 2007 could happen across the Earth as a result of global warming – a sobering prospect for everyone.

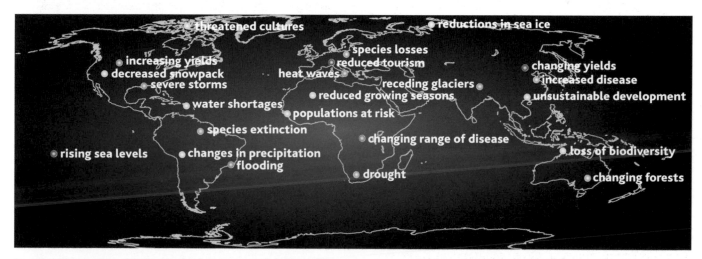

fig. 5.3.21 **The impact of global warning threatens to be huge. This diagram, based on a report from the IPCC in 2007, looks both at what is already happening and at predictions of what may happen in the future.**

Questions

1 The models for global carbon dioxide stabilisation show a great deal of uncertainty and variety. Explain why the models are so uncertain.

2 a Using data from **fig. 5.3.17**, calculate the percentage increase in average global temperature and Northern Hemisphere snow cover between 1930 and 2000.

  b What was the increase in average sea levels over the same period of time?

c Suggest how these data might be linked to rising carbon dioxide levels and each other.

3 Explain how a change in atmospheric carbon dioxide levels can have an impact on disease in both animals and humans.

4 Draw up a table to summarise the main effects of global warming. Then use this information to develop a flowchart of events which illustrate the best current model of the events linked to global warming.

What can be done? 4, 5, 20

Global warming is happening – few people dispute that – but how much is caused by human activities, and what actions, if any, should be taken to reduce it are much more controversial issues. Issues such as this are not always taken on board by the politicians and policy makers who make decisions that affect the problem and its solution. The way scientific conclusions are interpreted and used can depend very much on who is making the decisions.

HSW Differing scientific conclusions

One problem is that scientists rarely agree among themselves! Whatever the consensus or scientific view in any area, there are almost always some scientists who disagree. So while many scientists are convinced that atmospheric carbon dioxide levels, including human emissions, are contributing to global warming in the twenty-first century, others have a different view. There is also considerable debate among scientists as to the long-term effects of the increase in greenhouse gases on the climate in the future, and about what, if anything, can be done.

This is accepted as normal in the scientific community. Science works by debate, discussion and disagreement until a new model emerges from the results of investigations or the old model is confirmed. However, it can be hard for non-scientists to understand such disagreements. This paves the way for uncertainties and for people to select the theory which best suits their world view.

fig. 5.3.22 When hundreds of scientists get together at conferences to share their ideas and exchange research data, differences of opinion are common and opposing theories are shared and debated. This is how science moves ideas and models forward.

Who decides?

The decisions about energy usage and carbon emissions are usually made by politicians, and they are influenced by many factors, such as their political perspective, as well as the scientific evidence. They are also influenced by pressure groups and lobbyists who will be biased by their own interests. Environmental campaigners and scientists are anxious that politicians tackle carbon dioxide emissions to reduce the impact of global warming. Many industrialists, particularly in the field of electricity generation and the petrochemical industry, have a vested interest in promoting alternative theories for global warming to avoid legislation that changes their industry. For example, under a recent US president with strong links to the petrochemical industry, it was easier to get research funding for projects looking into alternative theories of global warming than to get funding for research into anthropogenic greenhouse gas emissions.

Politicians also tend to make decisions based on short-term gain at the polls. As a result, policies that might prove unpopular with voters may be ignored. For example, policies that would affect individual car use by limiting petrol or raising the price of petrol, or those that would raise the cost of electricity may be shelved even if they make environmental sense.

So, in the real world, the conclusions reached from scientific evidence depend heavily on who is reaching those conclusions, who has funded the original research and on the financial and political pressures that the decision-makers are working under.

Planning for the future

Increasing carbon dioxide levels are a fact. Many possible solutions that would reduce human emissions are being proposed, such as controlling the use of fossil fuels and making industrial processes and car engines cleaner and less polluting.

In most cases the conclusions based on the science are not clear-cut and different people have differing priorities. For example many people have supported the use of **biofuels** to replace fossil fuels. Looking at the carbon cycle, it makes sense to grow plants and then use products from those plants as fuel. This sounds like an ideal, carbon-neutral solution to the problems of fossil fuels. The plants take carbon dioxide out of the air as they grow and it is released when they are burnt as fuels, leading to no net loss or gain of carbon dioxide in the atmosphere. Unfortunately it is not that simple. Cars would need converting to run on biofuels, and the amount of land needed to grow the plants could threaten food production around the world. For example, it has been calculated that to replace 5% of US diesel consumption with biodiesel would use up 60% of the soy beans grown in that country. If poorer countries try to increase income by growing crops for fuel rather than food, it could mean starvation for millions of the world's poorest people.

The use of alternative energy sources, such as wind or nuclear, would also reduce carbon emissions, but cause their own problems. Naturally, different interest groups have different opinions on how these should be developed.

fig. 5.3.23 Research is being done on the use of waste plant material, such as straw or wood pulp from paper making, as the raw materials for biofuels. This would reduce the use of fossil fuels without taking up crop space, and use more of the plant material we already grow.

Reforestation is another approach. Replanting trees to replace those that have been felled makes wood a sustainable resource and also removes carbon dioxide from the atmosphere into the tissues of the trees.

Anthropogenic greenhouse gas production raises questions for scientists and society alike. It is important that everyone pulls together to find the answers, and that conclusions are reached as fairly and transparently as possible.

Questions

1 Why is it difficult for politicians to enact legislation that would substantially reduce the use of fossil fuels on both a national and a worldwide basis? Consider social and ethical considerations as well as practical ones.

SC 2 Different groups give very different impressions of the causes and possible solutions to the problem of global warming. How can the views of major organisations vary so much?

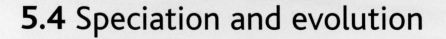

5.4 Speciation and evolution

Gene mutation, natural selection and evolution

4.5.21

DNA carries all our inherited information. It contains the genetic code in its sequence of the base pairs that determines the amino acid sequence in proteins (see *AS Biology* pages 72–9). Once the proteins (usually enzyme proteins) are made, they in turn construct the rest of the cell.

The **genome** is all the DNA of an individual. The **proteome** is all of the proteins produced from that DNA. There are far more proteins than there are genes. The proteins produced vary throughout life as a result of differential gene expression, and a gene can code for different proteins in different cells as a result of changes introduced through messenger RNA. Proteomics is the study of these different proteins and how they come about.

Gene and allele frequency

Mutations are changes in the DNA structure (*AS Biology* pages 82–3). These changes may be tiny, such as a change in a single base pair, or they may involve the obliteration or duplication of an entire chromosome. Some mutations have no effect at all on the phenotype, while others have severe or even lethal effects.

Mutations can increase the gene pool of a population by increasing the number of different alleles available. The relative frequency of a particular allele in a population is known as the **allele frequency**. If a mutation results

in an advantageous feature, the frequency of that allele in the population will be selected for and so increase in frequency. If the mutation is disadvantageous, natural selection will usually result in its removal from the gene pool. Changes in allele frequency due to natural selection may lead to the evolution of new species.

Many mutations are neutral, conferring neither advantage nor disadvantage. So for example on average a baby has 100 new mutations in its DNA compared with its parent's chromosomes but quite probably none will have an effect on the phenotype.

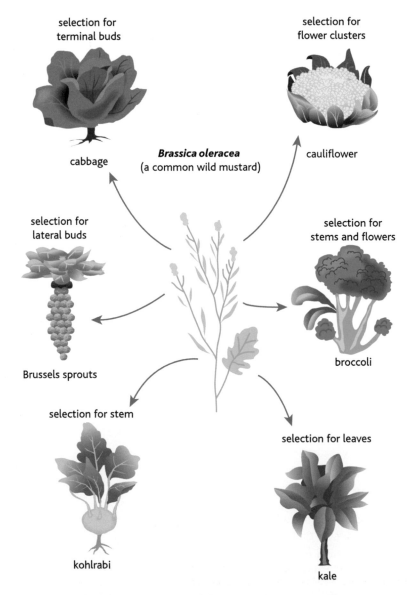

fig. 5.4.1 The wide variety of crop plants which have resulted from selective breeding of *Brassica oleracea* shows the huge amount of genetic variety in that gene pool. It is this variety that both natural and artificial selection act on.

Gene families and haemoglobin

For about half of your genes there is a single copy on each chromosome in a homologous pair. However there are multiple copies of the remaining genes. As mutations are random, some copies may be affected while others remain the same. The end result is a group of closely related genes known as **gene families**. One example is the gene that codes for haemoglobin, which is a conjugated protein made up of the protein globin and the iron-containing haem. The globin molecule consists of two α-globin and two β-globin amino acid chains. The family of genes which codes for α-globin, found on chromosome 16, has three functional members. The gene family for β-globin has five members and is found on chromosome 11. These family members code for slightly different amino acid chains and, during development, different members of the family are expressed, making normal adult haemoglobin, myoglobin (found in the muscles, see page 144) and foetal haemoglobin (formed in the foetal liver before birth and has a particularly high affinity for oxygen).

These mutations have been beneficial. However, some mutations in the haemoglobin family are positively harmful. A relatively common mutation in the gene coding for β-globin chains in adult haemoglobin replaces valine (a hydrophobic amino acid) at position 6 with glutamic acid (a hydrophilic amino acid). As a result, at low oxygen concentrations, the β-globin chains do not fold properly. They clump in a rigid structure, causing the red blood cell to form a characteristic sickle shape which makes it much less efficient at carrying oxygen and more likely to clog up the blood vessels. Individuals who are homozygous for this gene suffer **sickle cell disease**, which is debilitating and usually fatal without treatment.

	Allele frequency	Proportion of population with disease
US African–American	4%	1 in 500
Malaria-infected regions of Africa	16%	1 in 100

table 5.4.1 Allele frequencies for sickle cell and proportions of people affected by sickle cell disease in two populations.

HBB sequence in normal adult haemoglobin (HB A):

Nucleotide	CTG	ACT	CCT	**GAG**	GAG	AAG	TCT
Amino acid	Leu	Thr	Pro	**Glu**	Glu	Lys	Ser

HBB sequence in mutant adult haemoglobin (HB S):

Nucleotide	CTG	ACT	CCT	**GTG**	GAG	AAG	TCT
Amino acid	Leu	Thr	Pro	**Val**	Glu	Lys	Ser

fig. 5.4.2 The sickle cell mutation involves a tiny change in the order of the bases of the genetic code which has a major effect on the way the haemoglobin works. Around 6000 people have sickle cell disease in the UK. (NB: Only a section of the nucleotide and amino acid chain is shown here.)

Since sickle cell is a deleterious allele, it is usually removed from the gene pool through death before homozygotes can reproduce. Heterozygotes have mild anaemia but usually remain well. However, if their red blood cells become infected with malaria parasites, those containing the sickle haemoglobin will sickle and are removed by the spleen, removing the parasites as well. Being heterozygous for the sickle cell allele confers some resistance to malaria, so there is natural selection for heterozygotes in malarial regions and the allele frequency is higher than normal. In the United States, where there is no malaria, we can see natural selection in action as the frequency decreases in populations who originated from malarial regions of Africa. Interestingly, foetal haemoglobin is not affected, so sickle cell disease only appears after birth. Current research with mouse models and drug treatment aims to keep the foetal haemoglobin switched on in children and adults to overcome the sickle cell problems in homozygotes for the disease.

Questions

1 Explain the terms proteomics and genomics.

2 Use table 5.4.1 to help you explain the effect of natural selection on allele frequencies.

Evolution and speciation 4.5.22

There are a number of definitions of a species (see *AS Biology* pages 228–9), but one of the most commonly used is: *a group of closely related organisms that are all potentially capable of interbreeding to produce fertile offspring*. Another closely linked definition defines a species as *a group of organisms where the genes can flow between individuals*. In this spread you are going to look in some detail at the mechanisms by which speciation occurs.

As a result of random mutations, the variation in the DNA sequence between individuals of a species of animals or plants increases. Through natural selection this can lead to evolution and speciation. This requires isolation of some sort. In *AS Biology* (pages 236–45) you looked mainly at allopatric speciation, when populations are separated by geographical isolation. However speciation also occurs when there is no geographical barrier to interbreeding. This is sympatric speciation.

HSW 'Apple maggots' – a new species emerging?

Until the mid-1800s *Rhagoletis pomonella*, a tiny fruitfly, lived only on hawthorn bushes, laying their eggs on the fruits. The larvae respond to the smell of the hawthorns, and return as adults to hawthorns to reproduce. However, around 150 years ago along the Hudson River Valley in the United States many huge apple orchards were planted. Genetically, apple trees are quite closely related to hawthorns. Some female *Rhagoletis pomonella* laid their eggs on the apples, either by mistake or because they could not find hawthorns. The larvae did not do particularly well, but some survived to adulthood. These flies responded to the smell of apples, not hawthorns, and a breeding group of apple-dwelling flies evolved.

Now there are two breeding groups of *Rhagoletis pomonella* in the Hudson River Valley. One feeds on hawthorns, the other on apples. The two populations show increasing reproductive isolation because they mate only with flies on the same food source. The apple-dwelling flies have adapted to life on apple trees so they now emerge from their pupae at a different time of the year (see **fig. 5.4.3**). Apples provide more food and better protection for the maggots from parasitic wasps. Scientists have analysed the frequency

of a number of alleles in the flies and have found they are becoming increasingly different. It seems likely that two entirely different species will evolve which will no longer interbreed as their reproductive cycles will be completely out of synchronisation.

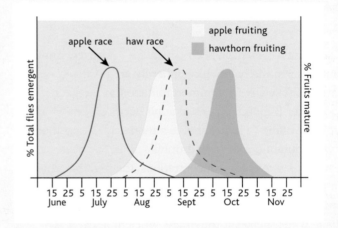

fig. 5.4.3 The apple race of flies now emerges earlier than the hawthorn race, so there is less chance for flies to interbreed and a greater chance this will lead to sympatric speciation. (Data from Reissig, 1991, Feder & Filchak 1999 and others.)

Mechanisms of speciation

Populations that have been isolated for millions of years can remain effectively the same species. For example, American and European sycamores (plane trees) have been geographically isolated for at least 20 million years yet they are still able to interbreed and produce fertile offspring. However, populations living next door to each other, such as *Rhagoletis pomonella* in the United States, can begin to form new species. Reproductive isolation is crucial to speciation and this occurs when fertilisation is prevented (prezygotic) or when the zygote fails or is unable to breed (postzygotic).

Prezygotic reproductive barriers

- Habitat isolation: Populations select different habitats in the same area so they do not come into contact during the reproductive season, e.g. *Rhagoletis pomonella*.

- Temporal isolation: Many organisms have mating or flowering periods which are very brief – a few hours or days. If two populations get out of synchronisation, they cannot mate with each other. Again *Rhagoletis pomonella* is an example.

- Mechanical isolation: Mutation may result in a physical barrier to fertilisation. For example the males of many insects have very complex reproductive organs which mean they can only mate with a particular group of females.

- Behavioural isolation: If the behaviour of animals changes, they may not recognise other members of the same species as mating partners. In some cases in plants, it is the behaviour of pollinators that may drive or prevent speciation (**see fig. 5.4.4**).

- Gametic isolation: If the female gamete fails to attract a male gamete, or the male gamete cannot penetrate the female gamete, then the individuals that produced the gametes cannot interbreed. If a common mutation causes this kind of incompatibility between individuals in a population, either two new species will result or some of the population will die out. For example, in many plants the pollen of one species cannot form an effective pollen tube on the stigma of another species. A similar process often prevents self-pollination and fertilisation in plants.

fig. 5.4.4 *Aquilegia formosa* (top) and *Aquilegia chrysantha* (bottom) grow in the Californian mountains. They can produce fertile hybrids, but *A. formosa* is pollinated by hummingbirds and *A. chrysantha* by hawkmoths. Each pollinator visits its preferred species almost exclusively, so cross-pollination is unlikely.

Postzygotic reproductive barriers

- Low hybrid zygote vigour: Zygotes fail to develop properly, and die during embryonic development or result in offspring with severe abnormalities so they cannot reproduce successfully.

- Low hybrid adult viability: Offspring fail to thrive and grow properly.

- Hybrid infertility: Offspring may appear healthy but are infertile, such as the mule which is the healthy, useful but infertile offspring of a horse and a donkey.

Questions

1 Suggest why the planting of orchards in the mid-1800s in the Hudson Valley triggered the beginnings of speciation in the fly *Rhagoletis pomonella*.

2 Investigate other examples of the main forms of pre-zygotic and post-zygotic isolation mechanisms. Write a short report to detail your findings.

Identifying individual species 4.5.23

In recent years scientists have developed the ability to analyse the DNA and proteins of different organisms. **DNA profiling** looks at the non-coding areas of DNA to identify patterns. These patterns are unique to individuals, but the similarity of patterns can be used to identify relationships between individuals and even between species. On pages 78–81 you will be looking at how techniques such as DNA profiling are carried out. Here you are going to discover some of the ways in which this information can be used to identify individuals and relationships between them.

The same ...

Identifying species from their phenotype can be difficult. External conditions can result in major differences in appearance of individuals of the same species. For example, red deer stags that live in woods and parkland have antlers which are much bigger and broader than stags that roam highland mountainsides. So they could easily be mistaken for different species, yet DNA evidence shows that they are the same.

... but different

In contrast, for many years the plant disease scab, which can destroy crops such as wheat and barley, was thought to be caused by a single fungus, *Fusarium graminearum*. Molecular geneticists in the United States have investigated the disease to try and help plant breeders and disease control specialists control it worldwide. DNA evidence, based on the divergence of six different genes, and the proteomic evidence of the proteins they produce, shows that there are at least eight different species of *Fusarium* pathogens, which have a similar effect on crop plants.

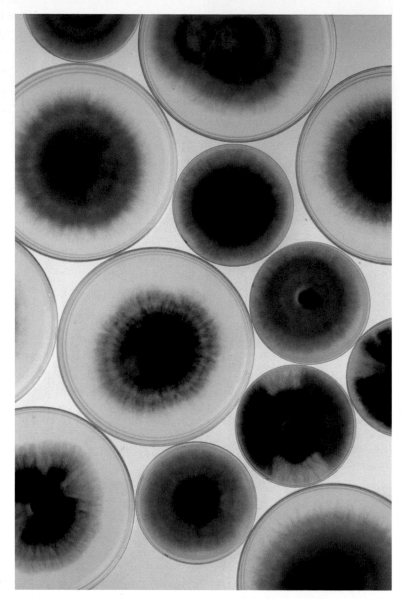

fig. 5.4.5 **All of these cultures may look very similar – but DNA data shows that they represent distinct species of fungi all capable of causing similar diseases in plants.**

The caviar con

Caviar is a luxury food and the very best – and most expensive – is Beluga caviar, the eggs of the Beluga sturgeon. DNA profiling is used by scientists to identify different but closely related species. Scientists from the American Museum of Natural History developed a series of profiles for different sturgeon species, as some of them are becoming very rare. They then ran DNA profiles on lots of different tins of caviar and discovered that around 25% of the tins claiming to be full of Beluga caviar actually contained the eggs of other, less prestigious species! This is an example of bringing cutting-edge science into the ethics of the marketplace.

HSW Project DNA Barcode

If scientists raise an organism in the lab, they usually know what species it is. But organisms found in the field may not be identified easily. The Consortium for the Barcode of Life (CBOL) is a large group of scientific organisations who are developing DNA barcoding as a global standard for species identification. This involves looking at short genetic sequences from a part of the genome common to particular groups of organisms. For example, a region of the mitochondrial cytochrome oxidase 1 gene (*CO1*), containing around 650 bases, is being used as the standard barcode for most animal species. So far this sequence has been shown to be effective in identifying individuals of fish, fly and bird species.

This region cannot be used to identify plants because it evolves too slowly in these organisms to give sufficient differences between species. However, botanists at Kew Gardens, and in other areas of the world, have identified other gene regions which could be used to produce a standard barcode for plants, for use in the same way as the animal barcodes.

Some scientists have doubts about the project, both relating to the ability of barcoding to distinguish between relatively newly evolved species and because it may undermine the traditional study of taxonomy and comparative anatomy which has been used to identify species for generations. However, many hope that eventually field instruments will be developed from these which can be used to analyse genes and identify species as scientists work with organisms in their natural habitats.

The CBOL project recognises that it will take a long time to barcode all the species of living organisms but rapid progress is being made. For example the ABBI – All Birds Barcoding Initiative – aims to obtain at least five barcode records to represent every one of the 10 000 or so known bird species within 5 years. Fortunately the tests needed to get the barcode from the DNA are both fast and relatively cheap. Within the next 20 years it is not unrealistic to think that all species will be identified and barcoded based on DNA analysis.

695-bp region of cytochrome oxidase gene

DNA

PCR, nucleotide sequencing

0   332
333   666
667   694   DNA barcode

fig. 5.4.6 **The DNA barcode of a living organism – each colour represents a different base.**

Questions

1   Why is it so important to be able to identify individual species?

2   Certain individual proteins such as cytochrome oxidase and haemoglobin, and the genes which code for them are widely used by scientists both to indentify individual species of animals and relationships between them. Why are these particular molecules so useful?

New evidence for evolution 4.5.23

Much of the old evidence for evolution relied on similarities in the appearance of living organisms and on fossil evidence. This can cause problems, particularly when two species look similar because they have evolved in response to similar niches, such as moles living underground. Now DNA profiling and proteomics give scientists new insights into evolutionary links.

The more differences (mutations) there are in the DNA from two individuals, the longer the time since they had a common ancestor. Using an agreed mutation rate as a kind of 'molecular clock', you can even estimate how long ago that common ancestor lived. However there are problems because DNA starts to degrade immediately after death. In the most favourable conditions, fragments can survive for 50–100 000 years. Also the rate at which different parts of the DNA mutates can vary. So the evidence has to be viewed with caution.

Fossil DNA and human evolution

Human evolution has always been difficult to follow owing to limited fossil evidence. Now scientists can extract DNA from suitable fossils under 100 000 years old, and analyse it using the polymerase chain reaction (which amplifies minute traces of DNA) and DNA profiling (see pages 80–81).

At one time it was thought that Neanderthals, who lived 30 000–100 000 years ago, were the ancestors of modern humans. Comparing DNA from a number of Neanderthal fossils with DNA of modern humans has shown both that Neanderthals were not our ancestors, and that interbreeding between Neanderthals and modern human ancestors is unlikely to have taken place.

DNA, lice and human evolution

It is not only human DNA that is useful in unravelling human evolution. Modern humans have three types of parasitic lice: head lice, pubic lice and body lice – the latter hang onto clothing but feed off the body. Head and body lice are related to chimpanzee lice. DNA evidence suggests that the common ancestors of humans and chimps diverged about 6 million years ago, and the head lice species diverged at the same time.

DNA analysis of the human head louse and body louse shows that they formed separate species around 72 000 years ago. Body lice live in close-fitting fabric, so this suggests when woven clothing became common. This work was published by R. Kittler, M. Kayser and M. Stoneking in the journal *Current Biology* in 2003.

DNA profiling also shows that the pubic louse is more closely related to the gorilla louse than to other human lice. Work by David Reed and Jessica Light, published in 2007 in the *BMC Biology* journal, shows that human and gorilla ancestors diverged about 6 million years ago, but that pubic and gorilla lice only diverged about 3 million years ago. This suggests that by then humans had lost most of their body hair, and the texture of the pubic hair was already different from the head hair. One explanation is that human ancestors picked up pubic lice from gorillas by using plant bedding which gorillas had slept on. Overall, the DNA evidence from

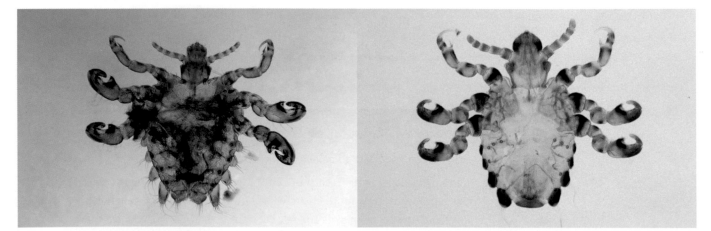

fig. 5.4.7 It isn't easy to get hold of gorilla lice for DNA analysis, but this shows that (a) the human pubic louse *Pthirus pubis* is closely related to (b) the gorilla louse *Pthirus gorilla*.

the lice suggests humans had head lice with chimpanzee louse ancestors, and pubic lice with gorilla louse ancestors, long before they began wearing woven clothes and body lice evolved. So the ability to weave clothes was developed long after most of our body hair was lost.

New models support old theory

Scientists use evidence from the DNA analysis of many species to help build diagrams that model the evolution of species from a common ancestor. The process relies heavily on how data are interpreted using statistics and computer analysis. It is possible that the same evidence can be interpreted differently. This is why it is important to look for evidence from traditional studies based on appearance, behaviour or fossil data. In an ideal situation evidence from a variety of sources like this all agree. An example is in primate evolution (**see fig. 5.4.8**).

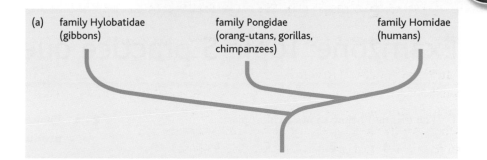

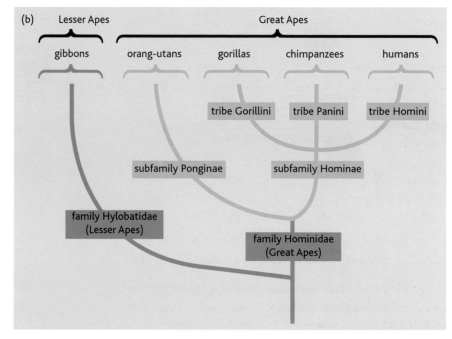

fig. 5.4.8 Evolutionary trees showing relationships between the apes. based on (a) the fossil evidence available at the time along with morphology and (b) more recent fossil and DNA evidence, show how important it is for scientists to keep developing new approaches.

HSW Differing scientific conclusions

The scientific community plays an important role in validating new evidence, as shown in the example of the evolution of human lice and their relevance to the loss of body hair and the development of clothing. When a piece of research produces useful results and conclusions, it is submitted to a scientific journal. Some of these journals are very famous, others are smaller and very specialised. When an article is submitted, it goes through a process of peer review when it is read by a number of experts to see if it is reliable. If so, it will be published. A paper should provide enough information for other scientists to carry out the same or similar investigations, so that the conclusions can be validated.

At scientific conferences scientists working in the same field get together to discuss ideas – for example, such as how accurate is the molecular clock for primates? This helps to promote the development of new techniques in research as well as provide opportunities to challenge the validity of results that are being presented.

Questions

1 a Describe some of the limitations of using fossils to show evolutionary relationships.

   b Explain why DNA profiling is of limited use when building models of evolution.

   c Explain why using evidence for evolution from various sources increases its validity.

SC 2 Explain the role of publications and scientific conferences in validating new scientific research.

Examzone: Topic 5 practice questions

1 The diagram below shows a chloroplast.

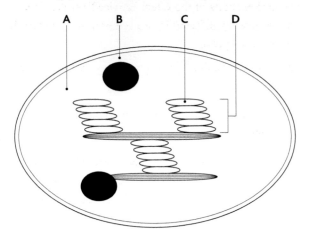

a i Name the parts labelled A, B, C and D. **(2)**

ii State the part of the chloroplast, shown on the diagram, where oxygen is produced. **(1)**

iii Explain how oxygen is produced in chloroplasts during photosynthesis. **(3)**

b Oxygen inhibits the enzyme that catalyses the fixing of carbon dioxide. High concentrations of oxygen, within a chloroplast, can reduce the rate of photosynthesis.

Describe and explain the effect of high concentrations of oxygen on the rate of carbohydrate production in a chloroplast. **(3)**

c Suggest **two** environmental conditions that could increase the rate of oxygen production by plants.

(2)

(Total 11 marks)

2 a Explain what is meant by the term **gross primary production** (GPP). **(2)**

b The table below shows the flow of energy in a tropical rainforest.

Trophic level	Energy entering trophic level/$kJ\,m^{-2}\,year^{-1}$
Producers	180.0×10^3
Primary consumers	5.0×10^3
Secondary consumers	4.5×10^3
Tertiary consumers	3.4×10^3
Decomposers	28.4×10^3

i Energy is transferred between trophic levels. If the producers lose $145 \times 10^3\,kJ\,m^{-2}\,year^{-1}$ in respiration, calculate the percentage of net primary production (NPP) which is passed to the primary consumers. Show your working. **(3)**

ii Explain the role of decomposers in a food chain. **(2)**

iii The productivity of a temperate forest in Europe is much lower than that of a tropical rainforest. Suggest reasons for this difference. **(2)**

c Describe how a forest could be managed sustainably in order to ensure a continual supply of timber for the future. **(3)**

(Total 12 marks)

3 A study of the distribution and abundance of three different seaweeds was carried out in the intertidal region of a gently sloping rocky shore. The intertidal region is the area that will be covered by water as the tide comes in and uncovered by water as the tide goes out.

The abundance of each seaweed was found by estimating its percentage cover at regular intervals from the high water mark at the top of the shore to the low water mark lower down the shore. The results of this study are shown on the graph below.

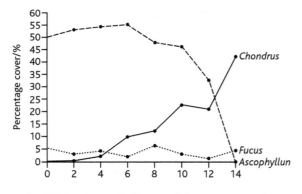

a i Write down the letter of the statement that could form part of a valid conclusion from the data shown in the graph.

A – *Ascophyllum* grows only in regions that are uncovered by water for long periods of time

B – *Fucus* grows better in regions that are never uncovered by water

C – *Chondrus* may not be able to compete with *Ascophyllum* (1)

ii With reference to the graph discuss the validity of statements **A**, **B** and **C**. (3)

b Suggest **two** abiotic factors, other than the length of time the seaweeds are out of water, that could affect the distribution of the seaweeds on this shore. (2)

c Describe a technique that you have used to study the distribution of a named organism within its habitat. (4)

(Total 10 marks)

4 Coral reefs are formed and maintained by very large numbers of simple animals called polyps. These polyps have single-celled algae (simple photosynthetic organisms) living inside their cells.

It is thought that when the sea is too warm the relationship between the coral polyps and the algae breaks down, and the reef begins to look white (becomes bleached). If the sea temperature falls again within a few weeks then the coral polyps and the algae reunite. If it does not, then the coral polyps die. In 1998, 16% of the world's coral reefs showed

some bleaching. Half of these damaged reefs are now recovering.

The Great Barrier Reef off the east coast of Australia has been badly bleached in the last few years. The average sea temperature on the reef has increased by 0.3 °C in the last century. It is feared that southern and central sections of the Great Barrier Reef are likely to be severely affected by sea temperature rises in the next 20–40 years.

a Name a method by which global sea temperatures can be monitored. (1)

b Suggest how the algae normally help the coral polyps to survive. (2)

c Some recovery in the Great Barrier Reef may be taking place at present. Suggest a possible explanation for this, other than change in sea temperature. (2)

(Total 5 marks)

5 If a horse, *Equus caballus*, is mated with a donkey, *Equus asinus*, a hybrid known as a mule is produced.

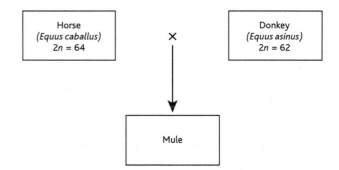

Mules are almost always sterile and produce no offspring. This phenomenon is an example of a post-zygotic isolating mechanism.

a State the diploid number of chromosomes in a mule and suggest why mules are unable to produce offspring. (3)

b State what is meant by the term **isolating mechanism**. Suggest why the production of a mule by mating a horse with a donkey is described as a post-zygotic isolating mechanism. (3)

c It has been suggested that the mule should be named as a new species, *Equus mulus*.

Suggest why this might not be acceptable to some biologists. (2)

(Total 8 marks)

Topic 6 Infection, immunity and forensics

This topic deals with some of the techniques used by forensic pathologists to identify bodies and establish a reliable time of death. Death can also be caused by infectious disease, and the way the body can be infected by pathogens and how it responds are also described.

What are the theories?

The unique structure of DNA not only codes for all the proteins in our body, but it can also be used to identify individuals and species. The use of DNA profiling has become increasingly important in forensic pathology, as the techniques of gel electrophoresis and use of the polymerase chain reaction (PCR) have been developed. The use of a range of forensic techniques, including state of decomposition and entomology, helps to determine the time of death with some accuracy.

The body has many defences against infection. If pathogens get past these, there are also non-specific and immune responses. However, if these responses are overcome, the host will become ill and may even die. Antibiotics can be used against bacterial and fungal infections to help kill those pathogens. Artificial immunity can increase the speed of the immune response and prevent illness.

What is the evidence?

The increasing number of cases of some diseases, such as tuberculosis and AIDS, shows that some pathogens are particularly good at evolving mechanisms that overcome the effects of antibiotics and even the responses of the human body. Over-use of antibiotics is also resulting in the evolution of 'superbugs', as the bacteria they are used on are evolving to be resistant. You will have the opportunity to carry out your own investigations on gel electrophoresis and PCR, as well as on the effect of different antibiotics on bacteria.

What are the implications?

The evolution of superbugs has highlighted the need for control over the use of antibiotics and other measures, such as improved hygiene, within hospitals and care homes where people are most at risk. The education of people on how to use antibiotics effectively is also needed if we are to win the evolutionary race against some of the more challenging pathogens. Winning against TB and AIDS may need new strategies.

The map opposite shows you all the knowledge and skills you need to have by the end of this topic. The colour in each box shows which chapter they are covered in and the numbers refer to the Edexcel specification.

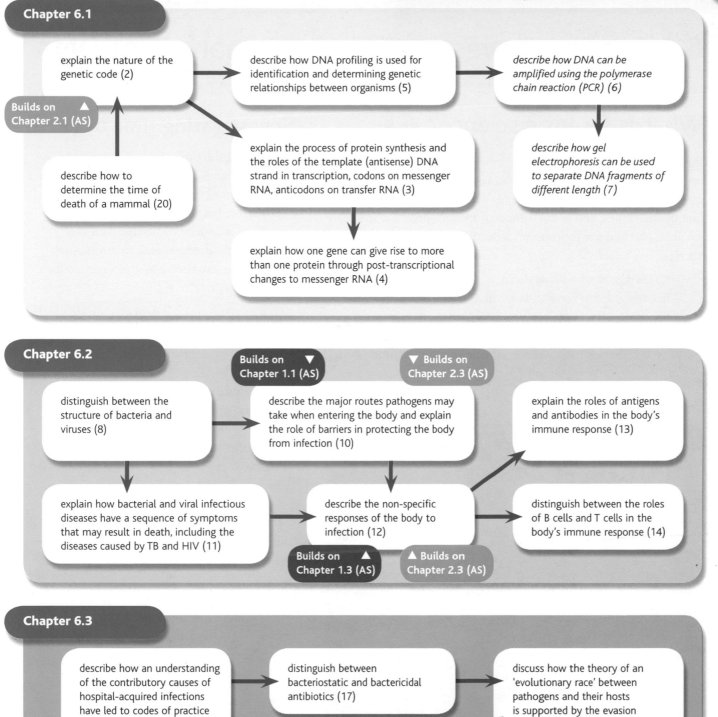

Chapter 6.1

explain the nature of the genetic code (2)

Builds on Chapter 2.1 (AS)

describe how to determine the time of death of a mammal (20)

describe how DNA profiling is used for identification and determining genetic relationships between organisms (5)

explain the process of protein synthesis and the roles of the template (antisense) DNA strand in transcription, codons on messenger RNA, anticodons on transfer RNA (3)

explain how one gene can give rise to more than one protein through post-transcriptional changes to messenger RNA (4)

describe how DNA can be amplified using the polymerase chain reaction (PCR) (6)

describe how gel electrophoresis can be used to separate DNA fragments of different length (7)

Chapter 6.2

Builds on Chapter 1.1 (AS) ▼

▼ **Builds on Chapter 2.3 (AS)**

distinguish between the structure of bacteria and viruses (8)

describe the major routes pathogens may take when entering the body and explain the role of barriers in protecting the body from infection (10)

explain the roles of antigens and antibodies in the body's immune response (13)

explain how bacterial and viral infectious diseases have a sequence of symptoms that may result in death, including the diseases caused by TB and HIV (11)

describe the non-specific responses of the body to infection (12)

distinguish between the roles of B cells and T cells in the body's immune response (14)

Builds on Chapter 1.3 (AS) ▲

▲ **Builds on Chapter 2.3 (AS)**

Chapter 6.3

describe how an understanding of the contributory causes of hospital-acquired infections have led to codes of practice relating to antibiotic prescription and hospital practice relating to infection prevention and control (19)

distinguish between bacteriostatic and bactericidal antibiotics (17)

describe how to investigate the effect of different antibiotics on bacteria (18)

discuss how the theory of an 'evolutionary race' between pathogens and their hosts is supported by the evasion mechanisms as shown by HIV and TB (16)

explain how individuals may develop immunity (natural, artificial, active, passive) (15)

6.1 Forensic investigations and analysis of DNA

What is forensic science? 5.6.20

Between March 2006 and March 2007 755 people were murdered in the UK – that's an average of at least two murders every day. Unsurprisingly, murder is the crime which most often hits the headlines, and is the subject of many a detective story. To secure a prosecution for murder, a number of facts need to be verified.

- Who died, and who killed them.
- What was used to commit the crime.
- When the victim died.
- Where the murder took place.
- Why the murder took place – the motive for the crime.

Forensic science provides us with tools with which to help solve murders and convict the murderer.

fig. 6.1.1 Specially trained officers collect evidence from crime sciences – you will be looking at the science behind these techniques for identifying both the innocent and the guilty.

Investigating time of death

Estimating the time of death is far more difficult than is usually portrayed, and once the body has been dead for more than 48 hours it becomes harder still. Forensic evidence is usually combined with the evidence of witnesses and circumstantial evidence to produce a best estimate of the time of death.

A number of changes take place in the body of any mammal after death which can be helpful in estimating the time of death. For example, the normal human body temperature is 37°C. At death, the metabolic reactions which have created the body heat begin to slow and eventually stop. At the same time heat energy is transferred from the surface of the body into the surroundings by radiation, conduction and the evaporation of water. But the body reactions do not all stop immediately, so that although the body temperature starts to fall straight after death, it plateaus for while before dropping steadily to room temperature. As a result the temperature of a body will give some indication of how long the person has been dead.

A number of other factors affect how quickly the body temperature drops. For example the outside of the body cools much more rapidly than the inside, and the amount of body fat affects rate of cooling because it acts as insulation. Soon after the point of death and depending upon a number of factors including mode of death, clothing, size of body and the environment surrounding the body, the body starts to cool in a fairly predictable manner. From analysing the cooling curve for bodies under known conditions it is possible to estimate the time of death.

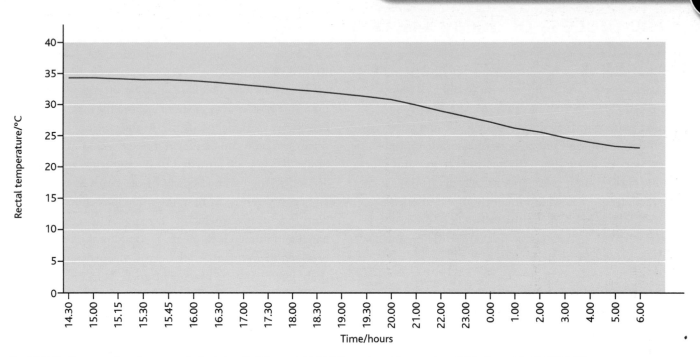

fig. 6.1.2 Cooling curve for a human male, body length 1.6 m, weight 70.76 kg, external temperature 10 °C, time of death 1330. This man had died from heart failure. Data from Len Nokes.

Rigor mortis

When someone dies, the heart stops pumping blood around the body and the brain dies within minutes. The brain cells respire actively and aerobically all the time, and contain little stored ATP, fat or glycogen so they are rapidly affected by a lack of oxygen. However, some tissues, such as the muscle cells, have large stores of ATP and glycogen and can continue to respire anaerobically for a time. ATP is needed to maintain the muscles in a relaxed state. As the muscle cells run out of ATP, the muscle fibres become permanently contracted and lock solid. This produces a stiffening effect which is known as **rigor mortis**. On average, rigor mortis starts about 2–4 hours after death and needs between 6 and 8 hours to take full effect. It begins in the muscles in the face and neck, progresses down the body, and spreads steadily to the larger muscles of the body. Rigor is seen clearly in all mammals, and in other animals too.

The main factor which will decide how quickly rigor mortis sets in is the amount of ATP stored in the muscles at the time of death. The level of ATP varies from person to person depending on their genetics and their level of fitness. It also depends on the level of activity before death. For example, rigor mortis usually sets in very quickly in drowning victims, because they have used up all their muscle ATP struggling to stay afloat.

The temperature of the person when they die and the temperature of the surroundings also affect how quickly rigor sets in. Rigor mortis is not permanent – it usually passes between 36 and 48 hours after death, although it can last considerably longer. The muscles soften as enzymes released from the lysosomes begin to break down the tissue. Using some basic mathematics it is possible to predict when the ATP store was 'full' and hence the time of death. Putting these data together with temperature changes can greatly improve the prediction of time of death.

Questions

1 a Explain why the body of a mammal cools down after death.

  b Why is the cooling rate slower in the first hours after death?

  c Explain how factors such as external temperature, whether the body is wet or dry and whether a body is wrapped or exposed will affect the rate of cooling after death.

2 What effect would death have on the temperature of an animal such as a frog or a lizard?

3 Why is rigor mortis of limited use in determining the time of death?

The process of decay 4.6.9, 4.6.20

Forensic experts can use the state of decay in a body to help estimate the time of death. Most bodies follow a similar pattern as they decay. As cells die and gut movement stops, the catabolic enzymes of the digestive system start breaking down the walls of the gut and then the surrounding cells. Also, as cells die from lack of oxygen, lysosomes within them rupture and release enzymes, which break down the cells. These processes make the body a more suitable habitat for the organisms responsible for further decay.

The stages of succession

A newly dead body is like a piece of freshly exposed soil or rock – it is a freshly available habitat. The principles of succession that you studied on pages 20–23 also apply to the succession of species on a human body after death. An understanding of this succession allows forensic specialists to date the time a body has been around very accurately.

The first stage of succession on a body involves the colonisers. Anaerobic bacteria, which do not need oxygen and thrive in the lactic acid-rich environment of the muscles after death, are the first colonisers. These bacteria, which in life are confined to certain areas of the body such as the gut, breed freely and take over. As enzymes break down cells, the bacteria spread.

However, they are quickly joined by several species of flies. The best known of these are the blowflies. These insects are extremely sensitive to the smell of dead organisms, and can arrive on a body within minutes of death. They are attracted to the moisture and smell around all the natural orifices of the body, as well as any open wounds. At first, the main attraction of the body is as a site on which to lay eggs. The maggots hatch and immediately begin feeding on the tissues, breaking them down. They burrow deeper into the flesh. Eventually the maggots pupate, turn into flies and immediately mate and start the cycle again. As the soft tissues of the body liquefy, adult flies can feed on this too.

Beetles also start to lay eggs on the carcass, as their larvae feed on maggots rather than eat the body itself. Then parasitic wasps arrive to lay their eggs in the fly and beetle larvae. Gradually, as the body is digested it also dries out, which does not suit the early colonisers. Different species such as the cheese flies and coffin flies move in. Eventually the body is too dry for maggots and a number of beetle species with strong, chewing mouthparts move in, including carcass beetles, ham beetles and hide beetles, which feed on the remains of the muscles and the connective tissues. At the very end, mites and moth larvae will feed on the hair until only dry bones are left.

fig. 6.1.3 The processes of decay turn a living animal, through stages of putrefaction which include bloating with gas, crawling with maggots and terrible smells, into a dry remnant of hair and bone.

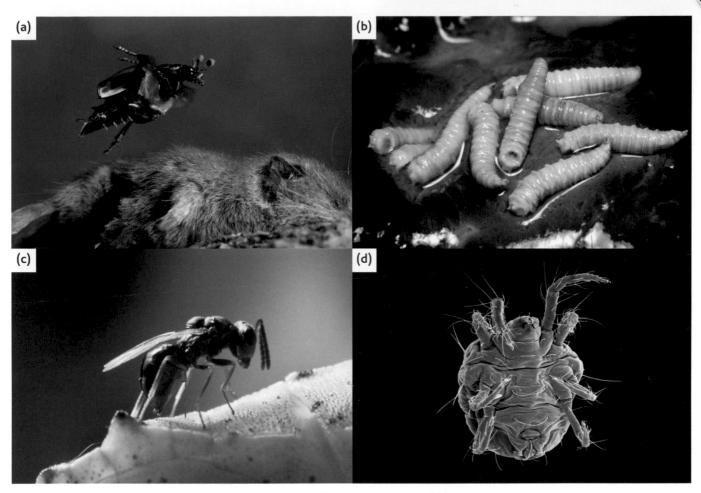

fig. 6.1.4 Corpse fauna include (a) carcass beetles, (b) blowfly larvae, (c) parasitoid wasps and (d) mites.

The stages of decay follow a regular pattern, but the speed at which they occur is variable and depends on a number of factors. Temperature is very important. The warmer the body, the faster the rate of decay as all the chemical reactions are speeded up. For example, in Zimbabwe, an entire elephant can be reduced to a skeleton in just 7 days. On the other hand, a body kept in a freezer will decay very slowly indeed. The level of exposure of the body is another factor. A buried body will decay more slowly than a body left in the open air because it is more available to flies and other decomposers. Also, the temperature will be lower and more stable. A body hidden in a house will be less exposed to insects, but usually warmer than a body outside, while a body in a bin bag outside will decay more slowly than a body exposed to the air.

Forensic entomology

Many of the organisms that colonise a body after death are insects, and the study of insect life as it relates to crime has developed into the science known as **forensic entomology**.

The first recorded case where insect evidence was used successfully in a UK murder investigation began on 27 September 1935 when the dismembered remains of Mrs Buck Ruxton and her maid May Jane Rogerson were found in a ravine on a Scottish mountain. Many of the body parts were found to be infested with maggots. The forensic team estimated the age of the maggots and showed that the remains had been dumped in the ravine 12–14 days earlier. This supported the rest of the evidence, which all pointed to Dr Buck Ruxton as the murderer. He was convicted and hanged.

Forensic entomologists not only know the detailed life cycles of blowflies and other insects that colonise dead bodies, they also know how the life cycles vary with different environmental conditions such as temperature. They can use this evidence to help estimate how long a body has been in the place it is found. For example, if a body found outside in the UK had no evidence of blowfly activity, this would tell the forensic team that the body had almost certainly been there for no more than 24 hours maximum – blowflies often find a body within minutes of death!

Blowflies lay their eggs in corpses – including human bodies – and when the maggots hatch they feed on the body and grow until they form a pupa and a new adult fly hatches. The flies lay their eggs in the natural openings of the body – like the eyes, nose and mouth, but will also lay eggs in knife and gunshot wounds.

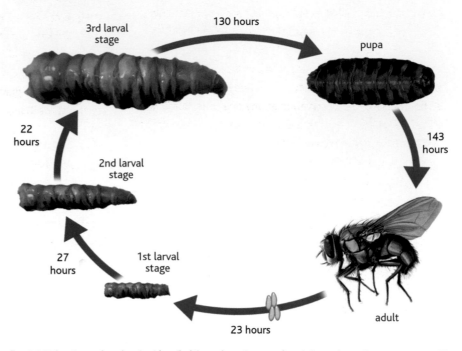

fig. 6.1.5 The time taken for the blowfly life cycle to be completed depends on the temperature. The times shown are at 21 °C. In colder weather the maggots grow more slowly.

When a body is discovered, eggs, maggots and pupae are collected. When live specimens can be saved, the forensic entomologists will grow them on to adults so a precise identification of the species of fly or beetle can be made. This makes calculating time of death even more accurate because each species has a different length life cycle.

Evidence from forensic entomologists carries a lot of weight in police investigations and in court. In another example a couple were found dead in their home in New South Wales. They had both been shot. The body of the woman, found in bed, was more decomposed and the maggots were more advanced than the body of the man found in the kitchen. Police gathered evidence from reported phone calls and sightings that the woman had been alive until the Saturday evening. There was a suspect – but he had a strong alibi for the Saturday night. However, when the evidence from the forensic entomologist was considered, a very different picture emerged. The minimum age of the oldest maggots taken from the woman was 4 days. This put the death at least one whole day earlier than the circumstantial evidence. When the witness evidence was checked again, it was discovered that there were mistakes. The maggots do not lie – and the prime suspect had no alibi for the Friday night. Faced with the evidence, he confessed. And why was one body more decomposed, with bigger, stronger maggots than the other? The woman had gone to bed with an electric blanket on which had kept her body warm and speeded up the chemical reactions of both decay and the development of the maggots.

HSW Moving knowledge forward

So how can forensic experts set about making their estimates more accurate? At the University of Knoxville in Tennessee, USA, forensic research teams have for some years been observing in great detail what happens when human bodies decay in a whole range of different conditions. The bodies they use are donated by individuals who want to help further scientific knowledge in this area. In a secluded site known by the local police as 'the Body Farm', around 30 bodies are under observation at any one time. Some are buried, some are not, some are rolled in carpet or stuffed into dustbin bags, some are in damp areas, others are exposed to the full sun, some are in freezers and others in the experimental equivalent of centrally heated homes. By monitoring the rate of change in these bodies, the research team can gain invaluable information that will help forensic pathologists throughout the world. They are also analysing the gases and fluids produced by decomposing bodies to try to develop advanced systems for detecting bodies which have been hidden after a murder.

Similar work is being done in other countries. For example, a big research project was carried out in Canada in the 1990s looking at the insect succession in buried carcasses. The Canadian study used pigs as human models, even dressing them up in human clothes before burial in the type of shallow graves often used by murderers to hide their victims. Using pigs removed many of the ethical and practical problems associated with this type of research – for example it can be difficult to get permission to bury human bodies just for observation! The results show some interesting differences in body temperature between exposed and buried bodies – just the sort of data that are useful to forensic experts – but of course it is based on pigs, not people.

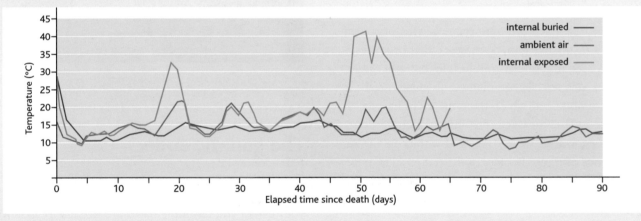

fig. 6.1.6 Internal temperature of buried and exposed pig carcasses compared to the ambient air temperature in the Cariboo Region of British Columbia. Measurements were taken using electronic probes in the pigs and weather station data.

Questions

1. Describe and explain the main stages of decomposition of a mammalian body and the organisms you would expect to be involved.

2. The conditions in which a body is kept after death have a major effect on the speed at which decomposition takes place. Select two factors and explain how they affect decomposition rates.

3. How is the process of succession helpful to forensic scientists in determining the time of death?

SC 4 a Using **fig. 6.1.6**, describe the pattern of temperature changes in both an exposed and an unexposed body in relation to the ambient air temperature and explain the patterns you see.

   b These data were collected using pigs in human clothes as mimics of the human body. What are the advantages and disadvantages of using pigs in this type of investigation?

   c What are the problems and advantages of using human bodies in forensic research?

The importance of DNA 4.6.2, 4.6.3, 4.5.4

In any murder both the body and who carried out the killing need to be identified. In recent years, advances in biotechnology have made it much easier for police and forensic experts to produce evidence which is reliable and can be used to convict a killer – or prove innocence. This evidence is commonly known as DNA profiling (or sometimes DNA fingerprinting when applied to criminal proceedings). To understand the way in which patterns in the DNA can be analysed and used to identify people, it is important to be familiar with the details of the way our genetic code works.

DNA and the genetic code

DNA is the molecule that carries all our inherited information. It has a double helix structure, which contains chains of nucleotide bases – adenine, thymine, cytosine and guanine – joined together in pairs (see *AS Biology* page 75). Each different type of living organism must have a distinctive genetic message that produces, for example, sea urchin cells rather than daffodil cells. Also, within each species are many individuals, each of which is unique and which must therefore have its own unique genetic message. The information needed to give this enormous variety is found within the DNA. The sequence of the base pairs in the molecule is used as the genetic code. The code determines which amino acids are joined together to form proteins.

Proteins are the key to how the genetic code works. As we have seen, proteins are vital components of almost all parts of a cell. Almost all enzymes are proteins, and enzymes control the synthesis and biochemistry of the cell and the whole organism.

How does DNA influence and control protein synthesis?

Proteins are formed from amino acids. There are only 20 naturally occurring amino acids, but joined together in different combinations they make up an almost infinite variety of proteins. The amino acids are joined together on the surface of the cell organelles known as **ribosomes**. The order in which the amino acids are joined is a result of the genetic code.

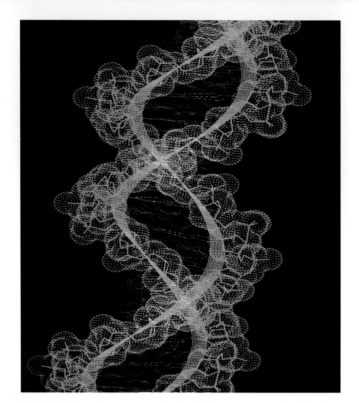

fig. 6.1.7 DNA – the master molecule which acts as a template for the proteins made during the life of a cell. Recent research has shown there is a lot more to the process than we originally thought!

The genetic code

In a double helix of DNA, the components that vary along the structure are the bases. As you know from your earlier studies, three bases are needed to code for one amino acid.

A **triplet code** of three bases gives $4 \times 4 \times 4 = 64$ possible combinations, more than enough for all the possible amino acids. A sequence of three base pairs on the DNA is transcribed to give the corresponding base pairs of messenger RNA in the nucleus as part of the process of protein synthesis. A three-base sequence of DNA or RNA is known as a **codon**. The 'dictionary' of the genetic code is more often shown for RNA than for DNA codons, as they are directly linked to the amino acids formed (see **table 6.1.1**). Some codons code for a particular amino acid while others code for the beginning or the ending of a particular amino acid sequence. However, the genetic code is not only a triplet code, it is non-overlapping and **degenerate** as well.

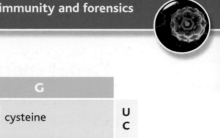

	second letter of the codon				
	U	**C**	**A**	**G**	

<table>
<tr><td rowspan="4">U</td><td>UUU
UUC phenylalanine
UUA
UUG leucine</td><td>UCU
UCC
UCA serine
UCG</td><td>UAU
UAC tyrosine
UAA stop codon
UAG stop codon</td><td>UGU
UGC cysteine
UGA stop codon
UGG trytophan</td><td>U
C
A
G</td></tr>
</table>

first letter of the codon						third letter of the codon
U	UUU / UUC phenylalanine UUA / UUG leucine	UCU / UCC / UCA / UCG serine	UAU / UAC tyrosine **UAA** stop codon **UAG** stop codon	UGU / UGC cysteine **UGA** stop codon UGG trytophan	U / C / A / G
C	CUU / CUC / CUA / CUG leucine	CCU / CCC / CCA / CCG proline	CAU / CAC histidine CAA / CAG glutamine	CGU / CGC / CGA / CGG arginine	U / C / A / G
A	AUU / AUC / AUA iscieucine **AUG** methionine; start codon	ACU / ACC / ACA / ACG threonine	AAU / AAC asparagine AAA / AAG lysine	AGU / AGC serine AGA / AGG arginine	U / C / A / G
G	GUU / GUC / GUA / GUG valine	GCU / GCC / GCA / GCG alanine	GAU / GAC aspartic acid GAA / GAG glutamic acid	GGU / GGC / GGA / GGG glycine	U / C / A / G

table 6.1.1 The mRNA codons of the genetic code with the amino acid messages they carry.

A non-overlapping code...

Once scientists had worked out that the genetic code was based on triplets of DNA bases, the next question was how is the code read? Do the triplets of bases follow each other along the DNA strand like beads on a necklace, or do they overlap? For example the mRNA sequence UUUAGC could code for two amino acids, phenylalanine (UUU) and serine (AGC).

On the other hand, if the code overlaps, it could code for *four*: phenylalanine (UUU), leucine (UUA), a nonsense or stop codon (UAG) and serine (AGC).

An overlapping code would be very economical – relatively short lengths of DNA could carry the instructions for many different proteins. However, it would also be very limiting, because the amino acids which could be coded for side by side would be limited. In the example given, only leucine out of the 20 available amino acids could ever follow phenylalanine, because only leucine has a codon starting with UU–.

HSW Evidence for a non-overlapping code

Scientists have relied on experimental observations to help decide whether the genetic code is overlapping or not. If a codon consists of three nucleotides and is completely overlapping, and a single nucleotide is altered by a point mutation (see *AS Biology* page 82), then three amino acids will be affected by that single change. If the code is only partly overlapping, then a single point mutation would result in two affected amino acids. But if the codons do not overlap at all then a single nucleotide mutation would affect only one amino acid, which is what has been observed, for example in sickle cell disease. All the evidence available suggests that the code is *not* overlapping and this is generally accepted among scientists.

...and a degenerate code

When you look at the genetic code it appears that the code is degenerate (also known as redundant). In other words it contains more information than it needs. If you look carefully at **table 6.1.1** you will see that often only the first two of the three nucleotides in a codon seem to matter in determining which amino acid results. This may seem a rather useless feature at first, but if each amino acid was produced by only one codon, then any error or mutation could cause havoc. With a degenerate code, if the final base in the triplet is changed, this mutation could still produce the same amino acid and have no effect on the organism. Only methionine and tryptophan are represented by only one codon. Mutations can happen any time the DNA is copied – the degenerate code at least partly protects living organisms from their effects.

HSW Evidence for the triplet codons

The first breakthrough in decoding the genetic code came in 1961 when M.W. Nirenberg and J.H. Matthaei in the United States prepared artificial mRNA where all the bases were uracil. They added their polyU – chains reading UUUUUUUUUUUU ... – to all the other ingredients needed for protein synthesis (ribosomes, tRNAs, amino acids, etc). When they analysed the polypeptides made, they found chains of a single type of amino acid, phenylalanine. UUU appeared to be the mRNA codon for phenylalanine. So the DNA codon would be AAA. The scientists soon showed that CCC codes for proline and AAA for lysine. Evidence for the triplet code – three non-overlapping bases with some degeneracy – built up swiftly from this early work.

It was also shown that the minimum length of artificial mRNA that would bind to a ribosome was three bases long – a single codon. This would then bind with the corresponding tRNA.

From this point on it was a case of careful and precise work to identify all of the codons and their corresponding amino acids.

The practice of converting the DNA code into proteins is a continual process. However, it makes it simpler to understand if you look at the two main aspects of it separately. The events in the nucleus involve the **transcription** of the DNA message into an RNA molecule. In the cytoplasm that message is **translated** into polypeptide molecules and hence into proteins (see **fig. 6.1.9**).

Transcription of the DNA molecule

The DNA that carries the genetic message is in the nucleus, but proteins are made on the ribosomes. The message of the DNA has to be transcribed (copied) to form a **messenger RNA** molecule (**mRNA**). The breakdown of the hydrogen bonds between the bases making up the two strands of DNA is catalysed by enzymes called **DNA-directed RNA polymerase**, though this name is usually shortened to **RNA polymerase**. Only the 5′ prime DNA strand is transcribed to give a single strand of mRNA. This DNA strand is called the **template strand**, because it provides the template for ordering the sequence of nucleotides in an RNA transcript. The transcription of the DNA is also brought about by RNA polymerase. The enzyme joins many small nucleotide units together (polymerises them) to form mRNA in a way that is determined by the DNA.

Every triplet code on the DNA gives rise to a complementary codon (triplet of bases) on the mRNA. The available region of the DNA template strand is read 3′ → 5′ by the RNA polymerase, so the new RNA strand is synthesised in the 5′ → 3′ direction. Every thymine in the DNA template is replaced with uracil in RNA. Apart from this change, the newly synthesised RNA strand has the same sequence as the non-template or coding strand of the DNA. For this reason, scientists usually refer to the DNA strand that has the same sequence as the resulting RNA as the **sense strand**, while the strand which acts as a template is known as the **antisense strand**.

The relatively small mRNA molecules pass easily through the pores in the nuclear membranes (nuclear envelope), carrying the genetic message from the nucleus to the cytoplasm of the cell. They then move to the surface of the ribosomes (see **fig. 6.1.9**).

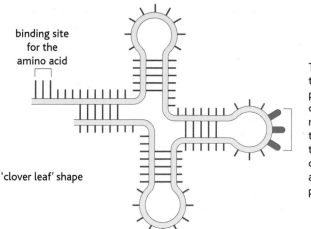

binding site
for the
amino acid

The anticodon – these
three bases determine
precisely to which piece
of mRNA on the
ribosomal surface the
tRNA will join. This in
turn decides the exact
order of the amino
acids in the resulting
polypeptide chain.

'clover leaf' shape

fig. 6.1.8 The structure of tRNA molecules is closely related to their function.

Protein synthesis – translation of the DNA code

There are three main forms of RNA in the cell. As well as mRNA there
is **transfer RNA** (**tRNA**) which picks up specific amino acids from the
protoplasm and carries them to the surface of the ribosomes and **ribosomal
RNA** which makes up the bulk of the ribosomes themselves.

Transfer RNA is found in the cytoplasm. Each tRNA molecule has a unit
of three bases at one end of the molecule which is known as the **anticodon**.
This picks up a particular amino acid from the vast numbers that are always
free there. Each amino acid has its own tRNA molecule. The tRNA molecules
carry all the necessary amino acids to the surface of the ribosomes ready for
synthesis into protein molecules.

Ribosomal RNA makes up about 50% of the structure of a ribosome and
is the most common form of RNA found in cells. It is made in the nucleus,
under the control of the nucleoli, and then moves out into the cytoplasm where
it binds with proteins to form ribosomes. The ribosomes are made up of a
large and a small subunit. They surround those parts of the mRNA which is
being actively translated, and then move along to the next bit. Their job is to
hold together the mRNA, tRNA and the enzymes controlling the process of
protein synthesis.

Each strand of mRNA has a start codon (AUG) at one end and a stop codon
(UAA, UAC or UGA) at the other. When the mRNA becomes attached to
a ribosome, the ribosome starts reading the mRNA at the start codon. This
codes for the amino acid methionine. When the ribosome meets the AUG
codon anywhere within the mRNA, normal methionine is inserted. Molecules
of tRNA carry individual amino acids to the surface of the ribosome. The
tRNA lines up its anticodon alongside a complementary codon in the mRNA.
Hydrogen bonds between the two bind the tRNA in place to the ribosome
while enzymes link the amino acids together by peptide bonds. Once its job
is done, the tRNA returns to the cytoplasm to pick up another amino acid.
The ribosome moves along the molecule of mRNA, revealing one codon
after another until the end is reached at the stop codon, leaving a completed
polypeptide chain.

Depending on the ribosome and the mRNA sequence the message may be read once or repeatedly, when many identical polypeptide chains are formed. All newly formed polypeptides start with methionine, because of the nature of the start codon. However, in many cases this first amino acid is removed by enzymes before the polypeptide becomes part of an active protein. This is one of a number of ways in which the protein which results from the original gene may be modified.

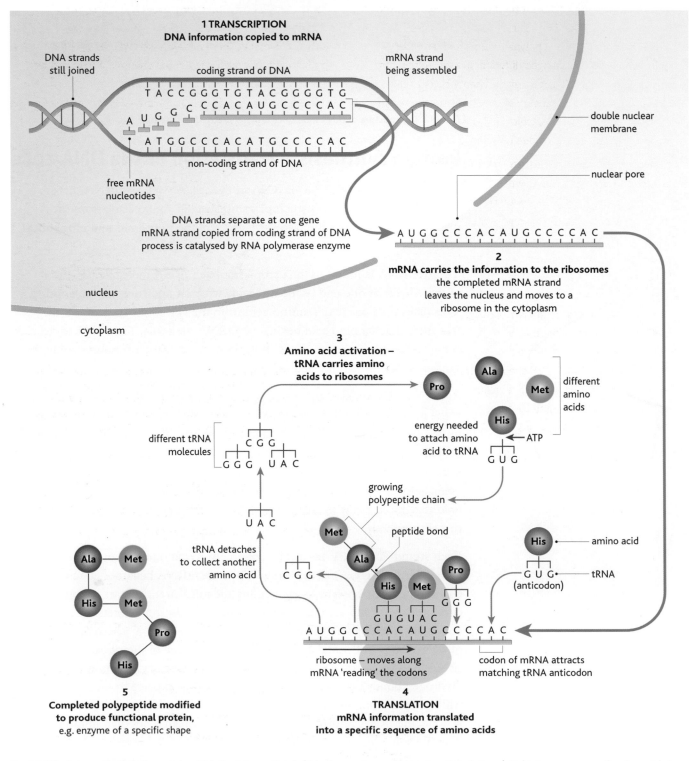

fig. 6.1.9 Protein synthesis is the way in which the information held in the sequence of bases in a gene is translated into a sequence of amino acids in a polypeptide chain.

HSW One gene, one protein?

In the 1940s George Beadle and Edward Tatum came up with the Nobel Prize-winning idea that each gene coded for one enzyme, based on their experiments using the mould *Neurospora crassa*. As understanding of proteins developed, this idea was modified to be 'one gene, one protein'. As the structures of complex proteins like haemoglobin were unravelled, scientists then realised that some proteins were made up of several polypeptide strands, and that different mutations changed different strands. This, in turn, led to a further modification of the theory to 'one gene, one polypeptide'. So in theory each gene is transcribed to give one strand of mRNA, which is then translated on a ribosome to produce a unique polypeptide sequence.

It now appears that the process is not as straightforward as this and the 'one gene, one polypeptide' theory is also an over-simplification. The RNA which is transcribed from the DNA is now referred to as **pre-mRNA**. It contains RNA copied from all the DNA in the gene, including nonsense sections which are not used to code for the protein. These areas are known as **introns**. The rest of the RNA is a copy of the areas of the DNA which code for the polypeptide chains – these areas are known as **exons**. So when the mRNA is first transcribed it is not quite finished. A number of processes take place before it lines up on the ribosomes, such as capping the ends of the RNA strand, so it is not attacked by enzymes, and the removal of the introns. The remaining exons are joined together to form a single long molecule during **RNA splicing**. This is carried out by large enzyme complexes known as **spliceosomes**. Sometimes some exons are removed as well, so that the code on the final mRNA is clearly different from the code on the DNA. Because strands of mRNA transcribed from the same bit of DNA may not be the same after these processes are complete, they may code for polypeptide chains containing slightly different amino acids, which in turn produce different proteins. These **post-transcriptional changes** to mRNA lead to more variety in the phenotype than is coded for directly in the genotype. So for example human DNA contains fewer than 25 000 genes, but codes for more than 90 000 different proteins.

fig. 6.1.10 One of the best known examples of pre-mRNA splicing takes place in the cells which form the inner ear of a chick. As a result a single gene gives rise to 576 different proteins which affect the sensitivity of the hairs in the inner ear. In turn this enables chicks to hear a range of sounds from 50 to 5000 Hz.

Questions

1 The genetic code is degenerate. Explain what this means and why it is important.

2 Summarise the processes of transcription of the DNA message and translation of the message.

3 Investigate the original 'one gene, one enzyme' theory proposed by Beadle and Tatum and describe the evidence for their theory.

4 Suggest why the statement was modified to become known as 'one gene, one protein' and then 'one gene, one polypeptide'.

5 How has the development of understanding of the processes of DNA transcription in the nucleus led to the breakdown of the 'one gene, one polypeptide' theory?

DNA and identification 4.6.5, 4.6.6, 4.6.7

One of the most important discoveries made about DNA was that you can identify individuals and species by patterns in the DNA. This has had enormous implications in many areas of science, including forensic science and species identification (see pages 58–61). The process is known as DNA profiling by scientists (and DNA fingerprinting by almost everyone else).

The human genome contains between 20 000 and 25 000 genes and the chromosomes are made up of hundreds of millions of base pairs. Less than 2% of the genome actually codes for proteins. Over 90% of the DNA is made up the introns and other repetitive coding regions between the genes. Their function is not yet fully understood, but they are inherited in the same way as the active genes. Introns are the regions of the chromosomes which are used in DNA profiling.

Within the introns, there are short sequences of DNA that are repeated many times to form micro-satellites and mini-satellites. In a **mini-satellite** a 20–50 base sequence will be repeated from 50 to several hundred times. A **micro-satellite** has 2–4 bases repeated between 5 and 15 times. The same mini- or micro-satellites appear in the same positions on each pair of homologous chromosomes. However, the number of repeats of each satellite will vary as different patterns may be inherited from your father and mother.

There are many different introns, and a huge variation in the number of repeats, so the likelihood of any two individuals having the same pattern of DNA is extremely remote, unless they are identical twins. However, the more closely related two individuals are, the more likely it is that similarities will be apparent in their DNA patterns.

How is a DNA profile produced?

The strands of DNA from a sample are chopped up into fragments using special enzymes known as **restriction endonucleases**. These enzymes cut the DNA at particular points in the intron sequences. There are many different restriction enzymes, each type cutting a DNA molecule into fragments at different specific base sequences known as **recognition sites**.

Using restriction enzymes that cut either side of mini- and micro-satellite units leaves the repeated sequences intact, giving a mixture of DNA fragments made up largely of mini- and micro-satellite sequences.

The fragments need to be separated and identified. This process starts with **gel electrophoresis** which is a variation of chromatography. The DNA fragments are placed in wells in an agarose gel medium in a buffering solution (to maintain a constant pH), with known DNA fragments to aid identification. The gel contains a dye (eg EtBr, ethidium bromide) which binds to the DNA fragments in the gel. The dye will fluoresce when placed under ultraviolet (UV) light, which makes the DNA bands. A dye is also added to the DNA samples. This does not bind with the DNA but moves through the gel slightly faster than the DNA so that the current can be turned off before all the samples run off the end.

An electric current is passed through the apparatus and the DNA fragments move towards the positive anode, because of the negative charge on the phosphate groups in the DNA. The fragments move at different rates depending on their mass and charge. Once the electrophoresis is complete the plate is placed under UV light. The DNA fluoresces and shows up clearly so it can be identified.

This is the original method of DNA profiling, which needs a relatively large sample of DNA. It shows up large DNA fragments containing a minimum of 50 base pairs – in other words, mini-satellites. The resultant DNA profile (fingerprint) looks very like a supermarket barcode. However, smaller regions of DNA and specific genes can now be identified using extensions of this technique.

The next stage is **Southern blotting**, named after its British inventor, Edwin Southern. An alkaline buffer solution is added to the gel after electrophoresis and a nylon filter or nitrocellulose paper is placed over it. Dry absorbent paper is used to draw the solution containing the DNA fragments from the gel to the filter, leaving the DNA fragments as 'blots' on the filter. The alkaline solution also denatures the DNA fragments so the strands separate and the base sequences are exposed.

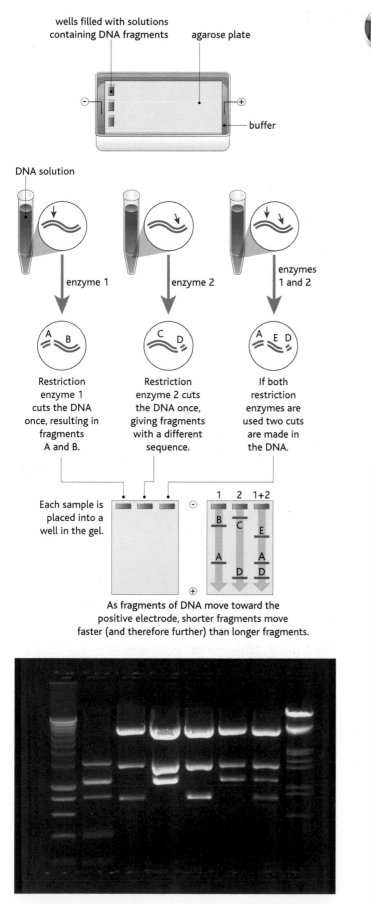

fig. 6.1.11 A summary of the process of gel electrophoresis and how the DNA bands are formed.

Using gene probes

Gene probes are short DNA sequences that are complementary to specific sequences which are being sought. Each probe is labelled, either with a radioactive element or (more recently) with a fluorescent molecule. Large amounts of the gene probes are added to the filter and bind with the complementary DNA strands in a process known as hybridisation. Excess probes are washed away and either X-ray pictures are taken of the filter, or the filter is placed under UV light to show up the DNA regions.

In forensic science gene probes are used for picking out **short tandem repeats** – micro-satellite regions which are now widely used in DNA identification. The more micro-satellites used to make up a DNA profile the more accurate it will be. Statistically the chances of two people matching on 11 or more sites is so small that it is counted as reliable evidence in court.

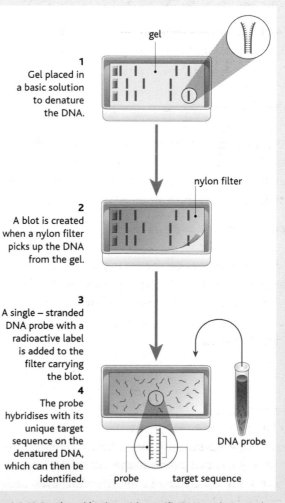

fig. 6.1.12 Southern blotting with specific DNA probes can give more accurate DNA profiles.

As a result of these different stages a DNA profile is produced as a graph (see **fig. 6.1.13**) with each peak representing the number of micro-satellite repeats in a fragment. It can be broken down to give a digital profile which provides numbers for the repeats at each micro-satellite. A single reading means that the same number of repeats was present on both chromosomes of a homologous pair.

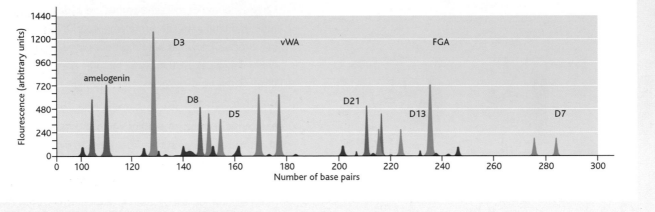

fig. 6.1.13 **Reading a DNA profile is a job for the experts!**

HSW **Professor Sir Alec Jeffreys and the fingerprinting breakthrough**

In the 1970s Alec Jeffries at Leicester University showed that when he used restriction endonuclease enzymes to chop the different regions of the chromosomes into smaller pieces, the repeating patterns in these units varied among individuals. Comparing seal and human myoglobin genes he discovered groups of repeating DNA sequences coding for the same polypeptide in two different species. Then, working with DNA from their lab technician and her family, the team noticed the repeating units were more similar between related people than between complete strangers. DNA fingerprinting had been born.

Polymerase chain reaction (PCR)

PCR – amplifying the DNA

Traditional DNA profiling needs at least 1 μg of DNA which is the equivalent of the DNA from about 10 000 human cells. In a crime investigation, there may only be a tiny DNA sample to work with. The **polymerase chain reaction** adapts the natural process in which DNA is replicated in the cell, making it possible to produce enough DNA for a profile from tiny traces of biological material.

The DNA sample which is to be amplified, DNA polymerase, primers (small sequences of DNA which must join to the beginning of the separated DNA strands before copying can begin) and a good supply of the four nucleotide bases are mixed together in a PCR vial and placed in a PCR machine. The mixture is heated to 90–95 °C which causes the DNA strands to separate as the hydrogen bonds between them break down. The mixture is cooled to 55–60 °C so the primers bind (or anneal) to the single DNA strands. Then the mixture is heated to 75 °C, which is the optimum temperature for the DNA polymerase enzyme to build the complementary strands of DNA.

These steps are repeated around 30 times to give around 1 billion copies of the original DNA. The whole process takes about 3 hours – and much of that is the time taken heating and cooling the reaction mixture in the PCR machine!

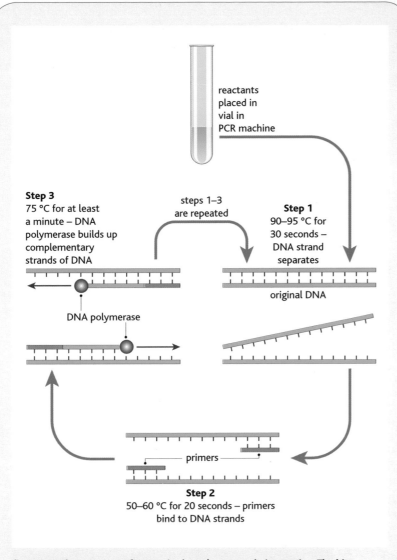

fig. 6.1.14 **The sequence of events in the polymerase chain reaction. The big breakthrough, for which Kary Mullis , the inventor of the process, was awarded the Nobel Prize in 1993, was to use enzymes from bacteria that lived in hot springs to replicate the DNA.**

Identifying individuals – forensic science in action

Helena Greenwood was a talented British biochemist working on DNA analysis in the United States. In 1984 David Frediani broke into her home, held Helena at gunpoint for several hours and sexually assaulted her. She persuaded him not to kill her by saying that she wouldn't tell anyone. Once he left she gave the police a description and they found Frediani. He was granted bail and a trial date was set for 1985.

Helena and her husband Roger were afraid Frediani might return and moved to San Diego. But 3 weeks before Frediani's trial, Roger found Helena dead in their garden, strangled and beaten. Frediani was the prime subject. Evidence from his credit cards showed he had been in the area just before the murder but police had no forensic evidence

linking him to Helena's body. Frediani stood trial for the original assault and was imprisoned for 3 years. There was no proof he was involved in Helena's death – but no other suspects emerged either.

Then, in 1999, the San Diego police reopened a number of unsolved murders to see if new forensic techniques such as PCR and DNA profiling could help. Skin fragments from Helena's attacker, where she had struggled to fight him off, were found beneath her fingernails when her body was examined. These were used to produce a DNA fingerprint which matched David Frediani! More than 15 years after he killed Helena Greenwood, he was tried, found guilty and sentenced to life imprisonment.

Questions

1 Explain the term DNA profiling.

2 Describe how gel electrophoresis is used to separate DNA fragments produced by restriction enzymes in the production of a DNA profile.

3 a Describe how DNA can be amplified in the polymerase chain reaction.

   b Explain why this has been an important development in DNA profiling.

4 a Explain why DNA profiling is useful for identifying different individuals in forensic investigations.

   b Individuals have been convicted of serious crimes partly because at some point another member of their family has committed a minor crime. Explain how this is possible.

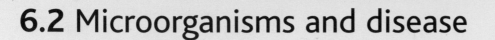

6.2 Microorganisms and disease

Viruses 4.6.8

Most deaths are not suspicious and many are caused by some form of disease, particularly infectious disease. Infectious diseases can be transmitted from one person to another, and are caused by invading microorganisms (known as **pathogens**) or the natural flora getting out of control and becoming pathogenic. The microorganisms often damage tissues directly, but in some cases they produce a poisonous **toxin** which causes the symptoms of disease. Some infectious diseases are so mild we hardly notice them and others are so virulent that they regularly cause death. There are five main groups of pathogens: viruses, bacteria, fungi, protoctista and metazoa (usually worms). In this book you will be focusing on bacteria and viruses.

What is a virus?

Viruses are the smallest of all the microorganisms, and range in size from 0.02 to 0.3 μm across, about 50 times smaller than the average bacterium. Viruses are not cells. They are arrangements of genetic material and protein that invade other living cells and take over their biochemistry to make more viruses. It is because of this reproduction, and the fact that they change and evolve in an adaptive way, that they are still classed as living organisms.

Most scientists working on viruses class them as obligate intracellular parasites, meaning they can exist and reproduce as parasites only in the cells of other living organisms. Since viruses invade and take over living cells to reproduce, they all cause damage and disease of some sort. They can withstand drying and long periods of storage while maintaining their ability to infect cells. There are very few drugs which have any effect on viruses, and those that do only work in very specific instances (eg acyclovir can help prevent herpes – cold sores and genital herpes).

HSW Discovering viruses

The presence of viruses as disease-causing agents was suspected in the late nineteenth century. They were developed as a model to explain the way certain diseases were passed from one individual to another, but it was not until 1935 that the first virus was identified by Wendell Stanley.

The leaves of tobacco plants are prone to an unpleasant blotchy disease which has a devastating effect on the plants, and no one could find the cause. Stanley pressed the juice from around 1300 kg of diseased tobacco leaves. After extraction and purification, this produced pure, needle-like crystals. If dissolved in water and painted onto tobacco leaves, these produced the symptoms of the disease. The particles were called **tobacco mosaic virus** (TMV). It was obvious that the crystals were not living in the usual sense of the word, yet they retained the ability to cause disease. Viruses cannot be seen using a light microscope because they are usually smaller than half a wavelength of light. With the development of the electron microscope the TMV particles were shown to be rod-like structures with a protein coat formed around a core of RNA.

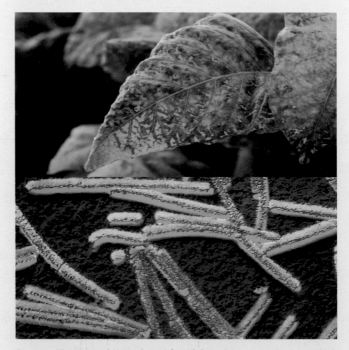

fig. 6.2.1 The tiny rod shaped particles of the tobacco mosaic virus, which causes the visible damage to plant leaves that you can see in the top photo.

The structure of viruses

Viruses are usually geometric shapes and have similar basic structures. However, there is considerable variation in the genetic material they possess, the structure of their protein coat and whether or not they have an **envelope**. The protein coat or **capsid** is made up of simple repeating protein units known as **capsomeres**, arranged in different ways. Using repeating units minimises the amount of genetic material needed to code for coat production. It also makes sure that assembling the protein coat in the host cell is as simple as possible. In some viruses the genetic material and protein coat are covered by a lipid envelope, produced from the host cell. The presence of the envelope makes it easier for the viruses to pass from cell to cell, but it does make them vulnerable to substances such as ether which will dissolve the lipid membrane.

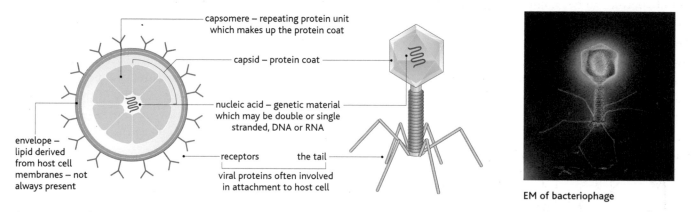

capsomere – repeating protein unit which makes up the protein coat

capsid – protein coat

nucleic acid – genetic material which may be double or single stranded, DNA or RNA

envelope – lipid derived from host cell membranes – not always present

receptors   the tail
viral proteins often involved in attachment to host cell

EM of bacteriophage

fig. 6.2.2 **General structure of a virus, including an electron micrograph of an individual bacteriophage virus.**

Viral genetic material can be DNA or RNA, and the nucleic acid is sometimes double stranded and sometimes single. The way in which the viral genetic material is used in the host cell to make new viruses depends on which form it is in. Viral DNA acts directly as a template for both new viral DNA and for the mRNAs needed to induce synthesis of viral proteins. Examples of DNA viruses include the smallpox virus, adenoviruses (which cause colds, etc), and **bacteriophages** (viruses that infect bacteria). Viral RNA, however, directs the synthesis of a special enzyme called **reverse transcriptase** which proceeds to make DNA molecules corresponding to the viral genome. This DNA is used as a template for new viral proteins and ultimately a new viral RNA genome. Examples of RNA viruses include tobacco mosaic virus and HIV (Human Immunodeficiency Virus).

Viruses attach to their host cells by means of specific proteins (antigens) known as virus attachment particles (VAPs) which target proteins in the host cell surface membrane. Because they respond to particular molecules of the host cell surface, viruses are often quite specific in the tissue they attack.

Questions

1 Explain how viruses are adapted to their particular way of life.

SC 2 Suggest valid arguments for the case that:
   a viruses *are* living organisms;   b viruses *are not* living organisms.

How viruses reproduce 4.6.11

People are in a constant struggle against the viruses that cause disease. In order to understand how they cause damage to the body, and to be able to target drugs effectively, it is important to understand how viruses reproduce in the human body.

Virus 'life cycles'

Viruses reproduce only within the cells of the body. They attack their host cells in a number of different ways. For example, bacteriophages inject their genome into the host bacterial cell but the bulk of the viral material remains outside the bacterium. The viral DNA forms a circle or **plasmid** within the bacterium. The viruses that infect animals get into the cells in several ways. Some types are taken into the cell by endocytosis – either with or without the envelope – and the host cell then digests the capsid, releasing the viral genetic material. Most commonly, the viral envelope fuses with the host cell surface, releasing the rest of the virus inside the cell membrane. Plant viruses usually get into the plant cell using a vector (often an insect, such as an aphid) to pierce the cellulose cell wall.

Once a virus is in the host cell there are two different routes of infection:

*   **Lysogenic pathway:** Many viruses are **non-virulent** when they first get into the host cell. They insert their DNA into the host DNA so it is replicated every time the host cell divides. This inserted DNA is called a **provirus**. mRNA is not produced from the viral DNA because one of the viral genes causes the production of a repressor protein which makes it impossible to translate the rest of the viral genetic material. During this period of **lysogeny**, when the virus is part of the reproducing host cells, the virus is said to be dormant.

*   **Lytic pathway:** Sometimes the viral genetic material is replicated independently of the host DNA straight after entering the host. Mature viruses are made and eventually the host cell bursts, releasing large numbers of new virus particles to invade other cells. The virus is said to be **virulent** (disease-causing) and the process of replicating and killing cells is known as the lytic pathway.

Under certain conditions such as when the host is damaged, viruses in the lysogenic state are activated. The amount of repressor protein decreases and the viruses enter the lytic pathway and become virulent (see **fig. 6.2.3**).

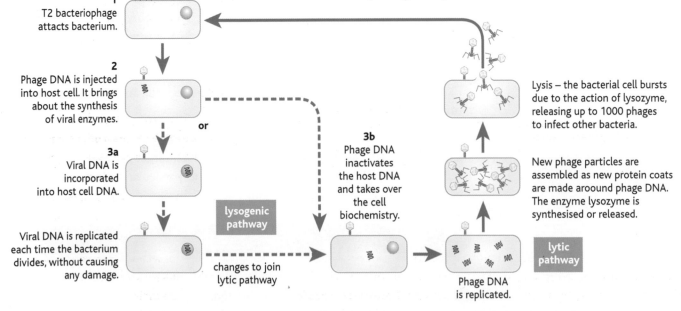

1 T2 bacteriophage attacts bacterium.

2 Phage DNA is injected into host cell. It brings about the synthesis of viral enzymes.

or

3a Viral DNA is incorporated into host cell DNA.

Viral DNA is replicated each time the bacterium divides, without causing any damage.

lysogenic pathway

changes to join lytic pathway

3b Phage DNA inactivates the host DNA and takes over the cell biochemistry.

Phage DNA is replicated.

New phage particles are assembled as new protein coats are made aroound phage DNA. The enzyme lysozyme is synthesised or released.

Lysis – the bacterial cell bursts due to the action of lysozyme, releasing up to 1000 phages to infect other bacteria.

lytic pathway

fig. 6.2.3 The life cycle of the T2 bacteriophage includes a lysogenic and a lytic phase. Some types of virus have both stages in their life cycle, but others move straight to the lytic stage after they have infected a cell.

A more complex life cycle

Retroviruses (including the HIV virus that causes AIDS and the Rous sarcoma virus that causes cancer in chickens) have a rather different and complex life cycle. Their genetic material is viral RNA. This cannot be used as mRNA but is translated into DNA by the specific enzyme reverse transcriptase in the cytoplasm of the cell. This viral DNA passes into the nucleus of the host cell where it is inserted into the host DNA. Host transcriptase enzymes then make viral mRNA and new viral genome RNA. New viral material is synthesised and the new viral particles leave the cell by **exocytosis** (see *AS Biology* page 109). The host cell continues to function as a virus-making factory, while the new viruses move on to infect other cells.

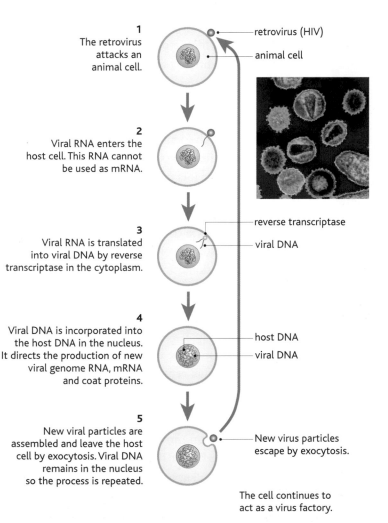

1
The retrovirus attacks an animal cell.

retrovirus (HIV)
animal cell

2
Viral RNA enters the host cell. This RNA cannot be used as mRNA.

3
Viral RNA is translated into viral DNA by reverse transcriptase in the cytoplasm.

reverse transcriptase
viral DNA

4
Viral DNA is incorporated into the host DNA in the nucleus. It directs the production of new viral genome RNA, mRNA and coat proteins.

host DNA
viral DNA

5
New viral particles are assembled and leave the host cell by exocytosis. Viral DNA remains in the nucleus so the process is repeated.

New virus particles escape by exocytosis.

The cell continues to act as a virus factory.

fig. 6.2.4 The life cycle of a retrovirus.

Viruses and disease

Viruses cause disease in animals and plants, and even in bacteria. They can cause the symptoms of disease by the lysis of the host cells, by causing the host cells to release their own lysosomes (see *AS Biology* page 142) and digest themselves from the inside, or by the production of toxins that inhibit cell metabolism.

Viral infections are often specific to particular tissues. For example, adenoviruses which cause colds affect the tissues of the respiratory tract but do not damage the cells of the brain or the intestine. This specificity seems to be due to the presence or absence of cell markers on the surface of host cells. Each type of cell has its own recognition markers and different types of virus can only bind to particular markers. The presence or absence of these markers can even affect whether a group of living organisms is vulnerable to attack by viruses at all. For example, the angiosperms (flowering plants) are vulnerable to viral diseases, but the gymnosperms (conifers and their relatives) are not.

Viruses are well known for causing diseases like flu, measles and AIDS. Research also shows that in some cases they play a role in the development of cancers. Certain animal cancers have been clearly linked to viral infection, and in humans there seems to be a link in certain specific cases. For example, the human papilloma virus responsible for warts on the skin, including genital warts, has been linked with the occurrence of pre-cancerous and cancerous changes in the cells of the cervix, and there is now a vaccination against it.

Questions

SC 1 Describe the main differences between the lytic and lysogenic pathways of infection.

2 a What is the main difference between retroviruses and other viruses?

b Explain how this structural difference affects their life cycle.

Bacteria 4.6.8

Bacteria are prokaryotic organisms, and probably the most common form of life on Earth. Some bacteria are pathogens and cause disease, but the great majority do no harm and many are beneficial to living organisms (e.g. in the human gut and in the nitrogen and carbon cycles; see page 38).

The structure of bacteria

All bacterial cells have certain features in common, although these vary greatly between species.

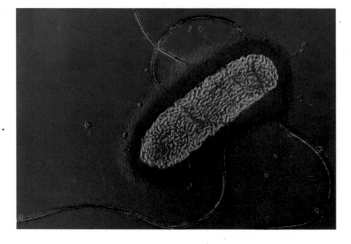

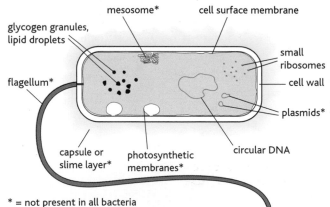

fig. 6.2.5 **Structure of a typical bacterium.**

All bacterial cells have a cell wall. The contents of bacterial cells are usually **hypertonic** to the medium around them, so water tends to move into the cells by osmosis (see *AS Biology* pages 106–7). The cell wall prevents the cell swelling and bursting. It also maintains the shape of the bacterium, and gives support and protection to the contents of the cell.

The cell surface membrane is similar in both structure and function to the membranes of eukaryotic cells.

However, bacteria have no mitochondria so the cell membrane is also the site of some of the respiratory enzymes. In some bacterial cells (e.g. *Bacillus subtilis*, a common soil bacterium) the membrane shows infoldings known as **mesosomes**. There is still some debate about their function. Some scientists think they may be an artefact from the process of preparing the cell for an electron micrograph, while others believe they are associated with enzyme activity, particularly during the separation of DNA and the formation of new cross-walls during replication.

Some bacteria have a **capsule** (or **slime layer** if it is very thin and diffuse) around their cell walls. This may be formed from starch, gelatin, protein or glycolipid, and protects the bacterium from phagocytosis by white blood cells. It also covers the cell markers on the cell membrane which identify the cell. So a capsule can make it easier for a bacterium to be pathogenic (to cause disease) because it is not identified by the host's immune system, such as the bacteria that cause pneumonia, meningitis, TB and septicaemia. However, many capsulated bacteria do not cause disease and it seems likely that capsules evolved to help the bacteria survive very dry conditions.

Some bacteria have from one to several hundred thread-like protein projections from their surface, called **pili** (or **fimbriae**) such as *Escherichia coli* and *Salmonella* spp. These seem to be used for attachment to a host cell and for sexual reproduction. However, they also make bacteria more vulnerable to viral infection, as bacteriophages can use pili as an entry point to the cell.

Some bacteria can move themselves using **flagella**. These are little bigger than one of the microtubules contained in a eukaryotic flagellum, and are made of a many-stranded helix of the protein flagellin. The flagellum moves the bacterium by rapid rotations – about 100 revolutions per second.

The genetic material consists of a single length of circular DNA lying free in the cytoplasm. Some bacterial cells also contain one or more much smaller circles of DNA known as plasmids. These code for particular aspects of the bacterial phenotype such as the production of a particular toxin or resistance to a particular antibiotic.

More about bacterial cell walls

Bacterial cell walls consist of a layer of **peptidoglycan** which is made up of many parallel polysaccharide chains with short peptide cross-linkages, forming an enormous molecule with a net-like structure. However, there are two different types of bacterial cell wall, which can be distinguished by **Gram staining**, a staining technique developed by Christian Gram in 1884 and still in use today. Before staining, bacteria are colourless. The cell walls of **Gram-positive bacteria** (e.g. methicillin-resistant *Staphylococcus aureus*, MRSA) have a thick layer of peptidoglycan containing chemicals such as **teichoic acid** within their net-like structure. The crystal violet in the stain binds to the teichoic acid and resists decolouring in the rest of the process, leaving the positive purple/blue colour.

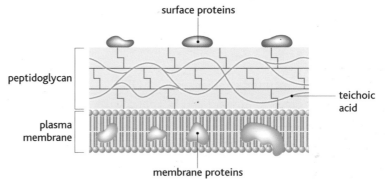

fig. 6.2.6 MRSA as seen under the light microscope. The blue/purple colour shows this is a Gram-positive bacterium, a result of a reaction between the bacterial cell wall and the Gram stain.

The cell walls of **Gram-negative bacteria** have a thinner layer of peptidoglycan, with no teichoic acid, between the two layers of membranes, and then an outer membrane-like layer made up of lipopolysaccharides. Any crystal violet which does bind is readily decolourised and replaced with red safranine in the Gram stain, so the cells appear red.

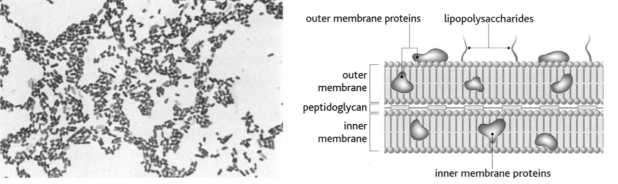

fig. 6.2.7 *E. coli*, the common gut bacterium, as seen under the light microscope. The red colour indicates that this is a Gram-negative bacterium. This difference in the cell wall structure accounts for the reaction with the Gram stain.

Classifying bacteria

Grouping bacteria simply by the way their cell walls do or do not take up Gram stains is of limited use in classifying the different types. Another way in which bacteria can be identified is by their shape. Some bacteria are spherical (**cocci**) while the **bacilli** are rod shaped. Yet others are twisted (**spirilla**) or comma shaped (**vibrios**).

Bacteria are also sometimes grouped by their respiratory requirements. **Obligate aerobes** need oxygen for respiration. **Facultative anaerobes** use oxygen if it is available but can manage without it. Many human pathogens fall into this group. **Obligate anaerobes** can only respire in the absence of oxygen.

Questions

SC 1 Draw up a table to compare and contrast the main structural features of animal cells, bacterial cells and viruses. Include characteristics such as size, genetic material and main structures.

How bacteria reproduce 4.6.11

Bacteria can reproduce in two main ways. By far the most common is asexual reproduction, by simple splitting in two (**binary fission**). Once a bacterium reaches a certain size, determined by the nuclear material to cytoplasm ratio, the DNA is replicated and the old cell wall begins to break down around the middle of the cell. While this happens the DNA appears to be associated with the cell surface membrane, and it may be held in position by the mesosome if one is present.

Enzymes break open the circular piece of DNA, allowing the strands to unwind and be replicated. New cross-walls are also laid down between the two new daughter cells, and again the mesosome appears to play a part in cells where it is present. New cell membrane and cell wall material extend inwards, forming a septum which eventually divides the cell into two new daughter cells, each containing a circular chromosome attached to the cell membrane. Plasmids often divide at the same time, so the daughter cells usually each contain both a copy of the original genome and any plasmids present in the parent cell. The time between cell divisions is known as the **generation time**. If conditions are favourable, bacteria can reproduce every 20 minutes.

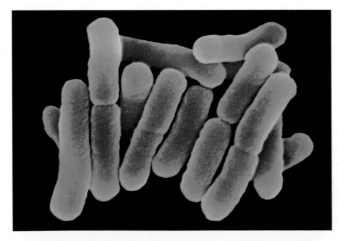

fig. 6.2.8 Binary fission in *E. coli*. In some places you can see now the cell wall and membrane are beginning to extend inwards to separate the two new cells.

In certain situations, some types of bacteria can reproduce using what appear to be different forms of sexual reproduction. These are very rare events, and none of them involves true sexual reproduction with the formation and transfer of gametes. However, they are methods by which genes can be transferred between bacteria, not necessarily the same species, and have important implications in our fight against disease.

There are three ways in which genetic material from one bacterium can be taken in and used as part of the DNA of another bacterium.

- During **transformation** a short piece of DNA is released by a donor and actively taken up by a recipient where it replaces a similar piece of DNA. This occurs only in certain types of bacteria.

- **Transduction** takes place when a small amount of DNA is transferred from one bacterium to another by a bacteriophage. Sometimes during the infection of a bacterial cell by a bacteriophage, small pieces of bacterial DNA may be included by mistake within a viral coat. If these new **transducing particles** are taken into another bacterium, they will become incorporated into the host DNA.

- The most common way by which bacteria exchange genetic information, although this is still a rare event, is by **conjugation**. Genetic information is transferred from one bacterium to another by direct contact, as described in *AS Biology* page 157. The donor cell (F^+) is analogous to a male cell and this produces a **sex pilus**, a cytoplasmic bridge between the two cells through which DNA is transferred to the recipient cell (F^-), analogous to the female cell. The 'male' cells contain the F (fertility) factor, a plasmid containing the DNA which codes for the formation of the sex pilus.

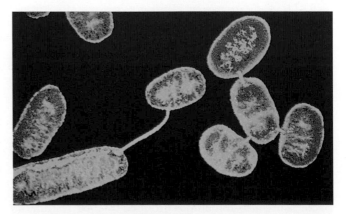

fig. 6.2.9 Bacterial conjugation is sexual reproduction from the point of view that DNA is exchanged between individuals, but otherwise does not resemble sexual reproduction in eukaryotic organisms.

HSW Modelling in the dark – investigating transformation in bacteria

Transformation was discovered by Frederick Griffith in 1928 working with *Pneumococcus*, a pneumonia-causing bacterium. He was working with two forms of the bacterium which looked different. The rough type R had no capsule and did not cause disease. The smooth type S had capsules and caused pneumonia. Griffith carried out a series of experiments as shown in **fig. 6.2.10**.

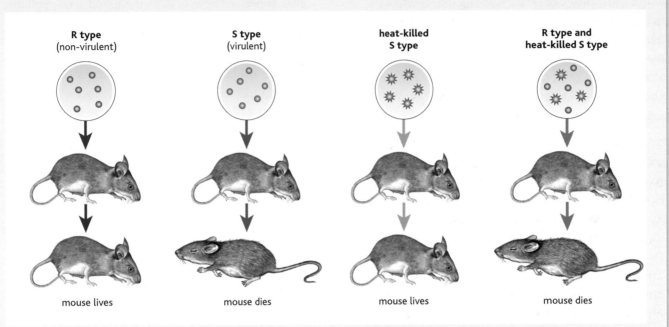

fig. 6.2.10 Summary of experiments carried out by Griffith on two strains of pneumonia-causing bacteria.

The mouse that received live R bacteria and dead S bacteria developed pneumonia and died a few days later. Living S bacteria were isolated from its blood. Griffith concluded that the living R cells had taken up a factor released from the dead S cells which transformed the R cells into S cells, enabling them to make a capsule, resist attack by the host cells and cause disease.

DNA and its role in inheritance was not recognised at the time of Griffith's work. However, work by Avery, Macleod and McCarthy in 1944 showed that the transforming factor was a piece of DNA (see **table 6.2.1**).

Method of treatment	Result after mixing transforming factor with R bacteria
Enzymes that digest carbohydrates	S bacteria produced – transformation occurred
Enzymes that digest proteins	S bacteria produced – transformation occurred
Enzymes that digest DNA	S bacteria not produced – no transformation

table 6.2.1: Evidence from the work of Avery, Macleod and McCarthy on the transforming factor in bacteria.

Questions

1 Explain why bacteria:
  a usually use asexual reproduction;
  b occasionally use some form of sexual reproduction.

2 a Explain what Griffith's work on transformation tells you about reproduction in bacteria.
  b Explain how the results in **table 6.2.1** provide evidence for DNA as the transforming factor in bacteria.

Bacteria – pathogens and benefactors 4.6.11

Bacteria do not cause disease in the same way as viruses. Once bacteria get into the body, they will often grow in a localised area unless they get into the blood when they can be carried all around the body. Bacteria make people unwell through the toxins they make, either as a by-product of their metabolism or as part of their parasitic lifestyle to incapacitate the host or its immune response. These can be classified as **endotoxins** and **exotoxins**.

Endotoxins are lipopolysaccharides, part of the outer layer of Gram-negative bacteria. They are rarely fatal and tend to cause symptoms such as fever, vomiting and diarrhoea, e.g. strains of *Salmonella* and *E. coli*. However, the symptoms they cause can lead indirectly to death, e.g. by dehydration. Exotoxins are usually soluble proteins that are produced and released into the body by bacteria as they metabolise and reproduce. There are many different types which tend to have specific effects – some damage cell membranes, causing cell breakdown or internal bleeding, some act as competitive inhibitors to neurotransmitters, while others directly poison cells. Exotoxins rarely cause fevers, but they include some of the most dangerous and fatal bacterial diseases. For example, *Clostridium botulinum* produces botulinum toxin, one of the most toxic substances known. It has been estimated that 1 mg of pure toxin could kill a million guinea pigs!

Bacterial meningitis is a very serious disease. The bacteria that cause it affect the meninges, the membranes that cover the brain. If the bacteria get into the blood, the toxins they produce damage the walls of the blood vessels so blood leaks out under the skin. This produces a typical rash, which doesn't disappear if a glass is pressed against it, as the blood is trapped there.

Beneficial bacteria

While some bacteria cause terrible diseases, the great majority of bacteria do not. The number of species of harmless and beneficial bacteria in the human body ranges from 500 to 10 000. Your body is an ideal environment for bacteria, such as in your gut where there is a regularly renewed supply of food in a warm, wet space. No wonder it is estimated that there are about 10^{14} bacteria in your body, weighing around 2.2 kg – that's 10 times more bacteria than body cells! While the majority of these bacteria are in the gut, others are found all over the body. Many of them are beneficial, helping to break down food and keeping pathogens at bay by outcompeting them. The normal growth of bacteria on your skin or in your gut is referred to as the 'skin flora' or 'gut flora'. Probiotic drinks and foods contain cultures of these 'good' bacteria to help support the normal healthy bacterial flora of the gut.

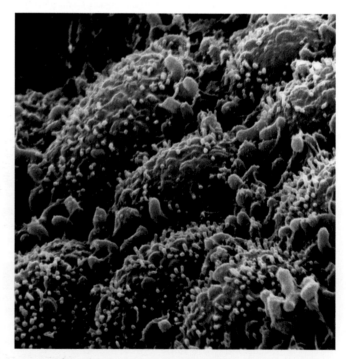

fig. 6.2.12 **The normal gut flora** – these bacteria can be destroyed if you have to take antibiotics for an infection. Probiotics can be useful in helping to repopulate the gut with the right kind of bacteria.

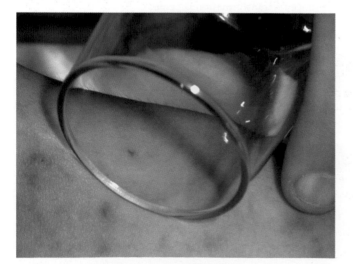

fig. 6.2.11 **The typical rash of severe bacterial meningitis.**

Bacteria also play a vital role in the ecosystems of the natural world. The majority of bacteria are decomposers. They break down organic material to produce simple inorganic molecules such as carbon dioxide and water. They release inorganic nitrogen (in the form of ammonia, nitrites and nitrates) which returns to the soil in the nitrogen cycle, and also sulfur compounds which return to the soil or water.

The role that decomposing bacteria play is a vital one. Living organisms die. Animals also excrete both solid and liquid waste in the form of faeces and urine. Without the decomposers, the surface of the Earth would be unrecognisable, because it would be covered in layer upon layer of the bodies of animals and plants along with the excrement from all of the animals which have ever lived. Bacteria, along with the fungi, are the main group of organisms which make sure this does not happen. On pages 68–9 you looked at the role they play in the decomposition of the human body. They play a similar part in every other living organism after death. One of the most important aspects of bacteria in the carbon cycle, for example, is the fact that some microorganisms produce the enzyme cellulase. This vital enzyme breaks down the cellulose produced in plant cell walls to give sugars which can then be used as food by a wide range of other microorganisms. The importance of their role in the carbon cycle is reflected in the fact that the decomposers (bacteria and fungi combined) release 25×10^{12} kg of carbon per year into the atmosphere. Compare this with the $6-7 \times 10^{12}$ kg per year (and rising) of carbon released into the atmosphere by the burning of fossil fuels and you will begin to recognise the importance of these microorganisms in the carbon cycle on Earth!

fig. 6.2.13 The actions of the decomposing bacteria which play such an important role in the carbon cycle break down organic material such as this cow dung and release carbon dioxide into the atmosphere.

Questions

SC 1 Compare the way in which bacteria and viruses can cause symptoms of disease.

2 Sketch the carbon cycle (if necessary look back to page 38 to refresh your memory) and indicate where microorganisms are involved in the process.

Invading the body 4.6.10, 4.6.12

Most infections are **communicable**. This means that the infection is capable of spreading from one person to another. Diseases can spread in many different ways. Sometimes part of the normal flora of the body will change and cause disease in response to a change in the body environment, but more often new microbes get into the body and cause problems.

For any disease to be passed on, the pathogen needs to get inside the body of the new host. There are a number of different ways in. The body openings – eyes, nose, mouth, ears, anus and urinogenital openings – provide relatively easy access. The alternative is for microorganisms to get straight into the blood through the skin – not quite so easy but a very direct route. Pathogens are transmitted in a variety of ways:

- *Vectors.* A living organism that transmits infection from one host to another is known as a **vector**. Many insects are vectors of disease. Examples: malaria, dengue, yellow fever.

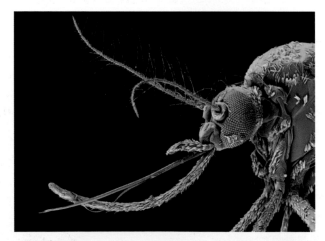

fig. 6.2.14 The virus that causes the disease dengue fever gets into the human bloodstream as a result of a bite by the *Aedes aegypti* mosquito.

- *Fomites.* Fomites are inanimate objects that carry pathogens from one host to another. Hospital towels and bedding can be a risk, or using someone else's make-up. Example: *Staphylococcus* infections.

- *Direct contact.* Direct contact is often important in the spreading of skin diseases in small children. Many sexual diseases are also spread by direct contact of the genital organs. Examples: impetigo, gonorrhoea, syphilis.

- *Inhalation.* When you cough, sneeze or talk, millions of droplets are expelled from your respiratory tract. If you have an infection of the respiratory system, those droplets all contain pathogens. Part of the water in these droplets evaporates, leaving very tiny droplets which are full of pathogens and small enough to remain suspended in the air for a long time. When these droplets are inhaled by another individual the pathogens gain entrance to a new respiratory tract and another infection is set up. Examples: influenza, measles, tuberculosis.

- *Ingestion.* Many of the pathogens that cause gut diseases are transmitted by contaminated food or drink. As many of these organisms are destroyed when food is heated thoroughly, the risk of infection is greatest from raw or undercooked food. Often only a small number of disease-causing organisms need to be taken in to cause disease. Examples: most forms of diarrhoea, hepatitis A, *Salmonella* poisoning.

fig. 6.2.15 Whenever a natural disaster or war results in thousands of refugees living in conditions like these, diseases such as cholera which are passed on through infected water become rife and can cause massive loss of life.

- *Inoculation.* A pathogen can be inoculated into the body directly through a break in the skin. This transmission might be via an injury from contaminated medical instruments or shared needles for drug abuse. An infected animal may bite, lick or scratch you – or you may pick up pathogens through a puncture wound from a contaminated knife, thorn or a stone. Examples: hepatitis B, HIV, rabies, tetanus.

Barriers to entry

The body does not make it easy for pathogens to enter. It has natural barriers that need to be breached before infection can occur.

Epithelial defences

The skin forms a natural barrier preventing the entry of microorganisms. It is an impenetrable layer toughened by keratin, a fibrous structural protein, and forms a physical barrier between the pathogen-laden environment and the delicate, blood-rich tissues beneath the skin. In addition, an oily substance produced by the skin, called **sebum**, contains chemicals that inhibit the growth of microorganisms. Sebum does not harm the natural skin flora which are adapted for survival on the skin surface. These natural skin flora also play a role in preventing disease by competing successfully for position on the skin and also, in some cases, producing substances that inhibit the growth of other microorganisms. Washing too often – and using antibacterial soaps – can reduce your resistance to disease by destroying the natural pH balance and surface flora of the skin! The pharynx and the large intestine have protective coverings similar to the skin.

The surfaces of the internal tubes and ducts (found in areas such as the nose, the respiratory system, the gut, urinary and reproductive tracts) are more vulnerable than the skin on the outside of your body as they are very thin and not toughened with keratin. However, these epithelial layers also produce defensive secretions. Many produce mucus, a sticky substance that traps microorganisms. Mucus contains **lysozymes**, enzymes capable of destroying microbial cell walls. These enzymes are particularly effective against Gram-positive bacteria, breaking down the cross-linkages in the peptidoglycans in the bacterial cell wall. Lysozymes are also present in tears, the secretions produced to keep the eyes moist and to protect them from the entry of pathogens. They are part of the non-specific defence of the body against disease (see pages 96–9).

fig. 6.2.16 The enzyme lysozyme ruptures bacteria by disrupting their cell walls. It is found in human tears, saliva and milk. Lysozyme is found in almost every member of the animal kingdom as part of the non-specific defence against disease.

The mucus produced in the respiratory system is constantly swept towards the outside of the body, while the lining of the urinary system is constantly washed through with urine. Cilia also move mucus in the reproductive tracts – for example along the Fallopian tubes. Phagocytic white blood cells which can engulf and digest pathogens are often present on the epithelial surfaces as well. These mechanisms are so successful that both the respiratory, reproductive and urinary systems usually have no bacteria in them except for the areas nearest to the outside world. However, if microorganisms are present in sufficient numbers they may breach these defences and get through to the areas where the cells are vulnerable to infection – for example cold and flu viruses can enter the body through the respiratory system.

The skin defences are breached when we cut ourselves, and this is when we become vulnerable to the entry of potentially disease-causing microorganisms directly into the blood, such as herpes viruses, *Clostridium tetani* and MRSA bacteria. In addition, some organisms like hookworms, ticks and biting insects can penetrate the skin for themselves either causing disease directly or introducing disease-causing pathogens, such as in malaria or Lyme disease. The first response of the body to a break in the skin is to seal the wound through the mechanism of blood clotting. This cascade of events involves fibrinogen, thrombin, blood platelets and red blood cells forming a solid clot, sealing the open wound and effectively preventing the entry of any further pathogens (see *AS Biology* page 17).

Going into the gut

The gut is also important in the natural defence of the body against disease. The saliva in the mouth has bactericidal properties. Some polypeptides produced in the salivary glands destroy bacteria while others slow down bacterial growth. The acid in your stomach – hydrochloric acid with a pH of around 2 – effectively destroys the majority of ingested microorganisms. Throughout the gut the natural flora usually competes successfully for both nutrients and space with any microorganisms which manage to get through the stomach. Like the skin flora the gut flora produces anti-microbial compounds.

Another way in which the stomach helps protect against disease – and a common symptom of illness – is vomiting. Vomiting is when the contents of the stomach are forcibly discharged out of the body through the mouth. It is a complex process which is coordinated partly through many different sites in the brain. Vomiting is caused by many things, including taking in toxins, bad smells, pregnancy and tumours. However, infection of the gut is one of the most common causes of vomiting. If the stomach is infected with bacteria or viruses, vomiting will effectively remove many of the microorganisms physically from the system. In most cases the disease is short-lived and self-limiting. However, in very young children and frail elderly people, or when the disease is longer lasting such as cholera and dysentery, the loss of fluids and electrolytes, often combined with high fever, can result in severe dehydration and death.

HSW Ulcers – changing the model of a disease

For many years gastric and duodenal ulcers were thought to be caused by stress increasing acid production in the stomach. The high levels of acid then damaged the lining of the stomach, causing an ulcer, a painful eroded area on the lining of the gut. Treatment involved drugs to reduce the amount of stomach acid and/or neutralise it, allowing the ulcer to heal. However ulcers often returned, presumably reflecting the continued stressful lifestyle of their owner.

Then in the 1980s an Australian pathologist, Robin Warren, observed bacteria (*Helicobacter pylori*) in the stomach cells of about 50% of the stomach **biopsies** he saw, and noticed that inflammation was always visible as well. The scientifically accepted view was that bacteria could not live in the stomach because of the acidic conditions. Barry Marshall was a young doctor who found these results very interesting and he and Warren started to work together. Marshall suspected the bacteria might be causing stomach ulcers and devised a series of tests to try to demonstrate this. These included infecting himself with the bacteria and observing the changes in his stomach! His work showed that not only were ulcers caused by bacteria, but that they could be treated with antibiotics that destroyed the bacteria so the ulcers did not return.

This cheap and simple solution met with resistance from gastrologists who spent a lot of time treating chronic ulcer sufferers, and the drug companies who produced the best-selling drugs to relieve ulcer pain and block acid production. It took 10 years for around 10% of doctors to be convinced by Marshall's work. Now most accept that *H. pylori* rather than stress is the major cause of ulcers. Barry Marshall went on to investigate a link between *H. pylori* and certain stomach cancers, which is also now an accepted causative relationship. Bacteria had never before been linked to cancer, but the WHO now classifies *H. pylori* as a class 1 carcinogen. In 2005 Robin Warren and Barry Marshall were awarded a Nobel Prize for their work.

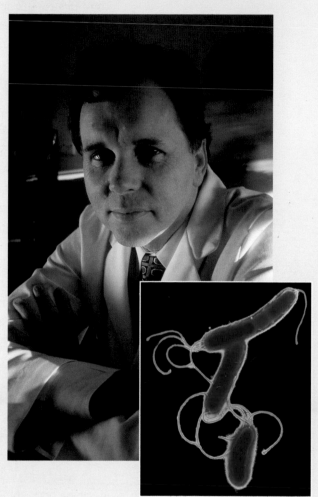

fig. 6.2.17 The Australian doctor Barry Marshall and *Helicobacter pylori*.

Questions

SC 1 Produce a table to summarise the main ways in which pathogens enter the body. For each way, explain how the natural barriers of the body help to prevent infection.

2 The enzyme lysozyme is almost universally present in animals. Explain its role in the non-specific defence against disease.

3 Explain the role of physical barriers, chemical barriers and biological defences in the way the skin and the gut help prevent the invasion of pathogenic microorganisms.

Non-specific responses to infection 4.6.12, 4.6.13

Even though the body has many barriers, millions of bacteria and viruses make their way in every day, but you do not constantly suffer from disease. This is because in most cases your body recognises that it has been invaded and destroys or inactivates the pathogens. This response is the result of a number of different defence systems in your body that depend on a process of cell recognition.

How do cells recognise each other?

Protruding from the outer surface of the cell surface membrane are many proteins, in particular glycoproteins which are protein molecules with a carbohydrate component (see *AS Biology* page 45). These chains of sugar molecules can be very varied, and they seem to be important in cell recognition in several ways. Similar sugar recognition sites may bind to each other, holding cells together. When tissues and organs are forming in embryonic development this kind of recognition and binding must be of great significance. These glycoproteins also act as **antigens** which are recognised by white blood cells during the specific responses to infection (see pages 100–103). An antigen is a substance that stimulates the production of an antibody when it gets into the body. Antigens are often chemicals on the surface of a cell such as proteins, glycoproteins or carbohydrates. They can also be toxins made by bacteria, or sometimes are whole microorganisms such as bacteria or viruses.

HSW Early evidence for cell recognition

Sponges are the most primitive of the multicellular animals – in fact until 1765 people thought they were plants. They are made up of many simple cells grouped together, but do not move about. Their cells show some differentiation into several types concerned with food extraction and water flow, but they do not have organs or organ systems.

In the early twentieth century H.V. Wilson split sponges into their individual cells by passing them through sieves (not really as unpleasant as it sounds as sponges have no nervous system to feel pain). The individual cells started moving and kept going until they met another cell. Groups of sponge cells formed, clearly demonstrating cell recognition, and these clusters went on to develop into new animals.

fig. 6.2.18 Sponges are simple animals that display clear cell recognition.

Once pathogens get inside your body tissues, other responses rather than physical barriers come into play. Some of these responses are non-specific, others are specific to particular pathogens which you will be looking at on page 100. The non-specific responses simply recognise the difference between self (your own cells) and non-self (a foreign cell or organism that gets into your body) and react against anything that is non-self.

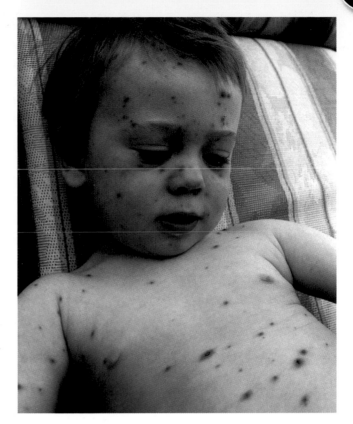

fig. 6.2.20 Some symptoms – like this chickenpox rash – are quite distinctive and can be used to diagnose a particular disease. However, red rashes are a common symptom of a wide range of bacterial and viral infections so they are not always so helpful for diagnosis.

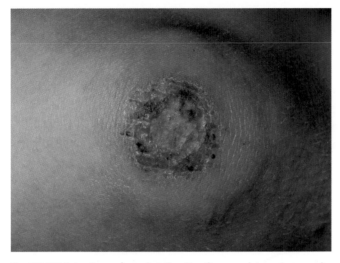

fig. 6.2.19 Histamines released at the site of a wound cause increased blood flow and swelling to protect against invasion by pathogens.

Inflammation is a common, non-specific way in which our bodies respond to infection. It generally occurs when an infection is relatively localised, for example when you cut yourself and bacteria get into the wound. The inflammatory response involves a number of stages. Special cells called **mast cells** are found in the connective tissue below the skin and around blood vessels. When this tissue is damaged, mast cells along with damaged white blood cells release chemicals known as **histamines**. These histamines cause the blood vessels in the area, particularly the arterioles, to dilate, causing local heat and redness. The locally raised temperature reduces the effectiveness of pathogen reproduction in the area. The histamines also make the walls of the capillaries leaky as the cells forming the walls separate slightly. As a result fluid, including plasma, white blood cells and antibodies, is forced out of the capillaries causing swelling (**oedema**) and often pain. The white blood cells and antibodies disable and destroy the pathogens. A fairly common symptom of a more widespread infection is a rash, which is a form of inflammation or tissue damage that particularly affects the skin, causing red spots or patches.

One early, and common, non-specific response to infection is a **fever**. Normal body temperature is maintained by the hypothalamus and follows a regular circadian (roughly 24 hour) rhythm, lowest in the early hours of the morning and highest at about 10pm. When a pathogen infects the body it causes the hypothalamus to reset to a higher body temperature, so that we become aware of 'running a temperature' – in other words, we have a fever. This might seem a strange response, but a raised temperature seems to help the body combat infection in two ways. Firstly, many pathogens reproduce most quickly at 37 °C or lower. Thus a raised temperature will reduce the ability of many pathogens to reproduce effectively and so they cause less damage (as is seen locally in inflammation). Secondly, your specific response system works better at higher temperatures and so will be more successful at combating the infection. In a bacterial infection the temperature rises steadily and remains fairly high until treatment is successful or the body overcomes the infection. In viral infections the temperature tends to 'spike', shooting up high every time viruses burst out of the cells and then dropping down towards normal again.

Although fevers can often be beneficial, if they get too high they can be damaging and even fatal. If your body temperature rises above 40 °C the denaturation of some enzymes takes place and you may suffer permanent tissue damage. If the temperature is not lowered fairly quickly, death may result. Sweating is often associated with fever – the body sweats in response to the high temperature. This can result in chills as the temperature falls. Also, if the fluid and electrolytes lost in the sweat are not replaced, dangerous dehydration and even death can result.

Phagocytosis is another non-specific response, often seen in association with inflammation. It involves white blood cells. There are two main groups of white blood cells, the **granulocytes** which have granules that can be stained in their cytoplasm, and the **agranulocytes** which have no granules. **Phagocyte** is a general term used to describe white blood cells which engulf and digest pathogens and any other foreign material in the blood and tissues (see *AS Biology* page 109). There are two main types of phagocytes – **neutrophils** which are granulocytes and make up 70% of the white cells, and **macrophages** which are agranulocytes and make up about 4%. They accumulate at the site of an infection to attack the invading pathogens. The phagocytes can sometimes be seen as pus – a build-up of dead cells which are mainly neutrophils. The pus may ooze out of a wound or spot, or it may be reabsorbed by the body.

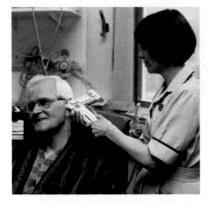

fig. 6.2.21 **Taking a patient's temperature is useful in tracking the course of many infections.**

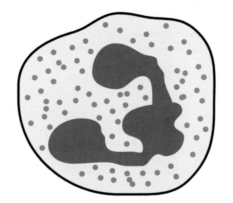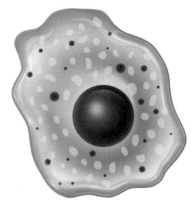

fig. 6.2.22 Neutrophils and macrophages are important in the non-specific responses to invasion by pathogens. Macrophages also play a vital role in the specific immune responses producing antibodies (see pages 102–103).

Another important non-specific defence mechanism is the production of lysozyme in tears, mucus and other body fluids. As you saw on page 93, lysozymes destroy bacteria by disrupting the bacterial cell walls.

All of these non-specific responses to infection are particularly effective against bacteria, but there is one response that is effective only against viruses. When cells are invaded by viruses they begin to produce a group of chemicals called **interferons**. Interferons are proteins that inhibit viral replication within the cells. An interferon diffuses from the cell where it is made into the surrounding cells. It binds to receptors in the surface membranes of uninfected cells, stimulating a pathway which makes the cells resistant to infection by viruses by preventing viruses reproducing. In this way it prevents the infection of more cells when the viruses break out of the first cell.

HSW Hijacking nature – interferon in medical treatments

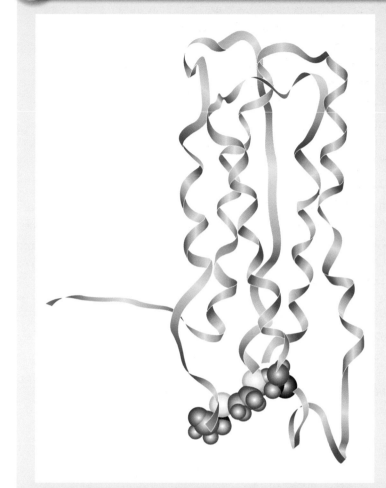

fig. 6.2.23 This is a modified version of interferon which can be produced fairly cheaply to treat hepatitis C. The new drug is currently in human trials.

Interferons aren't just effective against viruses in the body. They have also been shown to have an effect against the growth of some cancer cells. When interferons were first discovered, it was hoped that they would be 'wonder drugs' which would give us the same sort of control over viral diseases that antibiotics did over bacterial diseases. One problem has been that interferons are only made in very tiny quantities in human cells so it was almost impossible to get enough to use them therapeutically. Now scientists have genetically engineered bacteria and fungi to produce interferons in commercial quantities, although the drugs are still very expensive.

Interferon-alpha is used in the treatment of hepatitis C, a dangerous viral infection of the liver which affects about 2% of the world's population – that's about 170 million people. The problem is that interferons have not proved quite as effective against viral illnesses as the scientists had hoped, partly because they do not last long in the body and partly because they often cause unpleasant side effects. Current research suggests that in combination with other drugs they are more likely to result in a cure. However, research from 2007 suggests that using interferons and adding some very small RNA pieces (microRNA units) that are produced in response to interferons may make therapies much more effective. Another strand of research involves attempts to encourage the cells of the body to make more interferon themselves in response to a virus.

Interferons have also been shown to be an effective part of the treatment of certain cancers, including kidney cancers. However, here too they have not yet lived up to their initial promise.

Questions

1 Explain how inflammation protects the body against disease.

2 Inflammation and phagocytosis are used against pathogens that have invaded the body. Explain why they are still referred to as part of the non-specific defences of the body.

3 If someone is ill, people often try to get their temperature down. Explain:
   a why this isn't necessarily a good idea; **b** why it can be very important to lower the temperature.

The specific response to infection 4.6.13, 4.6.14

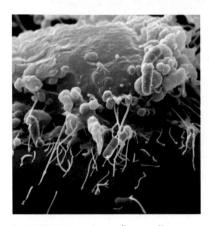

fig. 6.2.24 Macrophages (large yellow shape) play an important part in the immune system by engulfing pathogens, such as bacteria (pink rod shapes).

The **immune system** is the specific response of the body to invasion by pathogens. It enables the body to recognise anything that is non-self and to remove it from the body as efficiently as possible. Each organism carries its own unique set of markers, or antigens, on the cell surface membrane. Some are common to every member of a particular species, others to a particular individual. The more closely related two individuals are, the more antigens they have in common. Only genetically identical twins and clones have totally matching antigens.

There are two main types of white blood cells involved in the immune system. **Lymphocytes** are agranulocytes, made in the white bone marrow of the long bones. They move around the body in the blood and lymph, and are involved in recognising and responding to foreign antigens. Macrophages are also agranulocytes. They have left the bloodstream and move freely through the tissue.

The immune system of the body has four key characteristics:

- It can *distinguish 'self from non-self'*.
- It is *specific* – it responds to specific foreign cells.
- It is *diverse* – it can recognise an estimated 10 million different antigens.
- It has *immunological memory* – once you have met and responded to a pathogen, you can respond rapidly if you meet it again.

Different kinds of lymphocytes

There are two main types of lymphocytes involved in the immune system:

- **B cells** are made in the bone marrow. Once mature, they are found both in the lymph glands and free in the body. B cells have membrane-bound globular receptor proteins on their cell surface membrane, which are identical to the antibodies they will later produce. All antibodies are known as **immunoglobulins**, and these membrane-bound antibodies are known as **IgM**. Around 100 million B cells are formed as an embryo grows, each with a different membrane-bound antibody. Each then divides to form a clone of cells, giving a baby an immune system with the potential to recognise and tackle an enormous range of pathogens!

- **T cells** are made in the bone marrow but mature and become active in the thymus gland. The surface of each T cell displays thousands of identical T-cell receptors. There are two main types of T cells, **T killer** and **T helper cells**. The T killer cells produce chemicals that destroy pathogens. The T helper cells are involved in the process which produces antibodies against the antigens on a particular pathogen.

The working of many of these cells depends on special proteins known as **major histocompatibility complex (MHC) proteins**. These proteins display antigens on the cell surface membrane, as you will see later.

The immune response to infection is extremely complex so we will look at it one stage at a time.

The humoral response

The humoral response of the immune system consists of two main stages: the T helper activation stage and the effector stage.

In the T helper activation stage, when a pathogen enters the body, the non-specific response will rapidly bring it into contact with macrophages. The macrophage engulfs the pathogen by phagocytosis. The vesicle containing the pathogen fuses with a lysosome. The enzymes in the lysosome break down the pathogen and separate off the antigens. This is known as **antigen processing**. Inside the macrophage, the processed antigens combine with MHC proteins to form complexes which move to the surface of the cell outer membrane. The macrophage with these antigen/MHC protein complexes displayed on the cell surface is now known as an **antigen-presenting cell** (APC).

The next stage involves a T helper cell. CD4 receptors on the outer membrane of the T helper cell enable it to bind to the specific antigen of the antigen/MHC complex on the APC. This triggers the T helper cell to reproduce and form a clone of cells. These new cells have the same CD4 receptors as the original T helper cell, so they are specific for the original antigen.

Most of these cloned cells become active T helper cells which are then used in the rest of the immune system. The remainder of the cloned cells form inactive **T memory cells**, which remain in the body and rapidly become active if the same antigen is encountered again.

B cells and T helper cells are active in the effector stage. Some of the millions of different B cells will have immunoglobulins that are specific for the antigen presented by the pathogen and will bind to it. The B cell then engulfs the whole pathogen by endocytosis (see *AS Biology* page 109). As happens in a macrophage, the vesicle formed fuses with a lysosome. Enzymes break down the antigen to leave fragments of processed antigen. These become attached to MHC proteins within the cell, and the MHC/antigen complex is transported to the cell surface membrane where the antigen is displayed. This results in another type of APC.

A T helper cell from the active clone produced earlier recognises the specific antigen displayed on the MHC complex on the B cell and binds to it. This triggers the release of cytokines from the T helper cell which stimulate the B cell to divide and form a clone of identical cells. Two different clones of new cells result, **B effector cells** and **B memory cells**. The cloning of the B cells which, as you will see, eventually results in the formation of the correct antibodies to get rid of a pathogen, is known as **clonal selection**.

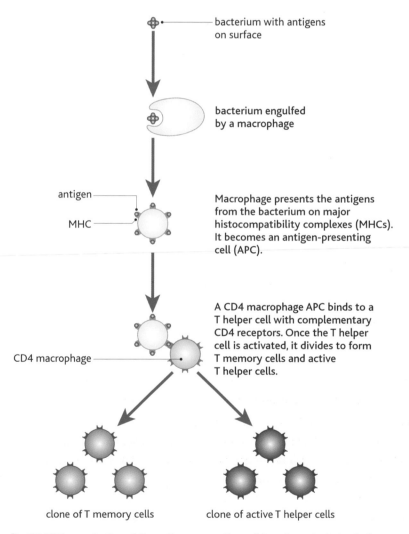

bacterium with antigens on surface

bacterium engulfed by a macrophage

antigen

MHC

Macrophage presents the antigens from the bacterium on major histocompatibility complexes (MHCs). It becomes an antigen-presenting cell (APC).

CD4 macrophage

A CD4 macrophage APC binds to a T helper cell with complementary CD4 receptors. Once the T helper cell is activated, it divides to form T memory cells and active T helper cells.

clone of T memory cells

clone of active T helper cells

fig. 6.2.25 The production of the antigen-presenting cell is an important step in the immune system of the body.

The majority of these new cells are B effector cells, which then differentiate into **plasma cell** clones. The plasma cells produce large amounts of antibodies. An **antibody** is a special protein which is released into the circulation. It will bind to a specific antigen on the particular pathogen which has triggered the immune system, causing its destruction in one of several ways (see below). Each plasma cell secretes antibodies which are identical to the immunoglobulin of the original parent B cell. Plasma cells live for only a few days but as they can produce up to 2000 antibody molecules per second this is long enough to be effective. They have extensive endoplasmic reticulum and many ribosomes, adaptations for their role in producing large quantities of protein antibodies.

Antibodies contribute to the defence of the body against the invasion of foreign material in a variety of ways:

- The ability of most pathogens to invade the host cells is dramatically reduced when they are combined with antibodies.

- When the antigens on pathogens are bound to antibodies, the microorganisms agglutinate or clump together and this helps to prevent their spread through the body.

- The antigen–antibody complex is readily engulfed and digested by phagocytes, another type of white blood cell, which travel through the circulatory system engulfing foreign material.

- The antigen–antibody complex may stimulate other reactions within the body, such as the destruction of the membrane of the antigen if it has one, or the release of histamine by the invaded cells, causing inflammation.

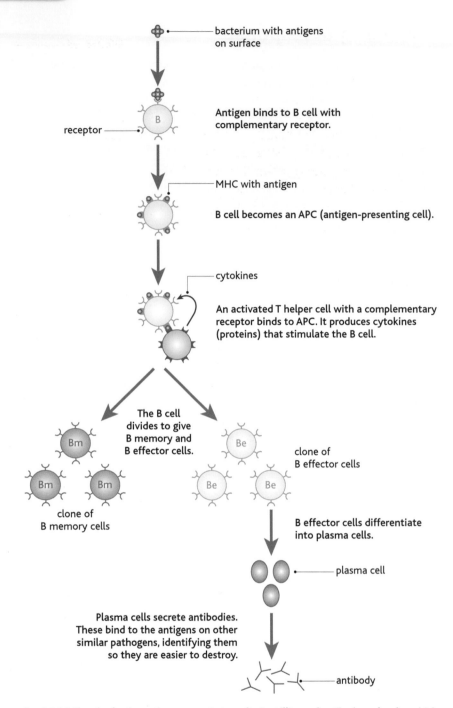

fig. 6.2.26 Clonal selection – the process that results in millions of antibody molecules which bind to and destroy pathogens.

B memory cells are also produced by the divisions of the B-cell APC. Unlike the plasma cells, B memory cells are very long-lived. They are important in allowing the body to respond very rapidly to a second invasion by the same antigen. When you have had a disease once, you usually do not catch it again. This isn't because you never come into contact with the disease-causing antigen again, but when you do encounter it the B memory cells help you produce the antibodies against it so rapidly that it is destroyed before the symptoms of the disease develop. As yet no one is entirely sure how memory cells provide immunological memory.

The cell-mediated response

Sometimes – particularly in viral infections – the pathogen is inside the host cells and the humoral response is not very effective against it. This is when the cell-mediated response is important. When a body cell is infected with a bacterium or virus, the pathogen is digested and the surface antigens become bound to an MHC in a similar process to that seen in macrophages. As a result the body cell becomes an APC.

The T killer cells present in the blood have complementary receptor proteins on the surface of their cell outer membrane. So T killer cells bind to the antigen/MHC complex on the surface of the body cell. If the T killer cells are then exposed to cytokines from an active T helper cell they undergo a rapid series of cell divisions to produce a **clone** of identical T killer cells which can all bind to infected body cells. The T killer cells release enzymes that make pores appear in the membrane of the infected cells. This allows the free entry of water and ions, so the cells swell and burst. Any pathogens which are released intact are labelled with antibodies produced by the B effector cells, and then destroyed. At the same time, some cloned T killer cells become T killer memory cells. These persist in the blood so that the body can produce a rapid response if the same pathogen invades again.

So why do we get ill? The specific response system is extremely effective, but it can take days or even weeks to become fully active against a particular pathogen. This is why we get the symptoms of disease – we feel ill when pathogens are reproducing freely inside our bodies, before the immune system has become fully operational against the pathogen concerned.

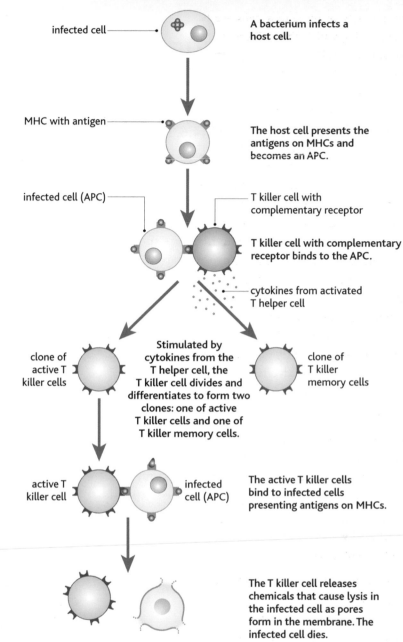

fig. 6.2.27 **The cell-mediated response.**

Questions

1 Produce a large diagram to explain in full how the immune system works.

2 Explain why the immune system does not attack the other cells of the body.

3 Distinguish carefully between the roles of the B cells and the T cells in the immune response of the body.

4 Describe the main differences between non-specific and specific immune responses.

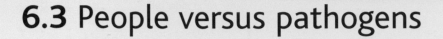

6.3 People versus pathogens

Controlling disease 4.6.19

It takes time for the body's immune system to overcome a pathogen it has not met before. During this time, the pathogen reproduces and causes damage, producing the signs and symptoms of disease. A sign of a disease is **objective evidence** – such as the typical chickenpox rash. **Symptoms** are what you feel – they are **subjective evidence** of disease, such as aching limbs or pain in the stomach. Often the immune system destroys the pathogens and you recover. However, there are some infectious diseases which can and regularly do result in death of the infected patient. Worldwide, infectious diseases kill more people than anything else.

The idea that diseases can be caused by microorganisms is central to the way we look at health and medical treatments, yet people have known about bacteria, viruses and other microorganisms only for about 150 years. For thousands of years people used simple remedies to try to overcome the ravages of disease. But from the middle of the nineteenth century in the developed world the battle against known and recognised pathogens became more focused. Not surprisingly, it also became more successful.

Asepsis and antisepsis

Asepsis is the absence of infectious organisms, and aseptic techniques are aimed at minimising infection. Some of the earliest steps in the control of bacterial diseases were simple aseptic techniques. In 1847 Ignaz Semmelweiss substantially reduced the number of cases of childbed fever (infections which frequently killed women in the few days after giving birth) by encouraging doctors to wash their hands between deliveries and examination of patients!

Then it was observed that if a surgical wound was coated in coal tar it was less likely to become infected. The coal tar kept out the air – and any microorganisms – and also contained an unrecognised antiseptic chemical, **phenol** (also known as carbolic acid). By 1860 the Scottish doctor Joseph Lister was using pure phenol as an antiseptic during and after surgery. Chemicals used to destroy bacteria in the environment are usually referred to as **disinfectants**, those used directly on people as **antiseptics**.

The combination of doctors using aseptic techniques and antiseptics meant that the number of deaths from infectious diseases began to fall. (Good hygiene and asepsis are still important aspects of disease control; see pages 110–111.) However, it was the development of medicines which could be used inside the body to target disease-causing microorganisms that gave people the hope of overcoming infectious disease.

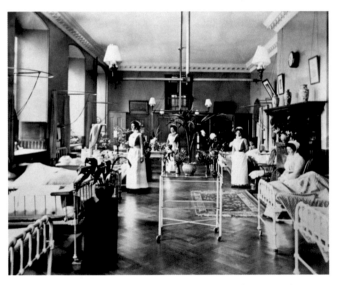

fig. 6.3.1 Disinfectants and antiseptics made hospitals much safer places for patients – but it wasn't until the arrival of antibiotics that infectious diseases could actively be cured.

Drugs versus microorganisms

It was not until well into the twentieth century that **antibiotics** became available. These drugs could be used to treat patients already suffering a bacterial infection and they had a dramatic impact. It is hard for us to imagine how many people died in the UK of infectious diseases caused by bacteria only 100 years ago. In 1901, 36.2% of all deaths (and 51.5% of childhood deaths) in the UK were from infectious diseases. By the year 2000, 11.6% of all UK deaths and only 7.4% of childhood deaths were from infectious diseases.

HSW Testing a new drug – or not?

In the 1930s a German chemist, Gerhard Domagk, tested a new dye (prontosil red) on bacteria in culture. It had little effect. But when he tested the dye on mice, rats and rabbits he found it cured bacterial infections. The drug was quickly used on people, without full trials. Anecdotal evidence tells of a doctor who heard of Domagk's work and used the dye to treat a 10-month-old baby dying of septicaemia. The baby recovered and lived.

Domagk didn't publish his results until 1935, but then doctors in many countries tried them. In the UK Leonard Colebrook and Méave Kenny tried out the new drugs on increasingly large numbers of patients with childbed fever. Most of the women, even the most seriously ill, recovered. Once these results were published, the new drugs were widely used to treat childbed fever and septicaemia. However, Colebrook and Kenny did not carry out a trial with **control patients** who did not receive the new drug (see *AS Biology* pages 224–7). Not to treat them seemed unethical, because it would have meant withholding the medicine and watching patients die. In a way these doctors had 'control patients' in their memory. In those days evidence-based medicine was not as important as it is today, and new drugs did not have to be tested in such a rigorous way.

fig. 6.3.2 The data that Colebrook and Kenny published in the *Lancet* in 1936. They did not test the new drug to modern standards, but long-term use has shown it to be a very effective antibiotic and similar drugs are still used today.

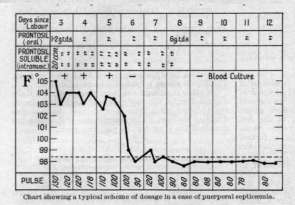

TREATMENT WITH PRONTOSIL OF PUERPERAL INFECTIONS
DUE TO HÆMOLYTIC STREPTOCOCCI *

By LEONARD COLEBROOK, M.B. Lond.
MEMBER OF THE SCIENTIFIC STAFF, MEDICAL RESEARCH COUNCIL

MÉAVE KENNY, M.R.C.S. Eng., M.C.O.G.
LATE RESIDENT MEDICAL OFFICER, ISOLATION BLOCK, QUEEN CHARLOTTE'S HOSPITAL, LONDON

And the members of the
HONORARY STAFF OF QUEEN CHARLOTTE'S HOSPITAL

Chart showing a typical scheme of dosage in a case of puerperal septicæmia.

TABLE III
Death-rate for all cases infected by Hæmolytic Streptococci (Queen Charlotte's Hospital)

—	Number of cases (all grades).	Deaths.	Deaths from peri-tonitis.*	Blood-positive cases (hæm. strept.) without general peri-tonitis, and death-rates.
1931	98	31 = 31·6 %	23	—
1932	90	19 = 21 %	16	1 (died = 100 %)
1933	97	20 = 20·6 %	14	9 (6 deaths = 66 %)
1934	120	20 = 16·6 %	16	15 (4 deaths = 27 %)
1935	90	22 = 24·4 %	15	13 (7 deaths = 53·8 %)
1936 Jan.–Aug.	64 (treated by prontosil)†	3 = 4·7 %	1	8 (2 deaths = 25 %)

Questions

1 Summarise the differences between disinfectants, antiseptics and antibiotics and explain how each can be effective in helping to prevent the spread of infectious diseases.

2 a Investigate the death rates in the UK from childbed fever in the 1800s and 2000.

 b In what ways was the work of Colebrook and Kenny important in the development of modern antibiotics, and in what ways did their work fall short of modern ethics and standards?

How antibiotics work 4.5.17, 4.5.18

All modern antimicrobial drugs work against microorganisms by the principle of **selective toxicity** – they interfere with the metabolism or function of the pathogen with minimal damage to the human host. The most commonly used and best known are the antibiotics, which can be used against both bacterial and fungal diseases.

Alexander Fleming is usually credited with the discovery of penicillin in 1928, the first modern antibiotic. He observed *Penicillium* mould infecting bacterial plates, leaving a clear area of agar jelly where the mould had destroyed the bacterial culture. However, penicillin is very difficult to extract in a usable form, and Fleming eventually moved on to other research. It was not until 1940 that Howard Florey and Ernst Chain developed penicillin for production as a drug. Many other scientists were also involved in this process. Penicillin does not work against all pathogens, so scientists searched for more antibiotics – a search which continues today. And although many other antibiotics have been discovered, penicillin is still commonly used to combat bacterial infections.

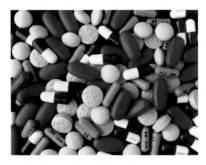

fig. 6.3.3 Antibiotic medicines come in a wide range of shapes and dosages, and they act in different ways – but they all help your body get on top of bacterial infections.

Antibiotic action

Antibiotics are effective because they disrupt the biochemistry of the bacterial cells in some way. Different classes of antibiotics interrupt different processes. The main classes of antibiotic drugs and the way they affect microorganisms are summarised in **table 6.3.1**.

Antimicrobial action	Examples of antibiotics
Antimetabolites interrupt metabolic pathways causing death, such as blocking nucleic acid synthesis	Sulphonamides
Cell wall agents prevent formation of cross-linking in cell walls so bacteria are killed by lysis (bursting)	Beta-lactams, e.g. penicillins, glycopeptides
Cell membrane agents damage the cell membrane, so metabolites leak out or water moves in, killing the bacteria	Some penicillins, cephalosporins
Protein synthesis inhibitors interrupt or prevent transcription and/or translation of microbial genes, so protein production is affected	tetracyclines, chloramphenicol
DNA gyrase inhibitors stop bacterial DNA coiling up so it no longer fits within the bacterium	Quinolone

Table 6.3.1 **Some methods of antibiotic action.**

When an antibiotic is taken, it may have one of two different effects. It may be **bacteriostatic**, which means that the antibiotic or the dose used completely inhibits the growth of the microorganism. This level of treatment is usually sufficient for the majority of everyday infections because, combined with the actions of our immune system, it will ensure that the pathogen will be completely destroyed. However, sometimes a particular drug, or the dose of a drug which is given, will be **bacteriocidal**. This means it will destroy almost all of the pathogens present. This type of treatment is particularly important in severe and dangerous infections. It is also used for treating infections where the immune system is suppressed such as in transplant patients, where suppressant drugs protect the transplanted organ, or in certain diseases such as TB and HIV/AIDS. A **broad spectrum antibiotic** destroys a wide range of harmful bacteria, pathogens, neutral and good bacteria alike. A **narrow spectrum antibiotic** targets one or two specific pathogens.

The effectiveness of any antimicrobial drugs depends on many factors. These include the concentration of the drug in the area of the body infected, which will be affected by how easily the drug can reach the tissue and how quickly it is excreted. Effectiveness will also depend on the local pH. Both the pathogen and the host tissue may destroy the antibiotic, which will obviously affect how well the drug can work. But one of the most important factors is the susceptibility of the pathogen to the particular antibiotic used. If the standard dose of a drug (in other words, what a doctor would normally prescribe) successfully destroys the pathogen and cures the disease then the pathogen is *sensitive* to that antibiotic. If an increased dose of the antibiotic results in successful treatment, the pathogen is *moderately sensitive*. However, there are increasing numbers of cases where a particular microorganism is not affected by an antibiotic, sometimes even one which may have been effective in the past. In these cases the microorganism is *resistant* to the antibiotic.

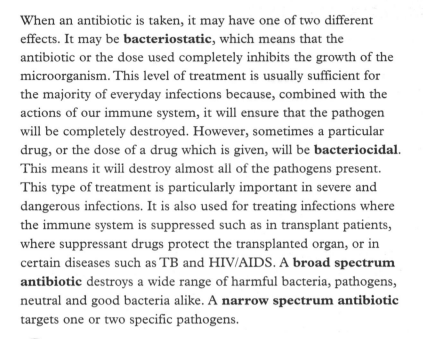

Practical box

You can investigate the effect of different antibiotics on bacteria using standard microbiological techniques. An agar plate is seeded with a known bacterial culture. Filter paper discs containing different antibiotics, or different concentrations of the same antibiotic, are placed on the agar and the plate sealed. A control culture of microorganisms with known sensitivity to the antibiotic is grown at the same time under the same conditions. The level of inhibition of bacterial growth gives a measure of the effectiveness of the drugs.

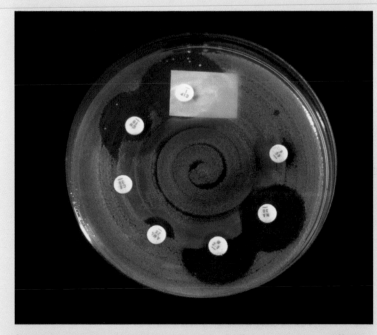

fig. 6.3.4 Using discs of known concentrations of different antibiotics, or different concentrations of the same antibiotic, the sensitivity of a pathogen to a particular antibiotic can be determined.

Questions

1 Investigate the discovery and development of penicillin. Write a paragraph on each of the following to explain their role in this: Ronald Hare, Dr Cecil Paine, Norman Heatley, Mary Hunt.

2 a Give two examples of how antibiotics affect bacteria.

   b Some antibiotics are bacteriocidal and others are bacteriostatic. Explain the difference.

   c A single antibiotic may be both bacteriostatic and bacteriocidal, depending on the conditions. Which factor is most likely to influence the way it works? Explain your answer.

Healthcare-acquired infections 4.5.16, 4.5.19

Antibiotic drugs provide an essential approach to controlling bacterial disease, but they are not the whole answer to the problem, and new problems are now arising which result directly from the over-use of these valuable drugs.

Creating drug-resistant bacteria

There is a constant 'evolutionary race' between pathogens and us, their hosts. We keep developing new medicines, and bacteria keep evolving resistance to these drugs. An antibiotic is effective only if the microorganism has a binding site for the drug and the metabolic process or biochemical pathway that the antibiotic interferes with. However, during bacterial reproduction there is always the chance that a mutation occurs, and some mutations might help the microorganism resist the effects of the antibiotic, such as by making the cell wall impermeable to the drug. Mutations like this will be selected for when the antibiotic is used, and the bacterial population will become increasingly resistant to the drug (see *AS Biology* pages 236–41). Mutations can also result in new biochemical pathways, or switch on or acquire a gene for the production of an antibiotic-destroying enzyme. These mutations will also be selected for when the antibiotic is used, and the pathogens will edge ahead in the evolutionary race.

Widespread use of antibiotics accelerates this process. As different antibiotics are used to tackle increasing resistance, this just increases the selection for bacteria that are resistant to all of them. This 'evolutionary race' is creating what are known as 'superbugs'. Unless there is another antibiotic that can be used, such 'superbugs' are quite capable of causing death. The only way to prevent this trend continuing is to reduce the selection pressure for resistance by using antibiotics sparingly, only when they are strictly necessary, and to use as few different antibiotics as possible, holding some in reserve for use only when all else has failed.

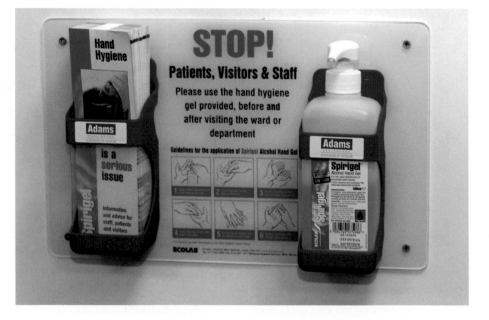

fig. 6.3.5 The superbug MRSA has evolved to be resistant to many antibiotics and causes hundreds of deaths every year. There is a constant battle in hospitals against the spread of these bacteria.

Hospital-acquired infections

'Superbugs' are commonly found in hospitals and care homes, where people are ill or have had surgery and antibiotic use is at its highest. **MRSA** (**methicillin-resistant** *Staphylococcus aureus*) and *Clostridium difficile* (*C. difiicile* or *C. diff*) are causing particular problems. Properly known as **healthcare-acquired infections**, they have a high profile in public awareness and are often referred to in the media as **hospital-acquired infections**. Patients who become infected have to stay in hospital much longer. This, combined with the treatment needed to overcome the infection, costs on average an extra £4000–10 000 per patient, as well as causing suffering to both the people involved and their families. Some people even die as a result of these infections. A 2006 study of NHS trusts found that 8.2% of patients in English hospitals have hospital-acquired infections.

MRSA

About one-third of people have the bacterium *Staphylococcus aureus* on their skin or in their nasal passages, without it causing problems. If the bacterium gets into the body it can cause boils and abcesses, or even infections throughout the body such as septicaemia. Many staph infections have been treated very effectively with methicillin (a penicillin-related antibiotic). However, a mutation has occurred in some of the bacteria that enables them to produce a penicillinase enzyme that breaks down methicillin.

In hospitals and care homes, patients weak with other infections often develop opportunistic *S. aureus* infections and have been treated with methicillin, and with other antibiotics when this hasn't worked. The result is MRSA – methicillin-resistant *Staphylococcus aureus*, known in the media as the hospital 'superbug'. In hospitals at least, *S. aureus* is now winning the evolutionary race as almost all the bacteria produce penicillinases. The infections can be treated, but only with high doses of a very small number of antibiotics which are used sparingly to prevent the same thing happening again.

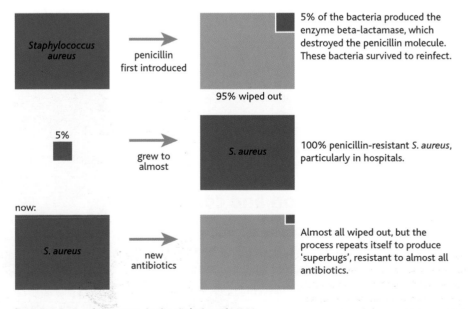

fig. 6.3.6 Some of the stages in the evolution of MRSA.

C. difficile

Clostridium difficile is an anaerobic bacterium that is found in small numbers in the large intestine of about 5% of the population. It is not affected by many of the commonly used antibiotics and produces extremely tough spores which can survive for months outside of the human body. In a healthy person *C. difficile* causes no problems, as its numbers are limited by competition with the normal gut flora (see page 90). Some common broad-spectrum antibiotics destroy the normal gut flora as well as the pathogens they are treating, and then *C. difficile* can rapidly increase in number. These bacteria produce two different toxins that damage the lining of the intestines, causing severe diarrhoea which can lead to bleeding from the gut and even death.

C. difficile is easily spread as the spores are passed through touching other people or objects. Weakened and ill patients are most at risk of serious infection, even death. A new strain of *C. difficile* has emerged recently that produces much higher levels of toxins than normal, because a gene that normally limits the levels has been replaced by a mutation. This new strain causes more serious disease and more deaths, and is a major cause for concern.

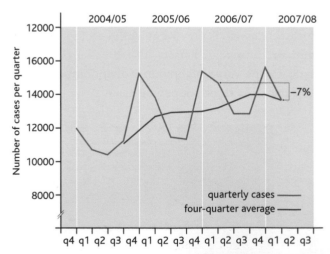

fig. 6.3.7 **Levels of hospital-acquired *C. difficile* infections in patients aged 65 and over, showing signs of hope in the battle against control.**

Infection prevention and control

Codes of practice have been drawn up for doctors, nurses and all healthcare workers to try to prevent the spread of healthcare-acquired infections, and to control them as effectively as possible when they do occur.

- *Controlling the use of antibiotics.* The careful use of antibiotics reduces the likelihood of resistant bacteria evolving. Antibiotics should be used only when absolutely necessary, and every course of antibiotics should be completed. If a patient takes only part of a course, the immune system is unable to cope with the numbers of bacteria remaining and does not destroy them all. Those bacteria that have some resistance will escape and can go on to infect other people. Use of different antibiotics just encourages a faster evolution of multiple resistance. This needs to be understood also by the general public, who still tend to demand antibiotics for every minor infection and often stop taking the medicine as soon as they feel better.

- *Hygiene measures.* Good hygiene within hospitals and care homes can have a major impact on healthcare-acquired infections. Examples of good practice include doctors, nurses and other healthcare professionals washing their hands or using alcohol-based gels between patients to destroy as many pathogens as possible. For example, MRSA can easily be spread by personal contact, but it is destroyed by alcohol and washing. However, the spores of *C. difficile* are not destroyed by the alcohol gels and need a chlorine-based disinfectant to destroy them. Another aspect of good hygiene are new guidelines about the clothing doctors and other staff should wear. For example, long ties which might dangle and carry bacteria from one patient to another are now banned, as are wristwatches and even long-sleeved shirts – the cuffs can carry bacteria.

fig. 6.3.8 **In some countries, health professionals wear sterilised scrubs all the time – and this may well be adopted in the UK in the near future.**

Thorough cleaning of hospital wards, toilets and equipment such as bedpans can also control the spread of disease. This is particularly important with diseases spread through faecal traces, such as *C. difficile*. Regular thorough cleaning is needed as well as the normal daily cleaning that occurs.

- *Isolation of patients*. Patients affected by a healthcare-acquired infection need to be isolated from other patients as quickly as possible. By nursing infected individuals in separate rooms with high levels of hygiene and infection-control nursing, the spread of disease to other patients can be minimised.

- *Prevention of infection coming into the hospital*. Screening patients as they come into hospital means people who are carrying MRSA (around 3% of the general public) or other infections can be treated immediately and isolated until the bacteria have been destroyed. This reduces the chance of the individual becoming clinically ill during treatment or of spreading the bacteria to others.

Another problem is that people visiting patients may bring infections into the wards. This is particularly the case with MRSA and many viral infections (e.g. Noro virus) which can cause sickness and/or diarrhoea. Hospitals advise people not to visit if they are unwell – but individuals may feel they need to see seriously unwell relatives and ignore the advice. People visiting patients should follow good hygiene procedures and keep their hands clean and washed. Most hospitals provide alcohol gels for people to use as they come in and out of the hospital – the biggest problem is getting people to use them!

- *Monitoring levels of healthcare-acquired infections*. It has been made mandatory that hospitals measure and report on levels of MRSA and *C. difficile* infections. These results are published and available to the general public as well as the Government. This has focused attention on the problem and led to increased efforts to reduce the problem and overcome the infections.

As a result of hospital trusts following these codes of practice there seems to have been a marked decrease in the incidence of these infections in recent years. For example, there was a 30% decrease in the incidence of MRSA bloodstream infections in 2007/8 compared

with 2006/7, and this was the fourth yearly decrease in a row. Levels of *C. difficile* infections also seem to be following a downward trend, but changes in the reporting year have made comparisons more difficult to make. Hopefully, as good practice over infection control continues to be given a high priority, levels of hospital-acquired infections – and perhaps most importantly, deaths resulting from them – will continue to fall.

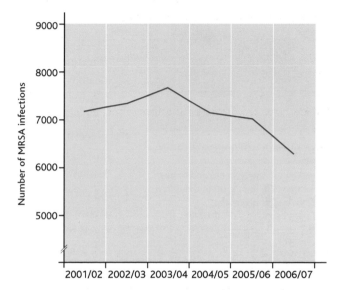

fig. 6.3.9 Figures from 2001 onwards show how the implementation of codes of practice, based on an understanding of how hospital-acquired infections are spread, is reducing the incidence of MRSA infections in hospitals.

Questions

1 Explain how bacteria develop resistance to common antibiotics.

(SC) 2 a Find out the current code of practice on the prescription of antibiotics.

   b Explain how can this help to reduce the development of further antibiotic-resistant strains of bacteria.

3 a Describe how the use of broad spectrum antibiotics is implicated in the spread of *C. difficile*.

   b Explain how minimal use of narrow spectrum antibiotics can help to avoid the problem.

4 Explain how an understanding of the causes and method of spread of hospital-acquired infections relates to the codes of practice on hospital hygiene.

Developing immunity 4.5.15

Once you have been exposed to a pathogen and your immune system has dealt with it you are unlikely to suffer illness as a result of infection by that microorganism again. This is because your immune system has a 'memory', based on B cells, T cells and immunoglobulins (antibodies).

Different types of immunity

Normally when the body comes into contact with a foreign antigen, the immune system is activated and antibodies are formed and the pathogen is destroyed (see pages 100–103). This is known as **natural active immunity**, because your body actively makes the antibodies. During pregnancy, preformed antibodies are passed from the mother to the foetus through the placenta. The newborn baby gets extra protection from antibodies taken in through breast milk, particularly the milk made in the first few days after birth known as colostrum. This provides the baby with temporary immunity until its own system becomes active. This is **natural passive immunity** – passive because your body does not make the antibodies. It tends to be quite short-lived because the antibodies are not replaced.

fig. 6.3.10 New-born mammalian babies are dependent on immunoglobulins received across the placenta and through their mother's milk to protect them from a wide variety of diseases.

Inducing immunity

An alternative approach to using drugs to treat a disease is to prevent it happening using **immunisation**. Immunisation is the process of protecting people from infection by giving them passive or active artificial immunity. It enables you to develop immunity by exposing your immune system to antigens in a safe way which does not put you at risk of developing the disease, so that antibodies and memory cells can be prepared for meeting the real thing. **Vaccination** is the procedure by which you immunise people to produce immunity.

The aim of immunisation is to protect individuals against diseases which might kill or harm them. However, it has a wider role in society – to eradicate, eliminate or control diseases which cause large numbers of deaths, disabilities or illnesses within a population and which therefore place a strain on the structure of that society.

Artificial passive immunity occurs when antibodies are formed in one individual, extracted and injected into another individual. This does not confer long-term immunity, because the antibodies are gradually broken down and not replaced, but it can be enormously valuable if someone has been exposed to a rapidly acting antigen such as **tetanus**. Tetanus, also known as lockjaw, results from a toxin produced by the bacterium *Clostridium tetani*. The toxin affects striated muscles, causing them to go into spasm (or tetanus), making swallowing and breathing impossible and so causing death. If someone may have been exposed to tetanus – for example, from a bad cut while gardening or while working with horses – they are injected with antibodies against tetanus. This prevents the development of the disease and death, but will not give prolonged immunity.

Artificial active immunity is the basis of most immunisation programmes. Here, small amounts of antigen (known as the **vaccine**) are used to produce immunity in a person. The pathogen is made non-infective without reducing its ability to act as an antigen. This can be done in a number of ways. If it is a toxin that causes the symptoms, a detoxified form with one or more chemical groups changed will be injected. Sometimes inactivated viruses or dead bacteria are used as vaccines, and in other cases **attenuated** organisms (living but modified so they cannot produce disease) are used. Increasingly, fragments of the outer coats of viruses and bacteria, or even DNA segments are used as vaccines.

Your immune system will produce antibodies against the antigen, and appropriate memory cells will be formed. Should you subsequently come into contact with the active antigen, the antigen will be destroyed without you experiencing the symptoms of the disease it causes (see **fig. 6.3.11**).

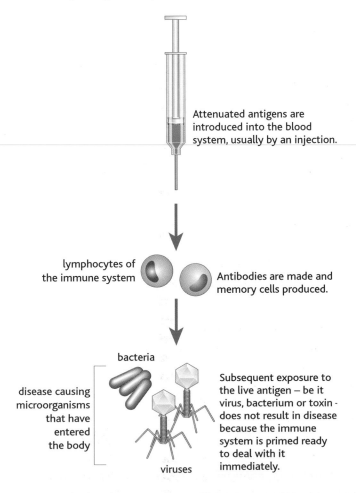

Attenuated antigens are introduced into the blood system, usually by an injection.

lymphocytes of the immune system

Antibodies are made and memory cells produced.

bacteria

disease causing microorganisms that have entered the body

viruses

Subsequent exposure to the live antigen – be it virus, bacterium or toxin - does not result in disease because the immune system is primed ready to deal with it immediately.

fig. 6.3.11 The process of vaccination manipulates the immune system so that an individual is immune to a disease before they become infected.

Eradicating disease

For centuries smallpox was feared – it killed millions and disfigured many more around the world. Now it has gone. Smallpox is the only disease which has been completely eradicated by a vaccination programme, although polio is close to being eradicated as well. Smallpox is no longer found either in people, animals or anywhere in the environment. The virus only exists sealed in two top-security labs.

Smallpox was very recognisable and had no non-human hosts, a long incubation period and a visible scar as evidence of immunisation. These features all made eradication possible.

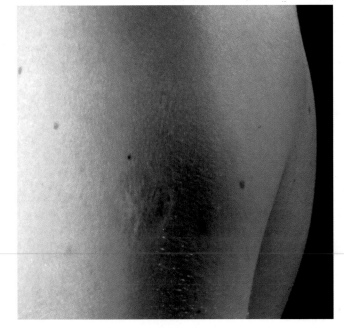

fig. 6.3.12 Since smallpox was officially eradicated worldwide in 1979, immunisation, which causes this distinctive scar, is no longer necessary.

There are many diseases where the pathogen survives in soil, water or animal hosts so there is always a massive reservoir of potential infection. For these eradication is not realistically possible and elimination and control have to be the aims of immunisation. Elimination is where the disease disappears but the pathogen remains in animals, the environment or in mild infections which are not recognised, and so immunisation must continue even when no clinical cases are being seen. When a disease is controlled it still occurs but not frequently enough to be a significant health problem. For some serious infectious diseases such as malaria, the development of a vaccine which is effective against the different forms of a pathogen that evolves rapidly has so far proved impossible.

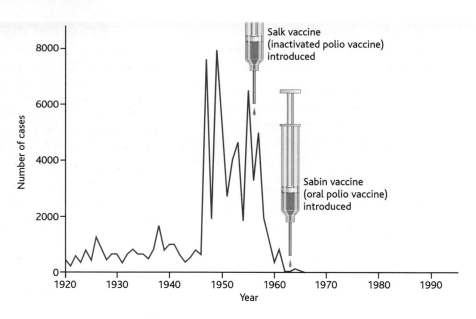

fig. 6.3.13 **The vaccination programme has not completely eradicated polio in England and Wales. Because live vaccine is used, there are occasional cases where an infant develops the disease – but the impact of the disease on the population as a whole has been reduced to a minimal level.**

HSW Dirty vaccines

Vaccines based on whole viruses – like the oral polio vaccine – easily stimulate the immune system. But as vaccines are made purer, it has become evident that many do not work effectively unless they contain an **adjuvant**. This is something added to the vaccine, old examples of which are detergent, aluminium hydroxide, oil and water, and dead bacteria which have nothing to do with the pathogen.

The role of these adjuvants seems to be to cause inflammation, and the worse the inflammation, the more effective the immune response to the vaccine. It is suggested that they alert the body to the presence of a foreign invader by mimicking a characteristic of the pathogen which is not present in the safe form in the vaccine. It has even been shown using mice that different adjuvants with the same vaccine can cause the stimulation of different parts of the immune system.

New adjuvants are being investigated and developed. The role of these 'added extras' in the vaccine mixture is constantly being checked and evaluated to ensure that they help and yet never, by stimulating too much inflammation, cause harm.

HSW The pros and cons of vaccination

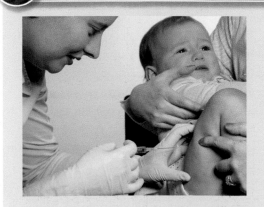

fig. 6.3.14 **Vaccination hurts for a short while but protects for a long time.**

Immunisation is widely believed to be a good thing. However, there are two sides to every debate. Usually the *pros* of a vaccination programmes are very obvious:

*   The child is protected against diseases which could kill or disable it.

*   Society benefits as the potential pool of infection is reduced with every vaccinated child – this helps to protect children who cannot be vaccinated because of allergies or immune system diseases and is known as **herd immunity**.

*   The cost of treating serious diseases and caring for those left permanently damaged by them is kept to a minimum for a relatively small financial outlay (most common vaccines are relatively cheap).

The cons have, until recent years, been less well known:

- Some of the live, attenuated vaccines are cultured in eggs, to which a number of children may suffer a violent allergic reaction. Children with these allergies are not usually vaccinated.

- A tiny minority of children become extremely ill after a vaccination with what may be an extreme immune response. Some of these children may die, others have been left severely brain damaged. It is very difficult to prove a direct link between the vaccine and the damage to a child – correlation and cause are not easy to distinguish here – but even when a link is proven it can be difficult to get any compensation.

- Some scientists have suggested that mass vaccination programmes are linked to the recent rise in childhood asthma and allergies (one of many different explanations for this phenomenon).

- Some vaccines, such as rubella for boys, are given more for the benefit of society than for the direct benefit of the child. The new vaccine to protect against cervical cancer is another example. Given to girls it benefits both individuals and society, but if boys are vaccinated it is only for the good of society at large.

Parents want to do the right thing for their child. Most decide that the benefits outweigh the risk and go ahead, but some parents decide against it – putting their own and other children at risk.

The safety and validity of immunisation have become an issue in the generation of people who (largely as a result of immunisation programmes) have little or no personal experience of the terrible infectious diseases which their children are vaccinated against. This debate remains a luxury available only to those living in a society relatively free from major infectious diseases – yet for each individual involved it is a real and serious issue.

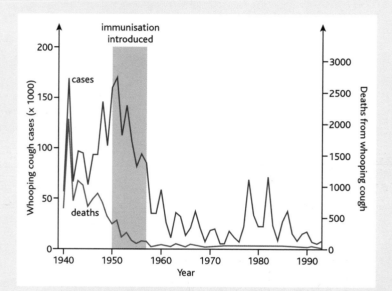

fig. 6.3.15 In the UK during the 1970s a link between whooping cough vaccination and serious brain damage in some children was suggested. Intense media coverage resulted in a sharp decrease in the numbers of children vaccinated. There followed, for the first time in years, an increase in the number of children affected by whooping infections and some died or were brain damaged. Levels of vaccine uptake are now back to around 96%, pre-scare levels.

Questions

1 Explain and give examples of natural active immunity, natural passive immunity, artificial passive immunity and artificial active immunity.

2 Explain why adjuvants are increasingly used in vaccines.

3 Some parents decide not to have their child vaccinated.

   a Explain how this puts their child at risk.

   b Explain how this puts other children at risk.

   c Is it ethical that parents should be allowed to choose whether their children are immunised?

4 Using the data from **fig. 6.3.15**, explain how the story of the whooping cough scare illustrates the importance of establishing the difference between correlation and causation before taking action. Research the story of the MMR vaccine for more evidence.

Case studies of disease – tuberculosis 4.5.16

Tuberculosis (TB) is one of the most common human infections. World Health Organization figures show that in 2006 there were around 9.2 million new cases of TB worldwide, and approximately 1.7 million people died of the disease. Up to a third of the population of the world have been infected by TB although many of them have no symptoms. At least one in ten of these symptomless people will go on to develop full-blown active TB, and without effective treatment, 50% of people with TB will die of the disease.

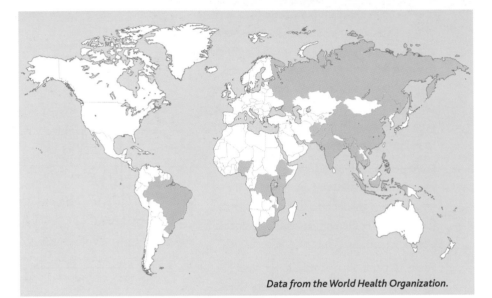

Data from the World Health Organization.

fig. 6.3.16 Eighty percent of the people affected by active TB are found in just 22 countries of the world.

The causes and symptoms of TB

TB is most commonly caused by the bacterium *Mycobacterium tuberculosis* which is spread by droplet infection. Crowded living or working conditions increase the likelihood of it spreading as people breathe, cough and sneeze near to each other. People who are malnourished, ill or have problems with their immune systems are more vulnerable to the disease and are much more likely to develop active TB than healthy, well-fed individuals.

The other common source of infection is from the bacterium *Mycobacterium bovis*, which particularly affects cattle. People become infected from drinking infected milk or living and working in close contact with cattle.

TB notably affects the respiratory system, particularly by damaging and destroying lung tissue. It also suppresses the immune system, making the body less able to fight the disease. The well-known symptoms of TB – coughing up blood and weakness – come at the end of the disease process.

Only about 30% of the people exposed to TB will actually become infected. Once the bacteria have been inhaled into the lungs they multiply slowly in the **primary infection**, often causing no obvious symptoms. If you have a healthy immune system, there will be a localised inflammatory response forming a mass of tissue called a **tubercule** containing dead bacteria

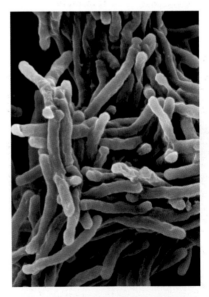

fig. 6.3.17 *Mycobacterium tuberculosis* – around the world this bacterium is responsible for almost 2 million deaths every year from tuberculosis.

and macrophages (hence tuberculosis). In about 8 weeks the immune system controls the bacteria, the inflammation dies down and the lung tissue heals. Primary TB infections often take place in childhood, and the majority (about 90%) heal without the infected individual ever realising they have had TB.

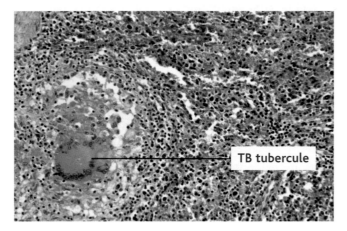

fig. 6.3.18 Although the bacteria in these tubercules are often completely destroyed by macrophages, they may survive for months or even years before resulting in active TB.

Mycobacterium tuberculosis can avoid the immune system, which means some bacteria may survive the primary infection stage. The bacteria produce a thick waxy outer layer which protects them from the enzymes of the macrophages. The bacteria with an effective coating will remain deep in the tubercules in the lungs, dormant or growing slowly for years until the person is malnourished, weakened or their immune system does not work well. They then produce **active tuberculosis**. In this way the most effective bacteria are selected and will be passed on. This helps to give them an edge in the evolutionary race between them and us!

Sometimes the active phase is simply the result of fresh infection. If a really heavy load of bacteria is taken down into the lungs, the infection takes hold before the immune system can respond properly. About 80% of people with active TB are suffering from a reactivation of an old, controlled infection rather than a fresh one.

With active TB, the bacteria multiply rapidly in the lungs. They cause all the typical symptoms of TB, including fever, night sweats, loss of appetite and loss of weight. Patients often feel increasingly tired and listless. Infection in the lungs causes a cough, which brings up sputum. As this gets worse, lung tissue becomes damaged and blood may be coughed up in the sputum. Without treatment the affected person will lose weight steadily, and the lungs will be steadily destroyed as the

alveoli break down to produce large, inefficient air spaces (see *AS Biology* pages 110–13).

Mycobacteria also target T cells, reducing the production of antibodies and so disarming a critical part of the immune system. The bacteria are temperature sensitive and stop reproducing above 42 °C. A patient with active TB will often run a temperature. However, human enzymes start to be denatured at around 40 °C, putting the patient at risk of dying before the bacteria are inhibited!

Eventually TB causes death, either because the individual cannot get enough oxygen from the air through their damaged lungs, or because their organs fail through lack of nutrition. And, since TB affects the immune system itself, sufferers often become very vulnerable to other, opportunistic infections such as pneumonia which may be what finally kills them.

Treatment and control

It is important to be able to diagnose TB as easily and cheaply as possible. A chest X-ray will show up TB damage to the lungs as opaque areas and large, thick-walled cavities. However, other diseases can give similar images. So chest X-rays can suggest that TB is present but not confirm it. New tests, examining the DNA of the bacteria, are being developed. Potentially these will be quick and easy, and give relatively immediate and reliable results.

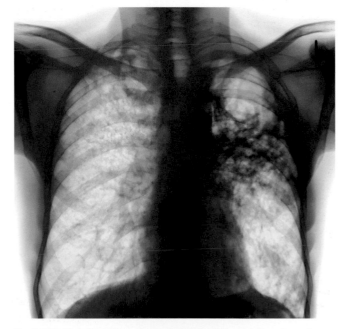

fig. 6.3.19 The shadowy area on the lung in this specially coloured X-ray is evidence of the damage caused by TB.

The main treatment for tuberculosis is with antibiotics for many months. For the first couple of months a cocktail of different antibiotics is used, so that even if the mycobacteria are resistant to some of the drugs there will be others which not only destroy the rapidly reproducing bacteria but also attack the ones that are metabolising slowly, hidden in cysts or within the immune system. This treatment is followed by another 4–7 months of taking two antibiotics. Most patients will be completely free of TB in about 9 months, but it can take 12–18 months before all traces of active disease have gone.

The most effective ways of controlling TB involve improving living standards. Less crowded housing and working conditions mean people are less likely to pass on the disease, and if people are better fed and generally healthier they are less likely to develop the full-blown disease after infection. Preventing and treating the disease in cattle, along with pasteurising or heating milk before it is drunk, help prevent the spread of *M. bovis*. In countries where TB is already rare, attempts are made to contact all the people in regular close contact with the patient so that they can be tested for TB and either immunised or treated as appropriate.

Immunisation has been very effective in the final reduction in cases of TB in countries such as the UK. The BCG (Bacillus Calmette-Guérin) vaccine is a live attenuated strain of mycobacterium which is given as a single injection. Until 2005, screening of schoolchildren followed by vaccination for those who needed it, was standard in the UK. Vaccination, particularly of very young babies, is increasing in developing countries, as they are much cheaper than treatment. Now, with such low rates of infection in the UK, vaccination is usually needed only for young babies and others at risk from infection, particularly immigrants from countries with a high infection rate.

Until recently, particularly in developed countries, it looked as if we were winning the race with the bacteria. However, the numbers of cases of TB are increasing again. This could be the result of a number of factors including deteriorating social conditions in some areas, immigration and the movement of refugees between countries, more foreign travel, an increase in intravenous drug use and most of all increasing numbers of people infected with HIV/AIDS. One worrying development is the evolution of multidrug-resistant strains of *M. tuberculosis*, making treatment more difficult and more expensive – and putting many more lives at risk.

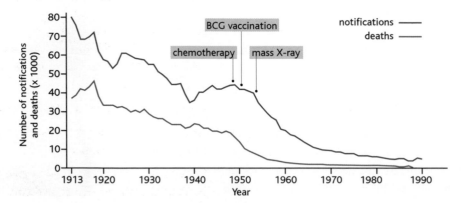

fig. 6.3.20 **A combination of approaches brought TB under control in the UK, but new developments may need different approaches to keep it under control.**

HSW Badgers and TB

Cows are particularly prone to *Mycobacterium bovis* and worldwide, many people get TB from drinking infected milk. UK milk is treated but the disease affects cows, reducing milk yields and eventually killing them. Around 30 000 infected cows and their contacts were slaughtered in 2007 in the UK and the figure is increasing by about 20% each year.

The bacteria also infect other species – such as badgers and deer. Badgers live around farmland, leaving faeces all over the grass. Much evidence shows correlation between TB in cattle and infections in badgers. There are different perspectives on whether to cull badgers in areas where bovine TB is high.

fig. 6.3.21 Would culling badgers control bovine TB in the UK?

- Badgers are protected in the UK and as populations have increased, so have bovine TB levels. Evidence from a large trial of badger culling, published in July 2007, showed TB incidence in cattle fell by around 23% in the culled areas, but rose by 24.5% in surrounding areas. A year later, bovine TB was down 54% in the culled areas and by about 23% in surrounding areas. Many British farmers, vets and scientists support the idea of a badger cull.

- There is research into vaccines for badgers and cows but they are not easy to develop. Vaccinating wild animals raises many problems, while European Union legislation bans the use of TB vaccines for cows, and milk or meat from vaccinated cattle cannot be sold for food. So immunisation may not be the solution.

- Conflicting evidence shows that when TB levels went up in cattle during the UK 2001 foot-and-mouth outbreak, TB rates in badgers also increased. Perhaps badgers catch TB from cows! An alternative source of infection could be deer.

Questions

1 Explain how *Mycobacterium tuberculosis* has evolved to become such a successful pathogen.

2 Describe the symptoms of TB and explain how these can lead to death.

SC 3 Look at **fig. 6.3.17**. Suggest reasons why these countries have such a problem with tuberculosis.

SC 4 Research the main scientific, economic, environmental and ethical issues affecting the introduction of a countrywide badger cull in an attempt to control bovine TB. Suggest what should be done and why.

Case studies of disease – HIV/AIDS 4.5.16

Acquired Immunodeficiency Syndrome (AIDS) is a relatively new disease, yet it is predicted that it could soon become the most prevalent cause of human death. We know the infective agent - the **Human Immunodeficiency Virus (HIV)** – and how it is transmitted, but even with huge amounts of funding for research so far we have failed to halt the spread of the disease.

HIV/AIDS was first noticed in the 1980s in the homosexual community in Los Angeles. It was eventually recognised that a range of common symptoms (fevers, persistent diarrhoea and weight loss, secondary infections such as TB, a rare type of pneumonia, Kaposi's sarcoma and finally death) resulted from infection by HIV, causing a disease called AIDS.

Infection by HIV does not lead to AIDS immediately. When people are infected by the virus but have no symptoms, they are **HIV positive**, as blood tests show the presence of HIV antibodies. **Table 6.3.2** shows the results from the Joint United Nations Programme on HIV/AIDS in 2007. They found that 90% of infected people live in the developing world. Thirty-two percent of all new HIV infections worldwide in 2007 occurred in Southern Africa.

In sub-Saharan Africa AIDS was the single largest cause of death. However, trends are as important as absolute figures. The numbers infected with HIV and dying of AIDS in Africa are beginning to fall. But in other areas of the world, such as Asia, new HIV infections increased by almost 20% in 2007.

fig. 6.3.22 In Sub-Saharan Africa, most families will lose at least one member to HIV/AIDS.

	Total	Adults	Children under 15 years
Number of people living with HIV in 2007			
	33.2 million (30.6–36.1 million)	30.8 million (28.2–33.6 million), including 15.4 million (13.9–16.6 million) women	2.5 million (2.2–2.6 million)
People newly infected with HIV in 2007			
	2.5 million (1.8–4.1 million)	2.1 million (1.4–3.6 million)	420 000 (350 000–540 000)
AIDS deaths in 2007			
	2.1 million (1.9–2.4 million)	1.7 million (1.6–2.1 million)	330 000 (310 000–380 000)

The ranges around the estimates in this table define the boundaries within which the actual numbers lie, based on the best available information.

Table 6.3.2 Table showing the extent of the AIDS problem worldwide.

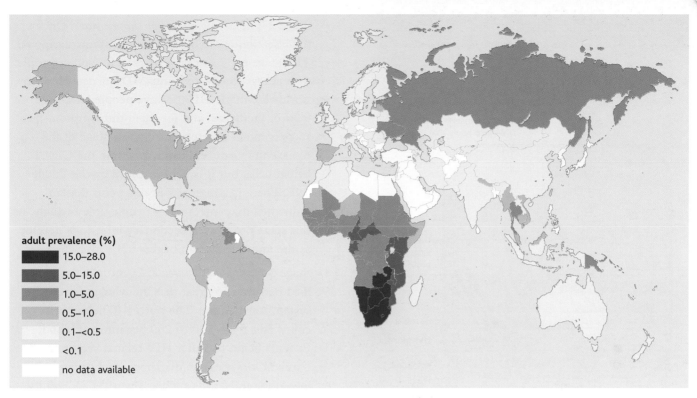

adult prevalence (%)

- 15.0–28.0
- 5.0–15.0
- 1.0–5.0
- 0.5–1.0
- 0.1–<0.5
- <0.1
- no data available

fig. 6.3.23 The estimated numbers of people living with HIV/AIDS in 2007.

How is HIV transmitted?

The Human Immunodeficiency Virus is very fragile and must be contained in human body fluids –it cannot survive in the air. The source of infection may be someone who is HIV positive (who may not be aware of their infective status) or someone with active AIDS. The virus can be transmitted from person to person in three main ways:

- through sexual contact – the most common way

- through infected blood, by intravenous drug users sharing needles and by the use of infected blood products (where these are not treated)

- from a mother to her foetus in the early stages of pregnancy, during birth, or through breastfeeding.

How does HIV cause AIDS?

fig. 6.3.24 A scanning electron micrograph showing the HIV virus attacking a helper T cell.

Most of the symptoms of AIDS result from the effect of HIV on the immune system. HIV attaches to the CD4 receptors on the T helper cells and infects them (see **fig. 6.3.25**). HIV is a retrovirus and, once inside the T helper cell, it takes over the host DNA and replicates (see page 85). When the new viruses leave the host T helper cell, it is destroyed. At the same time, host T killer cells recognise and destroy some of the heavily infected T helper cells. The result is a great reduction in the number of T helper cells, which in turn means that the activation of many macrophages and T killer cells simply does not take place. As a result the normal functioning of the T helper cells is lost or reduced, undermining the ability of the immune system to deal with other pathogens. This leaves individuals vulnerable to secondary infections which can kill.

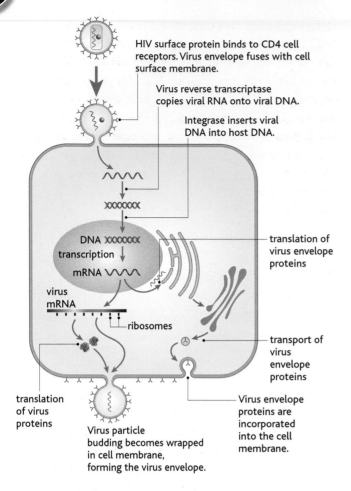

HIV surface protein binds to CD4 cell receptors. Virus envelope fuses with cell surface membrane.

Virus reverse transcriptase copies viral RNA onto viral DNA.

Integrase inserts viral DNA into host DNA.

DNA xxxxxxx transcription

mRNA ᨠᨠᨠ

virus mRNA

ribosomes

translation of virus envelope proteins

transport of virus envelope proteins

translation of virus proteins

Virus envelope proteins are incorporated into the cell membrane.

Virus particle budding becomes wrapped in cell membrane, forming the virus envelope.

fig. 6.3.25 Scientists look at all the stages by which HIV takes over a cell – and any one of them can be a target for a new drug or the development of a vaccine.

The course of an HIV/AIDS infection

The speed at which the disease progresses from infection to full-blown AIDS depends on many factors. A fit, well-nourished and healthy person is likely to remain well longer than someone who is malnourished and unhealthy. Some people have a better genetic resistance to infection than others – the immune system responds more effectively to HIV. And medical treatment can increase life expectancy by many years. There are four main stages:

- Stage 1 *Acute HIV syndrome*. In the first few weeks after infection, some people feel unwell. Symptoms include fevers, headaches, tiredness and swollen glands – similar to far less serious viral and bacterial diseases. Not everyone infected with HIV feels ill at all. Regardless of symptoms, 3–12 weeks after infection HIV antibodies appear in the blood, making them HIV positive.

- Stage 2 The *asymptomatic or chronic stage*. Once the infection is established all symptoms disappear. This stage can last many years in fit, young people with access to effective anti-AIDS drugs. However, worldwide many HIV-positive people have little food or medicine, and for them the symptom-free stage is much shorter. During this stage of the disease the virus replicates, infecting the CD4 T helper cells, but it is kept in check by the T killer cells. There is a high risk at this point that an individual may infect other people unknowingly. As this stage progresses, secondary infections develop as the immune system begins to be overwhelmed.

- Stage 3 *Symptomatic disease*. Eventually the viral load becomes so great that the whole immune system starts to fail. The normal T helper cell count falls from 500 to 200 per mm^3 of blood. Patients begin to suffer HIV-related symptoms – weight loss, fatigue, diarrhoea, night sweats and low-grade infections such as thrush. This rapidly progresses to the final stage.

- Stage 4 *Advanced AIDS*. As T helper cell numbers fall, severe symptoms begin to appear such as major weight loss, dementia as brain cells become infected, cancers (e.g. Kaposi's sarcoma) and serious infections such as TB and cryptococcal meningitis. The worldwide increase in HIV/AIDS is the main cause of the worldwide increase in cases of TB, for example.

The final stage of advanced AIDS is always death.

Treating AIDS

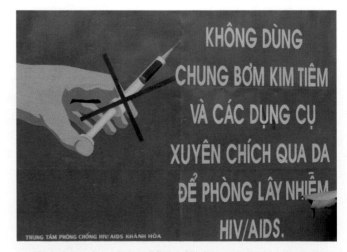

fig. 6.3.26 There is a lot of ignorance about the way HIV/AIDS can be spread – campaigns around the world aim to educate people to help keep them safe.

At the moment AIDS is an incurable disease, but various control methods are under investigation. The simplest is the attempt to limit the spread of the disease. Education programmes help people to understand the ways in which HIV is spread, and how to prevent it. Less promiscuous sex, the use of condoms and the use of clean needles if injecting drugs are important messages to get across. In countries which have made a big effort to educate people in simple ways to avoid infection, such as Uganda, there are signs that infection levels are lower than in surrounding countries.

The usual approach to controlling infectious disease is to produce an effective vaccine, but this is proving very difficult for HIV. The virus mutates rapidly so the antigens on the viral coat keep changing in the years after infection, making it harder for the immune system to recognise the virus and so target and destroy it. The rate of change only slows down as the T-cell count starts to fall seriously, when selection pressure on the virus is reduced. Natural selection also favours mutations that enable the virus to replicate particularly fast, allowing it to infect many cells as quickly as possible. By the time a vaccine has gone through all its development and safety tests the virus has changed and the vaccine doesn't work! Added to this, AIDS is a peculiarly human disease. Rhesus macaques and chimpanzees are some of the only other animals that seem to be susceptible to the virus, and so work on animals to develop vaccines is very limited.

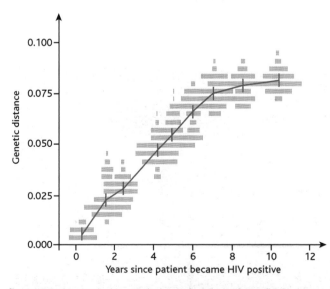

fig. 6.3.27 **This graph shows you the evolutionary change in the HIV population in one patient – you can see how it slows down with time after infection as the immune system collapses.**

Drug therapy is also very important. Combined drug therapies which are anti-viral and stimulate the immune system mean that AIDS is becoming a treatable, long-term disease. The drugs are quite expensive and so they are most widely used in the developed world. The major pharmaceutical companies have supplied huge quantities of drugs to many developing countries for nothing or at a minimal charge, but without comprehensive medical care (and where there is great political instability) they are often not available to those who need them.

None of the current drugs provides a cure, but they can delay the onset of full-blown AIDS for many years. Recent UK figures show that someone diagnosed HIV positive at around 20 years old can survive into their 60s with full treatment. The sooner treatment begins, the longer the patient can expect to live.

HIV evolution vindicates doctors

In 2007 six medical workers were sentenced to death in Libya, accused of deliberately infecting 426 children with HIV-infected blood. In 2008 biologists produced genetic profiles (see pages 78–9) from the HIV viruses infecting the children. By pinpointing the number of mutations which had taken place in the HIV viruses in the different children, they showed that the infection originated in a single case several years before the medics arrived at the hospital. What's more, the viruses were closely related to West African strains – the original virus was probably introduced accidentally by a West African worker or patient.

Questions

1 Describe the symptoms of HIV infection and explain how these may result in death.

SC 2 Compare HIV/AIDS and TB infections and comment on similarities and differences between them.

3 How do the mechanisms that allow HIV and *Mycobacterium tuberculosis* to evade the human immune system support the idea of an evolutionary race between pathogens and their hosts?

Examzone: Topic 6 practice questions

1 Amino acids are coded for by one or more DNA triplet codons. The table below shows some amino acids found in human proteins and their corresponding DNA triplet codons. A DNA triplet codon for the stop signal is also shown.

Amino acid	Triplet codons
Threonine	TGA TGG TGT
Glutamine	GTT GTC
Glycine	CCA CCG CCT CCC
Arginine	TCT
Alanine	CGG CGC
Stop signal	ACT

The diagram below shows part of a DNA molecule. This part of the DNA molecule is located near the end of a gene.

codon 47	codon 48	codon 49	codon 50	codon 51
T C T	C G G	T G G	G T C	C C A

a Give the sequence of amino acids found in the polypeptide chain that is coded for by this part of the DNA strand. **(2)**

b Give the next triplet codon that you would expect to see on this DNA strand if codon 51 coded for the last amino acid in the polypeptide chain. **(1)**

c Draw a diagram to show the sequence of bases on a molecule of messenger RNA synthesised from this part of the DNA strand. **(2)**

d Mutations can occur during DNA replication.

   i Suggest what would happen to the structure of the protein coded for by this DNA molecule if thymine in **codon 49** were replaced by cytosine. **(2)**

   ii Suggest what would happen to the structure of the protein coded for by this DNA molecule if adenine replaced the first thymine in **codon 47**. **(2)**

   (Total 9 marks)

2 Tuberculosis (TB) is caused by the bacterium, *Mycobacterium tuberculosis*.

a The table below lists five structural features that may be found in bacteria and viruses.

Copy the table and put a cross in the box if the structural feature is present.

Structural feature	Bacteria	Viruses
Mesosome		
Capsid		
Nucleic acid		
Cytoplasm		
Ribosome		

(5)

b The table below shows the number of new TB cases recorded in 1994 and in 2004 from four different geographical regions. These data exclude people who are HIV positive.

Year	Number of new TB cases per 100 000 of the population			
	Africa	Asia	South America	Europe
1994	148	629	98	48
2004	281	535	59	104

i Describe the trends shown by the data. **(2)**

ii HIV positive people were excluded from the data. If they had been included suggest how the data would differ. Give an explanation for your answer. **(3)**

SC **c** TB is increasing in some countries which have well-funded health services. Suggest **two** reasons for this. (2)

(Total 12 marks)

3 The graph below shows the changes in population size of bacterial cultures grown in the presence of three antibiotics, A, B and C. In each case the antibiotic was added at 7 hours.

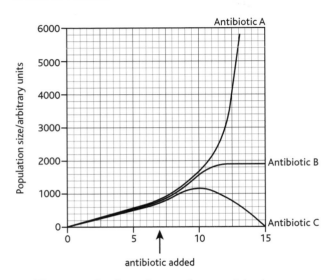

a Use examples from the graph to explain the differences between bacteriocidal and bacteriostatic antibiotics. (3)

SC **b** A previous investigation on the same bacterium using antibiotic A had produced a curve similar to that for antibiotic B. Suggest an explanation for the change in the response to antibiotic A. (4)

SC **c** Outline a technique that could demonstrate the effectiveness of antibiotics on bacteria. (4)

(Total 11 marks)

4 **a** Explain the meaning of the term pathogen. (2)

b Explain how each of the following reduces the chances of pathogens causing disease.

i inflammation (3)

ii lysozyme (2)

iii interferon (1)

(Total 8 marks)

5 Following the introduction of DNA profiling into forensic testing, many people have been freed from prison as a result of new evidence provided by the technique.

a Give reasons why confidence in the new evidence was strong enough to enable the release of these prisoners. (2)

b Give **one** example of physical evidence that could be retained from the original investigation and explain why the sample is suitable for a DNA test to be carried out. (2)

c Explain how the results of DNA profiling could be used to find the identity of a dead person. (3)

(Total 7 marks)

6 On 26th September, a forensic scientist was called to a room where a man was found dead. She was asked to determine the time of death.

She recorded the temperature in the room and she collected the larvae and pupae of several species of insect from the body. She took the pupae and larvae to her laboratory, where they were placed in a constant temperature of 23 °C.

On the 4th October, adults from four species of insect appeared, and another species appeared on the 6th October. One of the first species to be seen was the blowfly, which can lay eggs on a corpse within minutes of death, but which is rarely active at night.

Records of weather conditions for the area were consulted and the time of death was determined to be 14th or 15th September.

SC **a** Explain the importance of the temperature data in this investigation. (2)

b Suggest one reason why collecting data about several species of insect would make the estimate of time of death more reliable. (1)

c Suggest a reason why the scientist could not be more precise as to the time of death. (2)

(Total 5 marks)

Topic 7 Run for your life

This topic deals with various aspects of the body that make it possible for us to exercise, including the structure and function of muscles, and the supply of energy from aerobic and anaerobic respiration. It considers how homeostasis returns conditions in the body to normal after exercise, and looks at some of the effects of too little or too much exercise.

What are the theories?

The sliding filament theory helps us to understand how muscles contract and relax. Aerobic respiration provides most of the energy for muscle contraction, through the breakdown of food molecules via glycolysis, the Krebs cycle and the electron transport chain. When oxygen supply is insufficient, the breakdown of glucose to lactate in anaerobic respiration provides some energy so that muscles can continue to work.

Exercise changes conditions inside the body, particularly the need for oxygen and the internal temperature. Negative feedback mechanisms help the body respond to these changes and return conditions inside the body to normal as soon as possible when exercise ends. Longer term homeostatic changes are managed in the body by the switching on and off of genes.

What is the evidence?

There is plenty of evidence to show that moderate exercise correlates with an improvement in health by decreasing risks of obesity, coronary heart disease and diabetes, but proving a causal link is more difficult. Too much exercise is associated with increased wear and tear on the skeletal system and may also affect the immune system. You will have the opportunity to carry out your own investigations on the rate of respiration in organisms and on the effects of exercise on tidal volume and breathing rate.

What are the implications?

Damage to the skeletal tissues as a result of excess exercise can be remedied by keyhole surgery and the use of prostheses to replace damaged parts. This technology is also being developed to help those with physical disabilities, making it possible for some of them to participate in sports. However, the use of drugs to enhance performance in sport is raising more difficult, ethical issues that must be considered in relation to sports competition.

The map opposite shows you all the knowledge and skills you need to have by the end of this topic. The colour in each box shows which chapter they are covered in and the numbers refer to the Edexcel specification.

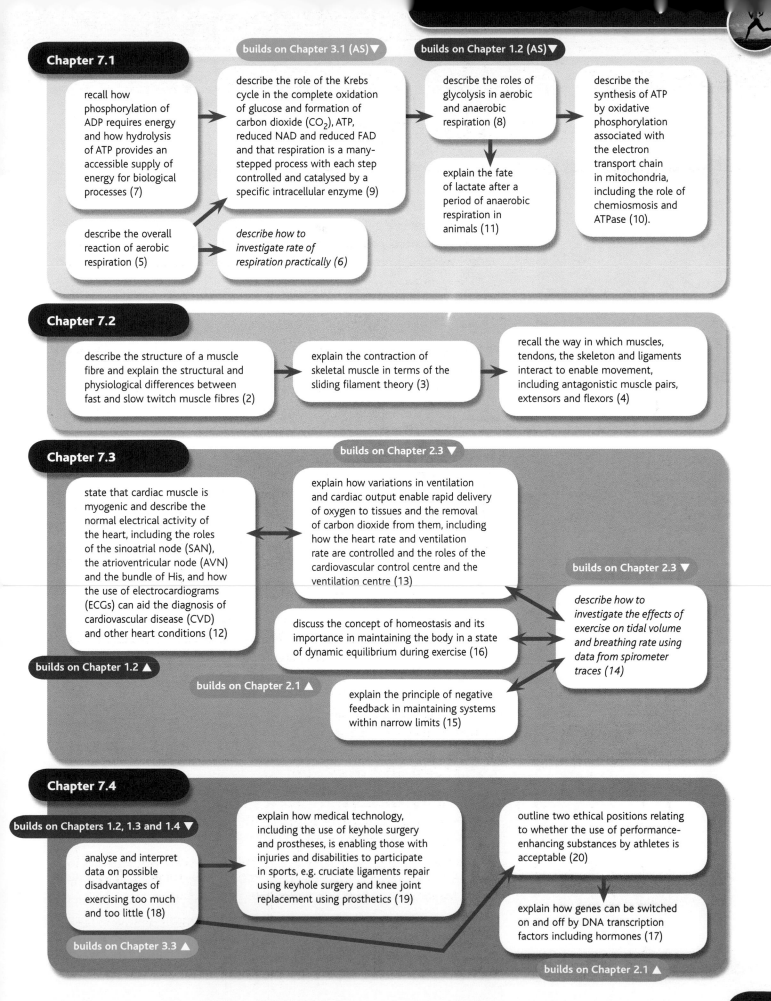

Chapter 7.1

recall how phosphorylation of ADP requires energy and how hydrolysis of ATP provides an accessible supply of energy for biological processes (7)

describe the overall reaction of aerobic respiration (5)

describe how to investigate rate of respiration practically (6)

builds on Chapter 3.1 (AS)▼

describe the role of the Krebs cycle in the complete oxidation of glucose and formation of carbon dioxide (CO_2), ATP, reduced NAD and reduced FAD and that respiration is a many-stepped process with each step controlled and catalysed by a specific intracellular enzyme (9)

builds on Chapter 1.2 (AS)▼

describe the roles of glycolysis in aerobic and anaerobic respiration (8)

explain the fate of lactate after a period of anaerobic respiration in animals (11)

describe the synthesis of ATP by oxidative phosphorylation associated with the electron transport chain in mitochondria, including the role of chemiosmosis and ATPase (10).

Chapter 7.2

describe the structure of a muscle fibre and explain the structural and physiological differences between fast and slow twitch muscle fibres (2)

explain the contraction of skeletal muscle in terms of the sliding filament theory (3)

recall the way in which muscles, tendons, the skeleton and ligaments interact to enable movement, including antagonistic muscle pairs, extensors and flexors (4)

Chapter 7.3

state that cardiac muscle is myogenic and describe the normal electrical activity of the heart, including the roles of the sinoatrial node (SAN), the atrioventricular node (AVN) and the bundle of His, and how the use of electrocardiograms (ECGs) can aid the diagnosis of cardiovascular disease (CVD) and other heart conditions (12)

builds on Chapter 1.2 ▲

builds on Chapter 2.3 ▼

explain how variations in ventilation and cardiac output enable rapid delivery of oxygen to tissues and the removal of carbon dioxide from them, including how the heart rate and ventilation rate are controlled and the roles of the cardiovascular control centre and the ventilation centre (13)

discuss the concept of homeostasis and its importance in maintaining the body in a state of dynamic equilibrium during exercise (16)

builds on Chapter 2.1 ▲

explain the principle of negative feedback in maintaining systems within narrow limits (15)

builds on Chapter 2.3 ▼

describe how to investigate the effects of exercise on tidal volume and breathing rate using data from spirometer traces (14)

Chapter 7.4

builds on Chapters 1.2, 1.3 and 1.4 ▼

analyse and interpret data on possible disadvantages of exercising too much and too little (18)

builds on Chapter 3.3 ▲

explain how medical technology, including the use of keyhole surgery and prostheses, is enabling those with injuries and disabilities to participate in sports, e.g. cruciate ligaments repair using keyhole surgery and knee joint replacement using prosthetics (19)

outline two ethical positions relating to whether the use of performance-enhancing substances by athletes is acceptable (20)

explain how genes can be switched on and off by DNA transcription factors including hormones (17)

builds on Chapter 2.1 ▲

7.1 Cellular respiration – the energy supply

fig. 7.1.1 Whatever your activity level, you need a constant supply of energy in your cells.

Introducing cellular respiration 5.7.5, 5.7.7

Muscles are very active tissues. They contract to move your body around, support you against the pull of gravity, squeeze the food through your gut, move blood around your body and much more. The energy needed to maintain this constant action comes from the food you eat.

Autotrophic organisms make their own food (usually by photosynthesis) while heterotrophic organisms eat and digest other organisms. This food provides the energy for all the metabolic reactions which occur in a cell or organism, including muscle contraction. In this chapter you will consider how the energy in the food molecules you eat is transferred to the molecules of adenosine triphosphate (ATP) needed by the cell.

Cellular respiration

The energy in your food is of no use to you until it is transferred from the chemical bonds in the food to the phosphate bonds of ATP (see page 10). Cellular respiration is the process by which organisms produce ATP. The food (known as the **respiratory substrate**, generally glucose) is usually oxidised as completely as possible. Oxygen from the air is used in the process, and carbon dioxide and water are formed as waste products. The volume of oxygen used and the volume of carbon dioxide produced change depending on the level of activity of the organism, the type of food being respired and other external factors such as temperature.

Cellular respiration is usually summarised as follows:

$$C_6H_{12}O_6 + 6O_2 \rightarrow 6CO_2 + 6H_2O + ATP$$
$$\text{glucose} + \text{oxygen} \rightarrow \text{carbon dioxide} + \text{water} + \text{energy}$$

ATP provides energy for all cellular reactions. When energy is needed, the third phosphate bond can be broken by a hydrolysis reaction catalysed by the enzyme ATPase. The result is adenosine diphosphate (ADP) and a free inorganic phosphate group (P_i). About 34 kJ of energy are released for every mole of ATP hydrolysed. Some of this energy is lost as heat, but the rest is available for any energy-requiring biological activity. The breakdown of ATP into ADP and P_i is reversible. The phosphorylation of ADP to ATP is also catalysed by ATPase and requires 34 kJ of energy.

ATP cannot be stored in the body in large amounts. As the raw materials to make ATP are almost always available, the compound is made as and when it is needed. Once the raw materials are used up, cellular respiration cannot continue and no more ATP is made. This is seen clearly with the onset of rigor mortis in a dead body. Once cellular respiration stops and ATP production ends, the contracting proteins of the muscles cannot work and the muscles lock solid.

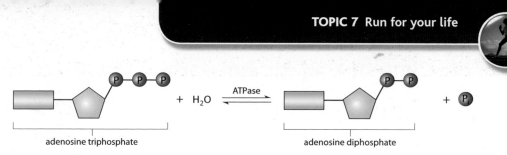

fig. 7.1.2 **ATP – the molecule which supplies the energy needed for all cellular reactions. When ATP is hydrolysed to ADP + P$_i$ (left → right) energy is released. The reverse reaction, where ATP is synthesised from ADP and P$_i$ *takes in* the same amount of energy – this energy is derived from respiration.**

The process of cellular respiration

The simple equation given above for cellular respiration hides the fact that the complete process is a complex series of reactions. Many of these reactions involve oxidation or reduction. For example, hydrogen is removed from glucose molecules and passed along an electron transfer chain (see pages 138–41), driving the formation of ATP and producing water using oxygen from the air. Carbon is also removed and oxidised to form carbon dioxide. As in all biochemical pathways, the reactions are controlled by enzymes. Because each enzyme is specific to a particular reaction, many different enzymes are involved. The rate of the reaction is controlled by inhibition of the various enzymes, usually by other chemicals in the reaction chain (see page 134).

The hydrogen acceptors

The simple equation for cellular respiration suggests that ATP is produced as a direct result of the breakdown of glucose. However, this is not the case. Most of the ATP produced during cellular respiration is made through a series of oxidation and reduction reactions in the electron transport chain. Reduction is the addition of electrons to a substance. In the cell this is brought about by the addition of hydrogen or the removal of oxygen. Any compound which has oxygen removed, or hydrogen or electrons added, is said to be reduced. Oxidation is the removal of electrons from a substance. Any compound which has oxygen added, or hydrogen or electrons removed, is said to be oxidised.

In most cases during cellular respiration, hydrogen is removed from compounds and picked up by a hydrogen carrier (hydrogen acceptor) which is therefore reduced. This happens in several places during the reactions of respiration, as you will see later. The hydrogen is then passed to the next hydrogen acceptor and along the electron transport chain. A series of linked oxidation and reduction (redox) reactions takes place and it is here that ATP is formed (see pages 138–9 for more details).

The most common hydrogen acceptor in cellular respiration is **NAD (nicotinamide adenine dinucleotide)**. NAD is a coenzyme, one of the small molecules that assist in enzyme-catalysed reactions. When it accepts hydrogen atoms from a metabolic pathway it becomes reduced to form **reduced NAD**.

FAD (flavine adenine dinucleotide) is another hydrogen carrier (and coenzyme), which accepts hydrogen from reduced NAD and forms reduced FAD. A molecule of ATP is formed in the process.

Questions

1 Explain why cellular respiration is such an important reaction.

2 Outline the strengths and limitations of this equation:

$$C_6H_{12}O_6 + 6O_2 \rightarrow 6CO_2 + 6H_2O + ATP$$

Finding out about cellular respiration 5.7.9, 5.7.6

Our understanding of the process of respiration has developed gradually over the years. In the early days the research was based on whole animals and plants. Now the work continues at the level of tiny cell fragments, evidence from which has become available to us using technology such as the electron microscope.

An outline of cellular respiration

Respiration takes place in two distinct phases. The first part of the process does *not* require oxygen – it is anaerobic. A little ATP is produced but more importantly the splitting of the respiratory substrate begins and the molecules are prepared for entry into the second stage of the process. This first stage is known as **glycolysis** (see page 132).

For the second set of reactions to proceed oxygen *is* needed – this is **aerobic respiration**. Aerobic respiration involves the **Krebs cycle** (see pages 136–7) and the electron transport chain (see pages 138–41).

The fuel for the process is usually glucose, although other substances can be used when there is a glucose shortage. Oxygen is the other major requirement for cellular respiration to proceed completely and the maximum amount of ATP to be produced from the food molecules. Most organisms depend on **aerobic respiration**, which means that they rely on the presence of oxygen to allow both parts of the respiratory process to occur and provide them with sufficient energy to survive. They may be able to cope with a temporary lack of oxygen, but only in the very short term. Some organisms can survive without oxygen – they rely on **anaerobic respiration**. There are a few groups which cannot use oxygen at all and may in fact be killed by it.

fig. 7.1.3 If this long-tailed tit (an aerobic organism) is deprived of oxygen it will survive for only a very short time as the cells cannot obtain enough ATP. Supply *Clostridium perfringens* (the bacterium responsible for gas gangrene in wounds) with oxygen and, as an obligate anaerobe, it dies!

Demonstrating respiration

It is not always easy to demonstrate the rate of cellular respiration without sophisticated biochemical techniques designed to measure the rate in isolated cell organelles. However, in a school lab a respirometer can give some valuable information about the rate of cellular respiration by measuring the uptake of oxygen or the output of carbon dioxide by whole organisms. A basic respirometer consists of a sealed chamber containing one or more living organisms, such as germinating seeds or live mice. As the summary equation for respiration on page 128 shows, the volume of carbon dioxide given off during respiration is equivalent to the volume of oxygen taken in. A chemical such as soda lime or potassium hydroxide is used to absorb the carbon dioxide produced during respiration and this loss is measured by observing the moment of fluid in a capillary tube (see **fig. 7.1.4**). The amount of oxygen used is calculated from this. By changing the external conditions (e.g. light levels, temperature) it is possible to measure their effect on the rate of respiration by recording changes in the uptake of oxygen.

This simple apparatus has obvious limitations but it can be used to give an overall impression of the rate of respiration of organisms in differing conditions.

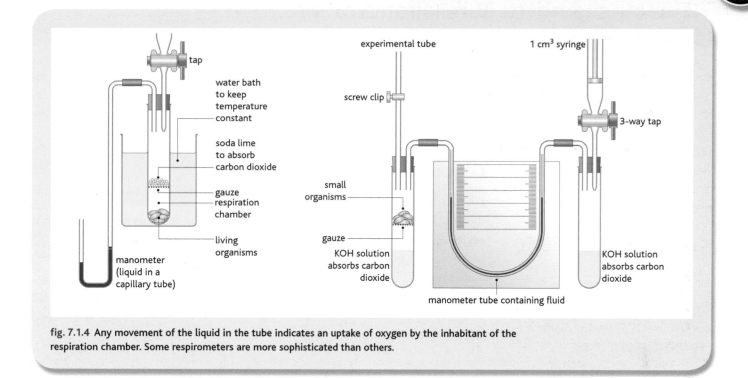

fig. 7.1.4 Any movement of the liquid in the tube indicates an uptake of oxygen by the inhabitant of the respiration chamber. Some respirometers are more sophisticated than others.

Where does cellular respiration take place?

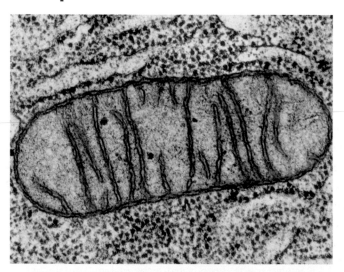

fig. 7.1.5 A mitochondrion – powerhouse of the cell and site of the Krebs cycle which provides most of the ATP needed by the cell. The stalked particles on the inner mitochondrial membranes are where ATP production takes place.

Glycolysis, the first part of the respiratory pathway, is not associated with any particular cell organelle. The enzymes controlling glycolysis are found in the cytoplasm. However, the rest of cellular respiration, including the reactions of the Krebs cycle and the electron transport system involved in producing ATP, takes place inside the **mitochondria** (see *AS Biology* pages 137–8).

Most cells contain mitochondria. They are relatively large organelles with a complex internal structure. There is a double membrane, with the inner one thrown into many folds called cristae. The matrix of the mitochondrion seems to contain the enzymes of the Krebs cycle, while the cristae carry the stalked particles associated with ATP synthesis. Those cells with very low energy requirements, for example fat storage cells, generally contain very few mitochondria, whereas cells that are very active, such as those of the muscles and the liver, have very large numbers of mitochondria packed into the cytoplasm.

Questions

1   a   Explain how respirometers are limited in what they can tell us about cellular respiration.
    b   Evaluate the two pieces of apparatus in **fig. 7.1.4** to show which you think would deliver more reliable evidence and why.

2   Describe the kind of evidence that would be needed to identify the sites of the various stages of cellular respiration in a mitochondrion.

The biochemistry of respiration 5.7.8, 5.7.11

The two pathways of cellular respiration, glycolysis and the Krebs cycle, are part of a coordinated sequence of reactions bringing about the oxidation of glucose and the production of ATP. To make understanding the biochemistry easier you are going to look at them separately, and then consider the overall situation.

Glycolysis

Glycolysis literally means 'sugar-splitting'. It takes place in the cytoplasm of the cell. In this initial part of the respiratory pathway glucose, a 6-carbon (6C) sugar, is split by a series of reactions into two molecules of the 3-carbon (3C) compound **pyruvate**. It is this pyruvate which is taken into the mitochondria and enters the Krebs cycle. The glucose for glycolysis may come directly from the blood or it may be produced by the breakdown of glycogen stores in muscle and liver cells (see *AS Biology* pages 38–9). The main stages of glycolysis are shown in **fig. 7.1.6**.

For a process designed to provide the cell with energy, glycolysis does not get off to a very good start! The first steps in the process actually use up some ATP as it is hydrolysed to provide the energy needed to phosphorylate the hexose (6C) sugar glucose, adding two phosphate groups. These are known as 'pump-priming' reactions as they activate the sugar and also make sure that it can no longer be transported readily across the cell membrane.

The phosphorylated sugar is then split to give two molecules of a 3-carbon compound, known as glyceraldehyde-3-phosphate (GALP). GALP is then converted by several steps into a molecule of **pyruvic acid**, which is found in solution as pyruvate ions. During these reactions a small amount of ATP is produced as follows.

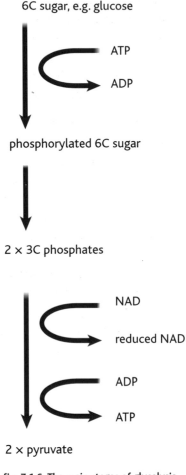

fig. 7.1.6 The main stages of glycolysis which result in the production of pyruvic acid in the form of pyruvate and a small quantity of ATP and reduced NAD. These reactions all happen within the cytoplasm of the cell.

- Two hydrogen atoms are removed from the 3C sugars and taken up by NAD, forming reduced NAD. This takes place in the cytoplasm of the cell. The reduced NAD then passes through the outer mitochondrial membrane into the electron carrier system (see pages 138–9). The energy made available through the electron carrier system is used to phosphorylate ADP (see page 10). Three molecules of ATP result from each 3C sugar passing through glycolysis.

- A small amount of ATP is also made directly from the energy transfer when the 3C sugar is converted to pyruvate. The phosphorylation of the sugar at the beginning of glycolysis is reversed when the final intermediate compound is converted to pyruvate. The phosphate group released is used to convert ADP to ATP.

If there is plenty of oxygen the pyruvate will enter the mitochondria and be used in the aerobic reactions of the Krebs cycle. If there is insufficient oxygen for this, the pyruvate is converted into either ethanol or lactic acid with a little ATP produced. This is anaerobic respiration.

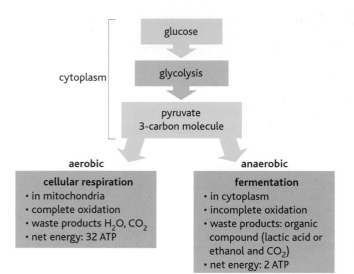

fig. 7.1.7 The alternative routes for the products of glycolysis.

Anaerobic respiration

At the start of exercise, before extra oxygen can be supplied, your muscles rely on a substance called **creatine phosphate** stored in the muscle fibres, which supplies the energy needed to produce ATP before aerobic respiration takes over again.

If the exercise is particularly hard, or lasts a long time and your muscles don't get enough oxygen to supply their needs, the products of glycolysis cannot go on to the Krebs cycle (the aerobic stage of cellular respiration). In anaerobic respiration the pyruvate is converted to **lactate** (also referred to as **lactic acid**),

another 3C compound. When glycolysis ends up with lactate, only two molecules of ATP are produced per glucose molecule respired instead of three, because some of the reduced NAD is used to reduce pyruvate to lactate instead of entering the electron transfer chain. The lactate moves out of the cells into the blood.

When exercise stops, the levels of lactate in the blood remain raised. The lactate must be oxidised back to pyruvate to enter the Krebs cycle to be respired, producing carbon dioxide, water and ATP. It takes oxygen to oxidise the accumulated lactate (which is toxic). This is why you continue to breathe deeply for some time after exercise has finished. The ways in which your body deals with the excess lactate in the system after exercise are complex (see the box on page 134).

Sprint athletes may run up to 95% of a race relying on the anaerobic respiration of their muscles. Long-distance runners have to maintain a much higher level of aerobic respiration, because their muscles could not continue to work for the length of time needed to finish the race if the lactate levels are not kept to a minimum. Training allows athletes both to get more oxygen to their muscles faster as a better blood supply develops, and to tolerate higher levels of lactate before the muscle fatigues. With repeated exposure to high lactate levels, more lactate transporter molecules develop in the mitochondrial membranes, resulting in faster processing of lactate to pyruvate when oxygen is available.

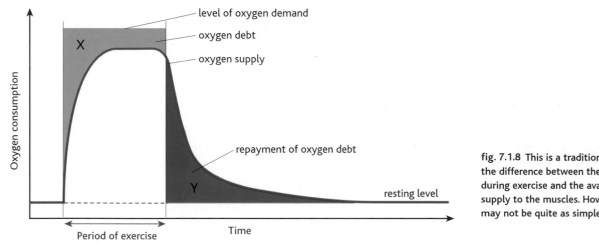

fig. 7.1.8 This is a traditional graph showing the difference between the oxygen demand during exercise and the available oxygen supply to the muscles. However, the picture may not be quite as simple as it appears.

HSW Oxygen debt and epoc – the figures don't add up!

fig. 7.1.9 Even elite athletes carry on breathing deeply for some time after the race is over – just what is happening in their bodies that demands all this extra oxygen?

The model of lactate metabolism after anaerobic respiration has remained the same for many years, with a picture of lactate being oxidised back to pyruvate and fed into the Krebs cycle. However, recently a more complex picture has started to emerge. Careful measurements have shown that the magnitude of the oxygen debt and the amount of oxygen taken in as part of the recovery profile simply don't add up. We definitely take in more oxygen after exercising than we appear to need simply from our measured lactate levels – this is excess post-exercise oxygen consumption, or epoc. There has been intense debate among scientists about the causes of this. The current consensus is that there are seven factors affecting our post-exercise oxygen needs:

- Oxidation of lactate to pyruvate to move into the Krebs cycle.

- Lactate removed from muscles and carried to the liver in the blood is converted back to pyruvate and then into glucose in a process called **gluconeogenesis**. The glucose is then carried around in the blood to replenish the glycogen stores in the muscles.

- ATP and phosphocreatine levels in the muscle fibres need to be restored, which takes oxygen from the Krebs cycle.

- Myoglobin in the muscles needs to be reoxygenated.

- All chemical reactions, including those of respiration, go faster – so more oxygen is needed. This is the result of raised temperatures in the muscles and hormones such as adrenalin which are released during exercise, both of which increase reaction rates.

- We need to breathe more deeply and rapidly during exercise – and so the muscles of the ribs and diaphragm use more oxygen.

- The heart rate is elevated for a time after exercise so the heart muscle needs extra oxygen supplies for the increased respiration required to support this.

HSW What is the evidence for glycolysis?

It took many years for the pathways of glycolysis and the closely associated processes of lactic and alcoholic fermentation to be worked out. There are several landmarks along the way, and many scientists have played their parts.

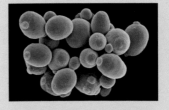

fig. 7.1.10 The experimental organism used in much of the work on glycolysis, from the early days onwards, has been yeast – easy to grow, no ethical issues and containing all the enzymes of glycolysis.

- In 1897 Eduard Buchner discovered that an extract of yeast without any cells in it could still convert glucose to ethanol. This showed that the enzymes of glycolysis and fermentation are not associated closely with the cell structure.

- In the early 1900s Arthur Harden and W.J. Young showed that phosphate was needed for the pathway to proceed and also that there were two elements of the yeast extracts needed before fermentation could go ahead. One of these was inactivated by heat – it contained the enzymes. The other was not affected by heat in the same way and contained NAD, ADP and ATP.

- After work with inhibitors had allowed some of the pathway intermediates to be studied, the German biochemists Gustav Embden and Otto Meyerhof worked out much of the rest of the sequence. Meyerhof received the Nobel Prize in 1922 for his work on glycolysis and lactate metabolism in muscles.

By the 1940s, all the individual steps of the glycolysis pathway had been worked out.

Controlling the rate of glycolysis

Although ATP is often described as an energy store, it is perhaps better described as a means of transferring energy from food molecules to the molecules of an organism. ATP is not stored – it is made as and when it is needed. This means the rate of glycolysis (and therefore the Krebs cycle) needs to be closely controlled. When energy demands are high, glycolysis must occur rapidly to supply plenty of pyruvate for the Krebs cycle. When energy demands are low, less oxygen is taken in. Glycolysis must slow down as the Krebs cycle reactions will proceed more slowly too.

Each of the individual steps in glycolysis is controlled by a specific intracellular enzyme. These enzymes are sensitive to various substrates and products of the reaction, giving various degrees of control. One enzyme – **phosphofructokinase** – is particularly important. It catalyses one of the early 'pump-priming' reactions, adding a phosphate group to the 6C sugar. It is affected by the concentration of one of its own substrates – ATP. The enzyme is inhibited by high levels of ATP and of citrate, one of the compounds of the Krebs cycle. So when there is plenty of ATP or the components of the Krebs cycle begin to build up, the process of glycolysis slows down. Conversely, when the cell needs energy and the components of the Krebs cycle are low, glycolysis speeds up to remedy the situation. By changing the rate of glycolysis the rate of the whole process of cellular respiration is controlled.

Most biochemical pathways have particular enzymes which, like this one, play a vital role in controlling the rate of the entire pathway. They are called **regulatory enzymes**.

Questions

1   Explain why the breathing rate and heart rate continue to be raised after exercise.

2   Produce an annotated diagram of glycolysis in which the important biochemistry of each step is labelled.

3   Summarise how the anaerobic oxidation of glucose releases useful energy for cell metabolism.

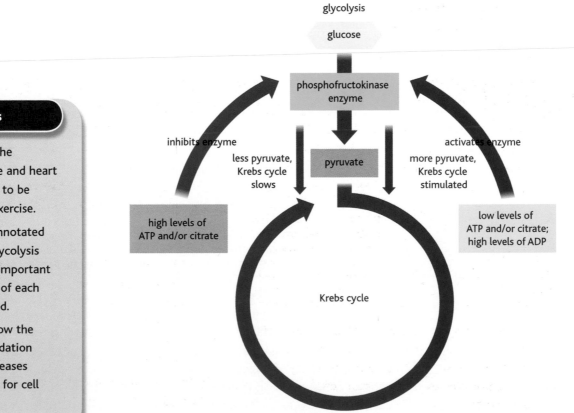

fig. 7.1.11 **Phosphofructokinase is one of the most important regulatory enzymes for aerobic respiration.**

The Krebs cycle 5.7.9

When there is plenty of oxygen available, the pyruvate produced as the end-product of glycolysis is fed through into the mitochondria where it enters the Krebs cycle. This is a series of biochemical steps which lead to the complete oxidation of glucose, resulting in carbon dioxide and water and relatively large amounts of ATP.

Like glycolysis, the Krebs cycle involves a many-stepped process, with each individual step controlled and catalysed by a specific intracellular enzyme. The reactions of the cycle take place in the matrix of the mitochondrion, but ATP is produced in the stalked particles on the inner mitochondrial membranes in the presence of oxygen.

You are going to be looking at the principles of the process but you do not need to learn the detailed biochemical steps that take place – although **fig. 7.1.12** gives you a flavour of just how complex it is!

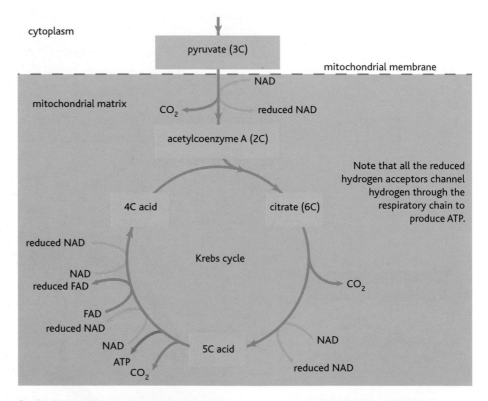

fig. 7.1.12 The Krebs cycle – this diagram shows the main principles of the cycle which supplies all your cells with energy. The cycle turns continuously and the rate of its turning is carefully controlled to ensure that the right amount of ATP is produced to meet the demands of the body.

- The 3-carbon compound pyruvate crosses the mitochondrial membrane from the cytoplasm. It is immediately converted to a 2-carbon (2C) compound known as **acetyl coenzyme A** (or **acetyl coA**). A molecule of carbon dioxide has to be removed to form the 2C compound, along with a molecule of hydrogen which reduces NAD. The reduced NAD is used later in the electron transport chain. The enzymes that remove carbon dioxide are known as **decarboxylases** and those that remove hydrogen are **dehydrogenases**.

- The 2C compound combines with a 4C compound to form the 6C compound citric acid (citrate). At this point it has entered the Krebs cycle (this is why the Krebs cycle is sometimes called the **citric acid cycle**).

- This 6C compound now goes through a cyclical series of reactions during which the citric acid is broken down in a number of stages to give the original 4C compound. Two further molecules of carbon dioxide are removed in the process. They are given off as a waste product.

- The 4C compound then combines with more 2C acetyl coA and the cycle turns again.

For each molecule of pyruvate that enters the Krebs cycle, three molecules of reduced NAD, one of reduced FAD and one of ATP are the direct result. The reduced NAD and reduced FAD then enter the electron transport chain. For each molecule of glucose which enters the glycolytic pathway, the Krebs cycle turns *twice* (6C glucose giving two 3C pyruvate).

HSW The Krebs cycle – developing the model

Hans Krebs first put forward his ideas for the now famous cycle in 1937. It was the result of brilliant reasoning and experimentation in the preceding years, both by Krebs and by others.

- In the period 1910–20 several biochemists including T. Thunberg, L.S. Stern and F. Batelli showed that dehydrogenases are active in minced animal tissues, transferring hydrogen atoms from certain organic acids known to occur in cells to a blue dye which turned colourless when it was reduced.

- In 1935 Albert Szent-Gyorgyi produced a sequence of enzymic reactions showing the oxidation of several organic acids from succinic acid, which we now know is part of the Krebs cycle.

- Krebs then carried out an elegant series of experiments to show that only certain organic acids are oxidised by cells, and that certain inhibitors could bring the oxidations to a halt. After much work he came up with the sequence we now know as the Krebs cycle. His master step was the discovery of the combination of the 2C molecule and the 4C molecule to form 6C citric acid. This was the 'missing link' which allowed him to show that the process was a cycle. Krebs also showed that all his suggested reactions could take place at a fast enough rate to account for the known pyruvate and oxygen use of the tissue. This suggested that his pathway was the main, if not the only, pathway for the oxidation of food molecules. He won the Nobel Prize in Physiology and Medicine in 1953 for his work, which changed perceptions of cell biology for ever.

fig. 7.1.13 Sir Hans Krebs. Krebs was banned from practising medicine in Germany by the Nazis because he was Jewish. He moved to Cambridge where he worked with Gowland Hopkins of vitamin fame (see *AS Biology* page 35) and during the 1930s he discovered both the Krebs cycle and the ornithine cycle which involves urea.

Questions

1 Summarise the differences between the Krebs cycle and glycolysis.

2 The Krebs cycle makes energy for the cell. Explain how this statement is incorrect.

SC 3 Investigate the work of Krebs and write a short description of how he built up his model of the cycle of reactions that take place in the mitochondria.

The electron transport chain 5.7.10

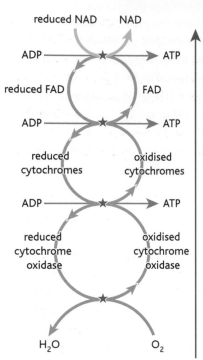

★ electron passed to next carrier – oxidation is loss of electrons   energy of electron

fig. 7.1.14 These are the main known components of the electron transport chain. As they become reduced and then oxidised again, sufficient energy is released to drive the production of molecules of ATP.

Aerobic respiration is the main source of ATP in aerobic organisms. Although it is hydrogen atoms that are removed from the compounds in glycolysis and the Krebs cycle, and hydrogen atoms that eventually join up with oxygen atoms to form water, it is in fact mainly electrons which are passed along the carrier system. This is why the system is known as the electron transport chain. The protons remain in solution. You can think of the various elements of the electron transport chain as being at different energy levels. The first member of the chain is the highest level, with subsequent steps down. Each electron is passed down from one energy level to another, releasing energy that powers the production of ATP (see **fig. 7.1.14**). The process is known as **oxidative phosphorylation** because ADP is phosphorylated in a process which depends on the presence of oxygen.

There are four main carriers involved. The coenzymes NAD and FAD both act as hydrogen acceptors for hydrogen released from the Krebs cycle. One molecule of ATP is produced as the FAD is reduced when it accepts hydrogen from the reduced NAD – which becomes oxidised in the process.

*   **Cytochromes** are protein pigments with an iron group rather like haemoglobin. They are reduced by electrons from reduced FAD which is oxidised again. A molecule of ATP is produced at this stage.

*   **Cytochrome oxidase** is an enzyme that receives the electrons from the cytochromes and is reduced as the cytochromes are oxidised. A molecule of ATP is also produced at this stage.

*   **Oxygen** is the final hydrogen acceptor in the chain. When the oxygen is reduced, water is formed and the chain is at an end.

As a result of each molecule of hydrogen passing along the electron transport chain, sufficient energy is released to make three molecules of ATP.

Where is ATP actually made?

The best current model of where ATP is produced has the main reactions of respiration taking place in the mitochondrial matrix, but the components of the electron transport chain and so the actual production of ATP taking place on the inner membrane of the mitochondria. This is folded up to form the cristae, which in turn are covered with closely packed stalked particles which seem to be the site of the ATPase.

fig. 7.1.15 Cyanide is well known in murder mysteries – and has been used in real murders too. The poison acts on cytochrome oxidase in the electron transport chain, preventing the production of ATP. The cells of the body cannot function without their energy supply, so the muscles spasm and the victim cannot breathe.

Over the years the model of ATP synthesis in the cell has developed and changed. There are several strands of evidence for the site of ATP synthesis which has resulted in the model which is widely accepted today.

* You can break open cells and centrifuge the contents to obtain a fraction containing just mitochondria. If these are kept supplied with glucose and oxygen they will produce ATP.

* High-powered electron micrographs show the surface of the inner membrane of the mitochondrion to be covered in closely packed stalked particles. These provide a greatly increased surface area which is an ideal site for enzymes to work.

* The stalked particles and the bits of membrane associated with them can be separated from the rest of the mitochondrial structure. Scientists have demonstrated that they alone out of the contents of the mitochondrion are capable of ATP synthesis.

As a result of this type of evidence, and more, the stalked particles have been accepted as vital for the formation of ATP. But exactly how does the process work? It took a stroke of genius to come up with a theory which fitted all the evidence – the chemiosmotic theory.

The chemiosmotic theory of ATP production

The link between the electrons that are passed down the electron transport chain and the production of ATP was first described by Peter Mitchell in 1961. He called it the chemiosmotic theory, and it provides a very elegant explanation. The theory explains what happens to the hydrogen ions (protons) that are left behind when the electrons are passed along the electron transport chain, and how the movement of the hydrogen ions is coupled to the actual production of ATP.

Peter Mitchell proposed that protons are actively transported into the space between the inner and outer mitochondrial membranes, using the energy provided as the electrons pass along the transport chain (see **fig. 7.1.16**). The inner mitochondrial membrane is impermeable to protons. This means that as a result of the active transport of the protons there are different hydrogen ion concentrations on the two sides of the inner membrane. The membrane space has a higher concentration of hydrogen ions than the matrix, so there is a concentration gradient across the membrane. As a result of the different hydrogen ion concentrations there is also a pH gradient. And because positive hydrogen ions are concentrated in the membrane space there is an electrochemical gradient too.

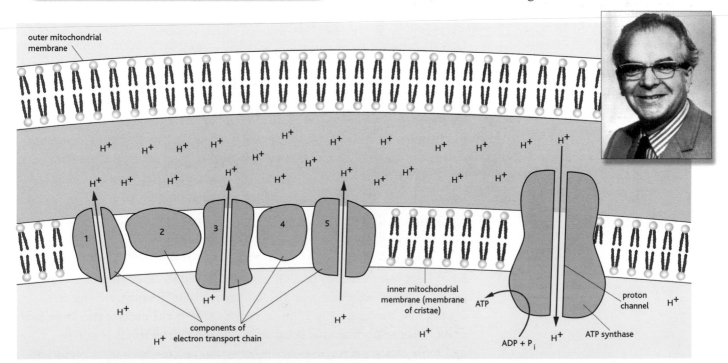

fig. 7.1.16 Peter Mitchell's chemiosmotic theory explains the formation of ATP not just in the mitochondria but also in chloroplasts and elsewhere. The use of the hydrogen ion gradient, produced using energy from the movement of electrons along the electron transport chain, explains all our current observations about the process. Numbers 1–5 represent carrier molecules in the inner membrane.

All of these factors mean that there is a tendency for the hydrogen ions to move back into the matrix. However, the membrane is generally impermeable to hydrogen ions. The only way they can move back into the matrix is through special pores. These pores are found on the stalked particles, and the movement of the hydrogen ions along their electrical, concentration and pH gradients is linked to an ATPase enzyme. The energy from the gradients is used to drive the synthesis of ATP. Thus the universal energy carrier is produced in a universal process, found in all living things.

HSW Fighting for the chemiosmotic model

In the 1960s, the widely held model for the formation of ATP in the cell was that a high-energy phosphate group was directly transferred to ADP from another intermediate, rather like the process at the end of glycolysis as pyruvate is formed. Unfortunately no one could find this intermediate compound. When Peter Mitchell put forward his explanation for the production of ATP in the mitochondria using his chemiosmotic theory, other scientists were sceptical at first because the idea was so very different from the accepted model. Over the next 10 years, evidence for Mitchell's ideas was built up – and no high-energy intermediates were found. By 1978 Mitchell's chemiosmotic theory was widely accepted and he won the Nobel Prize for Chemistry.

How much ATP is gained?

Although we look at respiration in terms of the two stages, it is important to remember that they work together. Glycolysis continually feeds into the Krebs cycle, and the control of the whole process depends on various enzymes and the levels of some of the substrates and products of the reactions.

Cellular respiration has evolved to produce energy in the form of ATP for use in the cells. The fact that the process is the same in almost all living organisms suggests that it evolved at a very early stage in the evolution of organisms on Earth and that it is a very effective method of producing available energy. If it wasn't, alternative successful life forms with a different system of respiration would doubtless have evolved long ago. But exactly how much ATP is gained during the oxidation of one molecule of glucose in its journey along the respiratory pathways?

The easiest way to look at this is to consider the whole process and where the ATP is produced (see **fig. 7.1.17**). For many years the average amount was said to be 36 molecules of ATP, assuming that glucose enters the cycle and that oxidation is complete. The actual total was taken as 38 molecules of ATP, but it takes two molecules of ATP to transport the reduced NAD molecules produced in glycolysis through the mitochondrial membrane, leaving 36 available for the body cells. If this is compared with the meagre two molecules of ATP that result when the breakdown of a glucose molecule is purely anaerobic, the importance of the oxygen-using process becomes abundantly clear. However, this figure was reached on the assumption that the yields of ATP are always in whole numbers.

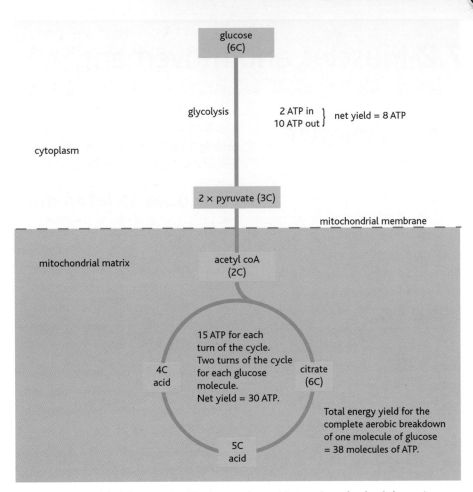

fig. 7.1.17 This model of the ATP gained by the complete oxidation of a molecule of glucose in cellular respiration has been accepted for a long time – but the figures are now being challenged.

As our understanding of the processes of the electron transport chain has increased over the past 40 years or so, the figures have become less certain. Scientists now think that ATP yields may not always be in whole numbers. Currently the biochemists' best estimates are that the oxidation of two molecules of reduced NAD supplies enough energy to make five molecules of ATP. Similarly they now think that the oxidation of two molecules of reduced FAD produces about three molecules of ATP. This gives an overall yield for the process of aerobic cellular respiration of around 31 molecules of ATP. In the future, this figure may well change again as understanding of the process develops and technology improves!

Questions

SC 1 Using **fig. 7.1.17** to help you, draw a large fully labelled diagram summarising the process of aerobic cellular respiration, starting with glucose.

2 Explain how the oxidation of glucose results in the formation of ATP.

3 Explain why aerobic respiration produces so much more ATP than anaerobic respiration.

4 What is Mitchell's chemiosmotic theory of ATP production and why is it so important to our understanding of cellular respiration?

7.2 Muscles and movement

What is muscle?

5.7.2

Muscle is a specialised tissue which is remarkably similar throughout the animal kingdom. Here we concentrate on mammalian muscle. Muscles are largely made up of protein. They consist of large numbers of very long cells known as muscle fibres bound together by connective tissue. They can contract (shorten) to do work. When they relax, they can be pulled back to their original length. Muscles have a good blood supply to provide them with the glucose and oxygen they need for respiration to supply the energy for contraction and remove the waste products which result. Muscles respond to stimulation from the nervous system and to chemical stimulation.

In mammals the muscle tissues can make up as much as 40% of the body weight. There are three main types of muscle, each specialised to perform a particular function – striated muscle, smooth muscle and cardiac muscle.

Striated muscle (skeletal muscle or voluntary muscle) is the muscle attached to the skeleton and involved in locomotion. It is under the control of the voluntary nervous system, and its appearance under the microscope is striated or stripy. It contracts rapidly, but

also fatigues or tires relatively quickly. You will be mainly studying striated muscle. The microscopic structure of striated muscle as revealed by the electron microscope gives many clues as to how the tissue contracts.

How does striated muscle contract?

Muscle fibres are made up of many **myofibrils** lying parallel to each other. Each myofibril is made up of **sarcomeres**, the individual units of the muscle structure. The proteins **actin** and **myosin** make up a large part of the structure of the sarcomeres. The cytoplasm of the myofibrils is called the sarcoplasm. It contains many mitochondria supplying the energy needed for muscle contraction. A network of membranes running through the system is called the sarcoplasmic reticulum, which stores and releases calcium ions.

Smooth muscle (involuntary muscle) is not striped and is under the control of the involuntary nervous system. It is found in the gut where it is involved in moving the food along, and in the blood vessels. It both contracts and fatigues slowly.

Cardiac muscle is found exclusively in the heart. It is striated and the fibres are joined by cross-connections. It contracts spontaneously and does not fatigue.

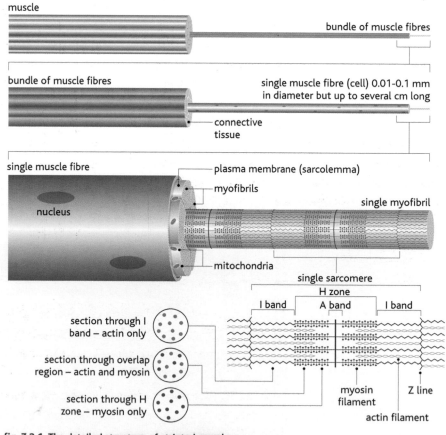

fig. 7.2.1 The detailed structure of striated muscle.

HSW Properties of skeletal muscle

Muscles respond to electrical stimulation. This has given scientists a way of investigating the way muscles work. If a calf muscle (gastrocnemius) from a frog is given a variety of different electrical stimuli the effects can be recorded on a revolving drum (kymograph). **Figure 7.2.3** shows the results from a single muscle fibre. If a whole muscle is used, the results are more confusing because different fibres have different thresholds and contract with different strengths.

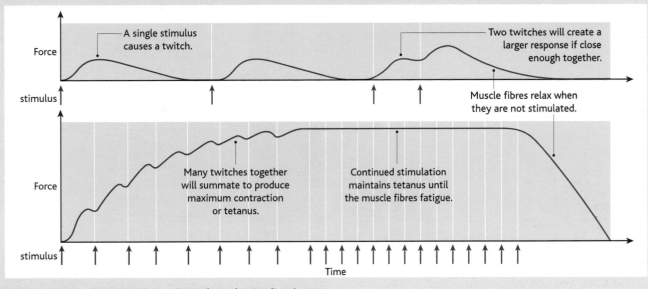

fig. 7.2.2 A series of kymograph recordings of muscle stimuli and responses.

A single stimulus causes a single contraction or twitch of the muscle fibre. It is an 'all-or-nothing' response. This means that if the stimulus is below a certain level, nothing happens. If it is above the **threshold** level, the muscle fibre twitches. But however big the stimulus, the size of a single twitch is always the same. Single twitches are relatively rare in whole muscles.

If two stimuli are given quite close together, however, the muscle fibre will contract a second time before it is fully relaxed, so it gets shorter than with a single twitch. Scientists discovered that if two stimuli are close enough together the two contractions are so close that there is no relaxing and lengthening of the muscle between them. This gives the appearance of a single larger contraction and is called **summation**.

When a series of rapid stimuli is given, the muscle fibre becomes fully contracted and as short as possible and stays like this. This is known as **tetanus**. This is the normal situation in a muscle when you are lifting an object or indeed standing up and maintaining your posture against gravity, with many fibres in tetanus.

A muscle cannot remain in tetanus continuously. Eventually it fatigues and cannot contract any more, when supplies of ATP and calcium are depleted.

Data like this showed scientists how muscle fibres react to stimuli. The development of the electron microscope and micro-investigation techniques has revealed just how they work.

Questions

1 Suggest an explanation for why a whole muscle might respond differently to a stimulus than a single fibre.

2 Summarise the similarities and differences between the three main types of muscle tissue.

Different types of muscle fibre 5.7.2

The cells of the skeletal muscles have certain features in common. They usually contain plenty of mitochondria. As you saw on pages 128–9, mitochondria are the site of aerobic respiration and they play an important role in supplying the active muscle cells with ATP. The muscle cells also contain **myoglobin**. This is a protein similar to haemoglobin, but it is made up of one chain rather than four. It has a much higher affinity for oxygen than haemoglobin so it readily accepts oxygen from the blood. It acts as an oxygen store in the muscles. Most muscles also have a blood supply to bring oxygen to the rapidly respiring tissue.

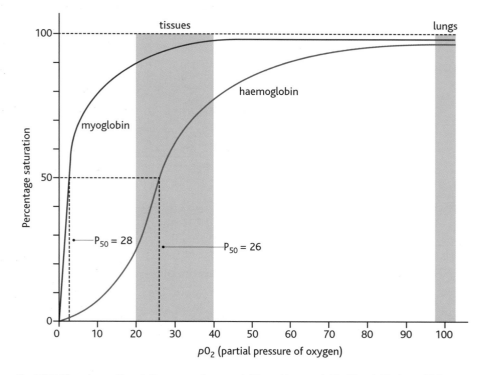

fig. 7.2.3 The oxygen dissociation curves for myoglobin and haemoglobin. Myoglobin has a higher affinity for oxygen, so will take oxygen from haemoglobin as blood passes through the muscles.

There are two types of skeletal muscle fibres in mammals, which give very different levels of performance. Most muscles contain a mixture of the different types of fibre. The balance will affect both the performance of the muscle and its colour.

- **Slow twitch muscle fibres** are adapted for steady action over a period of time. They contract relatively slowly and can stay in tetanus for a long time. They are used to maintain your body posture, and when long periods of activity are needed. These slow twitch fibres have a rich blood supply, lots of mitochondria and plenty of myoglobin so that they can maintain their activity without needing to respire anaerobically for any length of time. They are also known as **oxidative** or **red muscle fibres** because the rich blood supply and high levels of myoglobin mean they are a deep red colour. Slow twitch muscle fibres rely on glucose as a fuel, supplied by the blood vessels so they can continue to produce ATP for as long as oxygen is available.

- **Fast twitch muscle fibres** contract very rapidly, making them well suited for sudden, rapid bursts of activity. They often have to function anaerobically (without oxygen, using glycolysis, see page 132) and partly because of this they fatigue quite quickly. Compared with slow twitch fibres, fast twitch fibres are supplied with relatively few blood vessels, have low levels of myoglobin for storing oxygen and also contain a fairly small number of mitochondria. As a result they look much paler in colour. However, the fibres contain rich glycogen stores, which can be converted to glucose for both aerobic and anaerobic respiration. They also contain relatively high levels of creatine phosphate, which can be used to form ATP from ADP (see page 132). Fast twitch fibres are also known as **glycolytic** or **white muscle fibres**. Many more myofibrils are packed into fast twitch fibres as little space is taken up with mitochondria, etc. They cannot produce high levels of ATP over a sustained time, but they are capable of very fast, powerful contractions for a brief period.

Most people have roughly equal amounts of slow and fast twitch fibres in their muscles, but in some people the proportions can vary quite dramatically. For example, long-distance runners, cyclists, swimmers and other endurance athletes usually have particularly high proportions of slow twitch fibres. In contrast, weightlifters and sprinters, who need the maximum strength from their muscles in short bursts of activity, usually have an unusually high proportion of fast twitch fibres in their muscles.

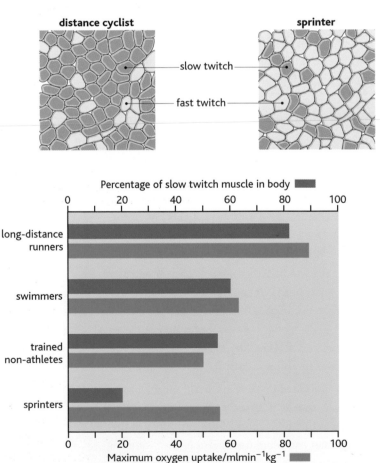

fig. 7.2.4 Scientists have found that athletes in different sports tend to have different distributions of slow and fast twitch fibres in their muscles.

So why does this difference occur? Part of the answer is training. The number of muscle fibres you possess does not change, but the size and type of the fibre can alter in response to exercise. So if you practise sprinting, you will develop more fast twitch fibres, while if you do endurance training then slow twitch muscle fibres will increase in number.

There are also a variety of different genes which affect the basic components of our muscles, which can then be enhanced with further training. So while most of us have about 50% of each type of muscle fibre, some people have around 75% fast twitch and others have 75% slow twitch. These differences are bound to make a difference to sporting potential. So for example, someone born with a high proportion of fast twitch fibres may well be a good sprinter but is unlikely to make a top-class marathon runner, while someone with more than average slow twitch fibres is unlikely to be a successful weightlifter but may well make an endurance athlete.

Scientists have also discovered 'superfast' twitch fibres, which contract even more quickly and strongly than usual. When the muscle structure of Colin Jackson, a former world 110 m hurdle record holder, was analysed, not only did he have 75% fast twitch fibres in his leg muscles, but 25% of those were superfast fibres – something which must have helped him in his sporting career.

HSW Explaining the difference

Currently there is a great deal of research into the genetics of sporting performance. However, it is an area which is fraught with ethical difficulties and examples of how the public perception of valid research may be skewed by media presentation.

For example, in the 2008 Olympics a young Jamaican sprinter, Usain Bolt, won both the 100 m and the 200 m gold medals with ease. Many headlines proclaimed that he – along with many other elite athletes of Jamaican origin around the world – possess what quickly became known as the 'sprint gene'. This gene affects one of the proteins (**ACTN3** or α-actinin-3) which make up the fast twitch fibres. It is not needed for fast twitch fibres to work but appears to help them contract faster and more powerfully. It has been claimed that 70% of Jamaicans make this protein compared with only 30% of Australians. In addition, media stories claimed that this gene makes all the difference and explains why athletes of African origins so often dominate sprint events.

Particular groups tend to excel in certain sporting areas – for example, people of Western African origin are highly represented in the sprint sports, from East Africa in the endurance races and white Caucasians in the swimming pool. As a result there are ethical issues with reporting research in this area, as some people feel that there are racial overtones to any work.

The real science behind this story is rather different and the following points somehow missed representation in the press.

- There are two alleles of the gene which codes for ACTN3 (referred to as R [dominant] and X [recessive]). Homozygous recessive (XX) individuals for ACTN3 (between a sixth and a quarter of the world population, or over a billion people) have no ACTN3 in their fast twitch muscle fibres at all and function perfectly well in everyday life.

- A number of studies by different groups in Australia, Europe and the US have suggested that XX individuals rarely make it as elite sprint or power athletes – and there is also evidence which suggests that lack of this protein increases endurance performance.

- There seems to be a trade-off – with ACTN3 you get explosive power, without it there is greater efficiency of respiration and more endurance. In evolutionary terms, the slightly more efficient XX genotype may have carried an advantage to early humans as they spread out across the world.

- The impact of the 'sprint' variant of ACTN3 on performance is only to give 2–3% increase in speed, not enough to have any effect on most people, but enough to make a difference when performing at the highest levels. This explains why almost all top sprint and power athletes have the RR or RX variant. Only one Olympic level sprint or power athlete investigated – a Spanish short-distance hurdler – is XX!

- There are dozens – and may even be hundreds – of genes that affect physical performance and the ACTN3 gene is just one of them.

- This gene cannot explain Jamaican dominance in sprint sports. The 70/30 percentage figures given in the media refer to the incidence of the homozygous RR state in Jamaican athletes compared with Australian athletes. However, when RX is considered as well (and the heterozygote state also produces the vital protein) the difference between the incidence in the Jamaican population (98%) and the European populations (82%) is much less striking. Both populations have plenty of potential elite sprinters to choose from. In fact around 5 billion people worldwide have this protein – and we're not all top athletes!

- The frequency of ACTN3 in Jamaicans is not unique. Research has shown even higher incidences of this variant (99% of people) in Kenya – a country renowned for its middle and long-distance runners rather than its sprinters!

- When the massively successful Usain Bolt ran in the 2008 Olympics, everyone he was competing against almost certainly had the same RX or RR genetic combination, giving them the useful ACTN3 protein. The superiority of Bolt's performance cannot be dismissed as a simple genetic advantage. Environmental factors such as training, hard work and motivation along with many other advantageous genes will have carried him to success.

fig. 7.2.5 Usain Bolt, the young Jamaican sprinter whose success in the 2008 Olympics brought the 'sprint gene' to greater public attention than ever before!

The team that has been behind much of the research into the ACTN3 protein and its genetic inheritance, lead by Katherine North, have extended their work in several ways. They are looking at the inheritance of muscle protein genes in human evolution and also, most excitingly, looking for application of their work for children with genetic diseases affecting the muscle protein such as muscular dystrophy.

Questions

1 Describe the roles of mitochondria and myoglobin in muscle fibres.

2 Describe how mitochondria and myoglobin vary between fast and slow twitch fibres.

3 Chickens are birds which spend much of their time walking around on the ground. If they are startled or frightened, they will fly up almost vertically to escape – but the flying doesn't last long. When carving a chicken to eat, the breast meat is pale and the leg meat is much darker. Explain these observations in the light of your knowledge about different types of muscle fibres.

SC 4 Draw up a table to compare slow and fast twitch muscle fibres.

How muscle contracts 5.7.3

Observations of micrographs show that whether a muscle fibre is contracted or relaxed, the dark A bands remain the same length. However, the light I bands and the H zone get shorter when a muscle fibre contracts and return to normal length when it relaxes again. This suggests that the two types of filaments slide over each other during contraction – the basis of the **sliding filament theory** (**fig. 7.2.6**)

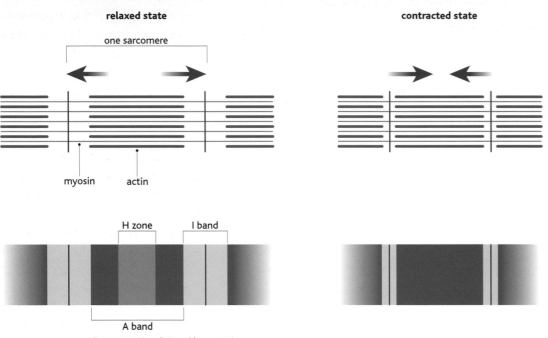

fig. 7.2.6 The sliding filament theory

If actin and myosin are extracted and then mixed together in the lab, nothing happens. If ATP is added, they form actomyosin (a different protein) and contract, so the process must be an active one. Increasingly clear electron micrographs have shown us the presence of 'bridges' between the actin and myosin strands, and it seems that these are formed and broken down during contraction. ATP is needed to break the actin–myosin bonds.

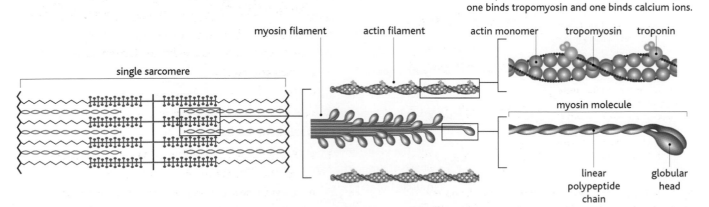

fig. 7.2.7 The structure of actin, myosin and the other associated protein molecules is crucial for the way they work in your body.

The diagram shows the actin and myosin unit before contraction starts. The myosin heads have ADP and Pi bound closely to them as well.

actin filament tropomyosin | troponin

Calcium ions bind to the troponin molecules, changing their shape, so troponin molecules pull on the tropomyosin molecules they are attached to. This moves the tropomyosin away from the myosin binding sites, exposing them ready for action.

Ca²⁺   exposed myosin binding sites

The myosin heads bind to the actin, forming an actomyosin bridge.

ADP and Pi are released from the myosin head. The myosin changes shape – the head bends forward moving the actin filament about 10 nm along the myosin filament, shortening the sarcomere.

Free ATP binds to the head, causing another shape change in the myosin, so the binding of the head to the actin strand is broken. This activates ATPase in the myosin head, which also needs calcium ions to work. The ATP is hydrolysed, providing the energy to return the myosin head to its original position, primed with ADP and Pi, ready to go again.

Ca²⁺   myosin binding site

With continued stimulation, calcium ions remain in the sarcoplasm and the cycle is repeated. If not, calcium ions are pumped back into the sarcoplasmic reticulum using energy from ATP. The troponin and tropomyosin return to their original positions and the contraction is complete. The muscle fibre is relaxed.

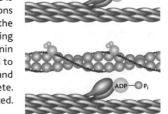

fig. 7.2.8 Muscles contract in response to a stimulation at a neuromuscular junction between a nerve cell and a muscle. This triggers the release of calcium ions (Ca²⁺) from the sarcoplasmic reticulum which then flood the sarcomeres.

Actin–myosin interactions

A sort of ratchet mechanism has been proposed for the contraction of the myofibrils. The shape of the myosin molecule enables it to attach to the actin to form cross-bridges of actomyosin. This changes the molecular shape and so pulls the actin filament across the myosin, increasing the interlocking region and shortening the sarcomere. The bridges then break and the process is repeated between 50 and 100 times per second. The combined effect of this happening in each sarcomere is a shortening of the whole myofibril. The shortening of many myofibrils together brings about the contraction of a muscle. For the ratchet mechanism to work, both calcium ions and ATP must be present.

To understand how the sliding filament theory explains the way in which muscles contract, it is important to understand the structure of actin and myosin. A myosin molecule is made up of two long polypeptide chains twisted together, each ending in a large, globular head which has ADP and inorganic phosphate molecules bound to it. In some circumstances the head can act as an ATPase enzyme. A myosin filament is made up of lots of these molecules bundled together, with their heads sticking out from the filament. An actin filament is made up of two chains of actin monomers joined together like beads on a necklace. The shape of the actin molecule produces myosin binding sites at regular intervals, where the globular heads of the myosin molecules can fit. However, wrapping around the double actin chains is another long chain protein molecule called **tropomyosin**. In a relaxed muscle, the tropomyosin chain covers up the myosin bonding sites. In turn the tropomyosin has molecules of another protein, **troponin**, attached regularly along the chain.

Questions

1 Draw and label the appearance of a sarcomere as you would expect it to look under an electron microscope:
   a fully contracted
   b fully relaxed.

2 Describe the role of calcium ions in the contraction of skeletal muscles.

3 a Explain why the presence of ATP is so important for the contraction of striated muscles.
   b Suggest how this explains what happens when rigor mortis sets in after death.

Tissues of the skeletal system 5.7.4

Imagine yourself moving – walking, running, jumping – and then try to imagine the variety of demands being made on your body. The properties of your skeletal tissues vary, as they are adapted to carry out these various functions effectively.

Bone is strong and hard, made up of bone cells embedded in a matrix of collagen and calcium salts. Bone is particularly strong under compression (squashing) forces. It not only needs to be strong and hard – it must be as light as possible to reduce the weight moved about.

Cartilage is a hard but flexible tissue made up of cells called **chondrocytes** within an organic matrix which consists of varying amounts of collagen fibrils. Cartilage is elastic and able to withstand compressive forces. It is a very good shock absorber and is frequently found between bones such as the vertebrae and in the joints. There are two main types of cartilage found in the skeleton:

- Hyaline cartilage is found at the ends of bones (and in the nose, air passageways and parts of the ear).

- White fibrous cartilage has bundles of densely packed collagen in the matrix. It has great tensile strength but is less flexible than the other forms of cartilage. It forms the intervertebral discs and is found between the bones in the joints.

Tendons are made up almost entirely of **white fibrous tissue**. This consists of bundles of collagen fibres and gives a tissue that is strong but relatively inelastic. This makes it ideal for joining muscles to bones. One end of the tendon is attached to a muscle and the other end attached either directly to a bone or to the fibrous cover of the bone. This makes a more secure attachment for muscles to bone and provides a little shock absorption if the joint is subjected to sudden stretch. However, if tendons stretched a lot, much of the work done by the muscles would be wasted as they would stretch the tendons without moving the bones!

Ligaments hold bones together and in the correct alignment, both around the joint as a capsule and within the joint itself. They need to be elastic to allow the bones of the joint to move when necessary. They are made of yellow elastic tissue which gives an ideal combination of strength with elasticity. Some ligament capsules are very loose, while others are very tight – different joints need different properties. The differences in the properties of the ligaments result from the presence of varying amounts of collagen and even some white fibrous tissue in the mixture.

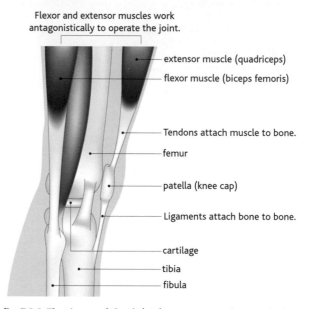

Flexor and extensor muscles work antagonistically to operate the joint.

- extensor muscle (quadriceps)
- flexor muscle (biceps femoris)
- Tendons attach muscle to bone.
- femur
- patella (knee cap)
- Ligaments attach bone to bone.
- cartilage
- tibia
- fibula

fig. 7.2.9 The tissues of the skeletal system – seen here at the knee – work together to hold the bones together, stop them wearing away and make movement possible.

Joints, muscles and movement

The joints are vital to allow movement and locomotion. Anyone who has experienced the pain of a dislocated joint will know that keeping the bones lined up correctly is essential to the working of a joint.

The ends of the bones at a joint are shaped to move smoothly over each other, and the way in which the two bones meet varies according to the type of movement required. The ball and socket joints found at the hip and shoulder give very free movement, whereas the hinge joints of the fingers and knees are much more restrictive.

The bones in a joint form two solid masses moving over each other while subjected to quite severe forces. If the joint consisted just of bone on bone, the ends would soon wear each other away. To prevent the bones from being eroded like this the joint is lined with a replaceable layer of rubbery cartilage which allows the joint to articulate smoothly. The most mobile joints also produce a liquid lubricant known as **synovial fluid** which fills the joint cavity and ensures easy friction-free movement (see **fig. 7.2.11**).

How is movement brought about?

Movement is brought about by the action of muscles on bones. Each of the skeletal muscles is attached by tendons to two different bones, spanning at least one joint. When muscles contract they exert a pull on a bone and so it moves relative to another. However, when they relax they do not exert a corresponding push – they simply stop

contracting and become capable of being pulled back to their original shape. Thus the muscles of the skeleton are found in pairs. One pulls the bone in one direction, the other pulls it back to its original position. Because they work in direct opposition to each other these muscles are known as antagonistic pairs. A clearer picture of how movement is brought about can be gained from **fig. 7.2.12**.

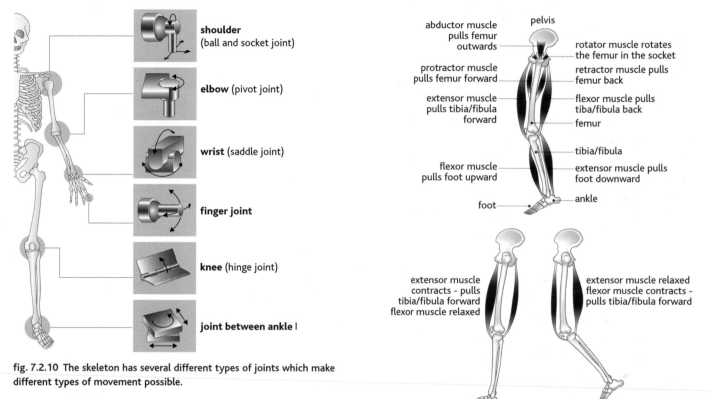

fig. 7.2.12 Some of the muscles involved in the movement of the leg.

fig. 7.2.10 The skeleton has several different types of joints which make different types of movement possible.

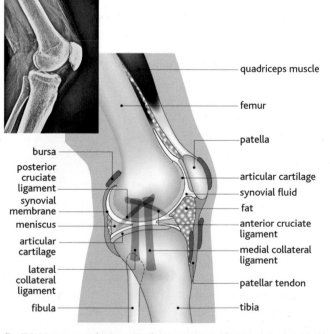

fig. 7.2.11 A synovial joint – the lubrication provided by the synovial fluid is vital for smooth, painfree movement in the most mobile joints.

Questions

1 Joints such as the knee, the hip and the shoulder have a synovial membrane and produce synovial fluid. Many other joints do not. Describe synovial fluid and explain why is it so important in some joints but not in others.

2 Describe how muscles, tendons, the skeleton and ligaments interact to enable movement.

7.3 The heart, energy and exercise

Controlling the heart 5.7.12

Your heart beats continually throughout life, with an average of about 70 beats per minute, although in small children the heart rate is much higher. The heart can respond to need. During physical exercise, when the tissues need more oxygen, your heart beats faster to supply more oxygenated, glucose-carrying blood to the tissues and to remove the increased waste products. Stress can also raise the heart rate, while rest and relaxation can lower it.

How is the heartbeat controlled?

In the very early embryo, cells which are destined to become the heart begin contracting rhythmically long before the actual organ forms. They have **intrinsic rhythmicity**. An adult heart removed from the body will continue to contract as long as it is bathed in a suitable oxygen-rich fluid. The intrinsic rhythm of the heart is around 60 beats per minute. This rhythm is maintained by a wave of electrical excitation similar to a nerve impulse which spreads through special tissue in the heart muscle (see **fig. 7.3.1**).

The area of the heart with the fastest intrinsic rhythm is a group of cells in the right atrium known as the **sinoatrial node (SAN)**, and this acts as the heart's own natural pacemaker.

- The sinoatrial node sets up a wave of electrical excitation (depolarisation) which causes the atria to start contracting.

- Excitation also spreads to another area of similar tissue called the **atrioventricular node (AVN)**.

- The AVN is excited as a result of the SAN and from here the wave of depolarisation passes into the **bundle of His**.

- The bundle of His carries the excitation from the AVN down to the **Purkyne tissue**.

- The Purkyne tissue penetrates down through the septum of the heart, spreading between and around the ventricles. As the depolarisation travels through the tissue it sets off the contraction of the ventricles, starting at the bottom and so squeezing blood out of the heart.

The speed at which the excitation spreads through the heart makes sure that the atria have stopped contracting before the ventricles start. It is these changes in the electrical excitation of the heart which are measured in an **electrocardiogram (ECG)** – see below.

Because your heart has its own basic rhythm, body resources are not wasted on maintaining such a vital but continuous event. However, many people have a faster resting heart rate than this basic rhythm – around 70 beats per minute is the average. This is because lots of other factors constantly influence the heart rate, as you will learn later in this chapter.

The sinoatrial node (SAN) or pacemaker where the wave of electrical excitation (depolarisation) starts.

The bundle of His, which carries the excitation from the AVN down to the Purkyne tissue.

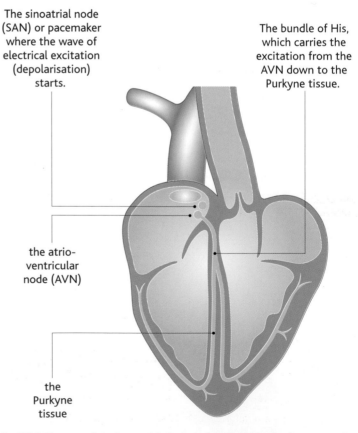

the atrio-ventricular node (AVN)

the Purkyne tissue

fig. 7.3.1 The area of the heart with the fastest intrinsic rhythm is a group of cells in the right atrium known as the sinoatrial node, which acts as the heart's own natural pacemaker.

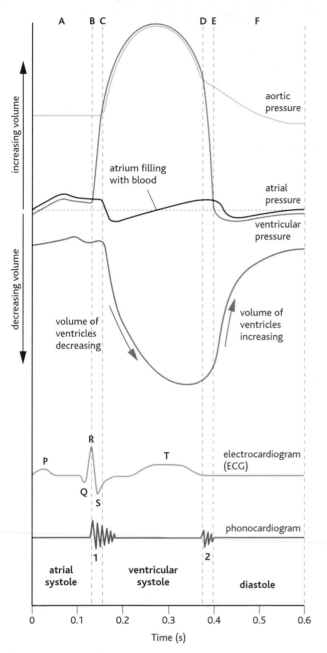

An ECG is used to investigate the rhythms of the heart by producing a record of the electrical activity of the heart. As you know, the rhythm of the heart results from the spread of a wave of depolarisation (electrical activity) through specialised tissue within the heart muscle itself. This depolarisation in the heart causes tiny electrical changes on the surface of your skin. An ECG measures these changes at the surface of your skin.

To take an ECG, 12 electrodes and leads are attached to your body. This is a completely painless process. Your skin is wiped with alcohol to remove any grease or sweat so the electrodes make good contact with your skin. Sometimes a special gel is applied to the electrodes to make sure they conduct electricity as effectively as possible. As the recording is made, information is fed back from each of the electrodes, effectively giving 12 views of the heart.

An ECG can show you what is happening in a normal, healthy heart. However, it is often used to indicate different

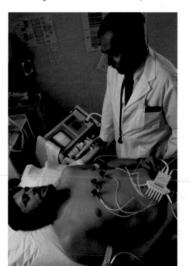

heart conditions, and to monitor patients with heart disease. It is usually done with the patient lying down and resting, but sometimes an ECG is carried out while a patient is exercising (known as a stress test) because some heart conditions show up only during exercise.

fig. 7.3.2 The normal pattern of the heartbeat from an ECG. In this diagram, you can see clearly how the peaks on the ECG relate to the changes going on in the heart itself.

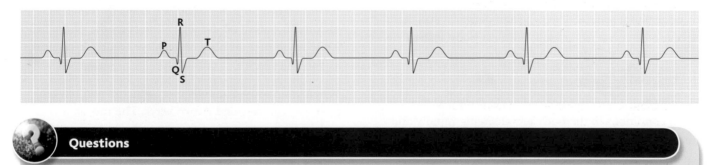

Questions

1 Explain how an artificial heart pacemaker, which delivers a regular electric shock to the right atrium, can help maintain a steady heart rate in people when the natural pacemaker is no longer working properly.

2 Describe how the events of the heartbeat are shown on an ECG.

Homeostasis and responding to exercise 5.7.13, 5.7.15, 5.7.16

The cells of the human body are very sensitive to change. For aerobic respiration to take place inside cells, the levels of oxygen and glucose need to be maintained within very narrow limits. Similarly, for many of the enzymes to work efficiently, the core temperature of the body has to be maintained at around 37 °C. So during vigorous physical exercise the body must control the internal conditions within a narrow range. This is a dynamic equilibrium, matching the supply of oxygen and glucose to the continually changing demands of the body, while removing carbon dioxide and maintaining an even temperature. The maintenance of a steady internal state in the body almost regardless of changes in either the external or the internal conditions is known as **homeostasis**.

Homeostasis involves a high level of coordination and control. Changes in the body are detected by a **sensor** (also called a **receptor**). This sends a message to an **effector** which either works to reverse the change or to increase it. **Negative feedback systems** are the most common, and they provide a way of maintaining a condition, such as the concentration of a substance, within a narrow range. A change in conditions is registered by receptors and as a result effectors are stimulated to restore the equilibrium. If the concentration goes up, the effectors bring it down again and vice versa. Alternatively, in a **positive feedback system,** effectors work to increase the effect which has triggered the response.

The communication in a feedback system may be by hormones (chemical messengers) or by nerve impulses (electrical messages). There is often a small overshoot or undershoot as a feedback system corrects, and that needs to be corrected as well. So most body system levels oscillate slightly around the ideal level in a dynamic equilibrium.

Homeostasis plays an important role during exercise, when conditions in the body are changing rapidly and demands on the systems are high. When you want to move somewhere fast your body must respond quickly, supplying your muscles with the glucose and oxygen they need and removing excess carbon dioxide. Negative feedback systems are vital in the coordinated response which enables you to exercise effectively, as both your heart and your respiratory system respond.

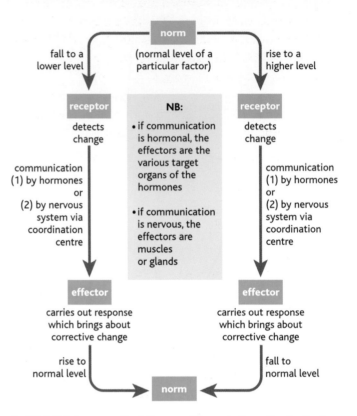

fig. 7.3.3 This is a generalised diagram of the sort of negative feedback which plays a vital role in homeostasis.

Changing cardiac output

The intrinsic rhythm of the heart is not sufficient to supply the needs of the body except at a most basic level. For example, during exercise, more oxygen must be carried to the rapidly respiring muscle tissues and the waste carbon dioxide and lactate which accumulate in the muscle fibres need to be removed. And once the exercise stops, your body needs to return to normal – even cardiac muscle cannot continue pumping at maximum output all the time! The response of the heart is the result of a number of negative feedback systems, as you will see.

When your body demands more glucose and oxygen the heart can respond in two ways. The rate at which the heart beats can increase. In addition, the volume of blood pumped at each heartbeat, called the **cardiac volume**, can be increased by a more efficient contraction of the ventricles. The combination of these two factors gives a measure called the **cardiac output**.

$$\underset{(\text{dm}^3\,\text{min}^{-1})}{\text{cardiac output}} = \underset{(\text{dm}^3)}{\text{cardiac volume}} \times \underset{(\text{beats}\,\text{min}^{-1})}{\text{heart rate}}$$

At rest in a normal individual the heart beats about 70 times a minute, and pumps between 4 and 6 dm³ of blood per minute. In a trained athlete the resting heart beats more slowly – around 60 beats per minute. When a fit individual anticipates exercise, the heart rate begins to increase before the exercise begins. The cardiac volume increases more slowly, as it becomes clear from the changes in the body that the exercise is going to continue. Cardiac output during exercise can go up to around 30 dm³ min⁻¹ (**fig. 7.3.4**).

fig. 7.3.4 The demands of your body change when you exercise. Several feedback systems make sure that your heart responds appropriately – whatever the external temperature.

Adjusting the heart rate

Different control systems enable the heart to respond to the varying demands of your body throughout the day.

Nervous control of the heart

The **cardiovascular control centre**, which controls changes to heart rate, is found in the medulla of the brain (see page 221). Chemical and stretch receptors in the lining of the blood vessels and the chambers of the heart send nerve impulses to the cardiovascular centre. Two types of nerves (see below) then carry impulses out to the heart, controlling the rate at which it beats.

Most of the nervous control of your heart is by the **autonomic (involuntary) nervous system**, so you don't have to think about it. The autonomic nervous system is divided into two parts:

- The **sympathetic nervous system is** usually **excitatory** – for example it speeds up the heart rate.

- The **parasympathetic system** is usually **inhibitory** – it slows the heart rate down.

Most of the body organs are supplied by both types of nerves, giving a level of fine control.

Nerve impulses travelling down the sympathetic nerve from the cardiovascular centre in the brain to the heart stimulate the SAN. This increases the frequency of the signals from the pacemaker region so that the heart beats more quickly. In contrast, nerve impulses in the corresponding parasympathetic nerve inhibit the SAN and slow the heart down.

We also have a certain amount of conscious control over our heart rate, so nerves from the conscious areas of our brains can also stimulate or inhibit the SAN. Some people can slow their heart rate right down just by concentrating on it!

Hormonal control of the heart

You are probably familiar with the way your heart beats faster when you are nervous, frightened or excited, and when you are anticipating exercise. This happens even if you are sitting still at the time so the change is not in response to exercise. When you are stressed, the hormone adrenaline is produced. This affects the SAN, speeding up the frequency of the excitation and so speeding up the heart, supplying you with extra oxygen and glucose for the muscles and brain in case you need to run away or stand and fight!

Responding to exercise

Some of the main control systems that regulate the heart rate involve a negative feedback response to the pressure of blood in the circulatory system. As the atria fill with blood at the start of the cardiac cycle, **stretch receptors** in the muscle walls of the heart respond to the stretching by sending nerve impulses to the cardiovascular control centre (see *AS Biology* page 26 for details of cardiac cycle and pressure changes). So for example, at the beginning of a period of exercise more blood than usual returns to the heart because the big muscle blocks in the legs and arms squeeze more blood along the veins as they work. As more blood flows into the atria, the receptors are stretched more than usual and send more nerve impulses to the cardiovascular centre in the brain. This in turn sends more nerve impulses along the sympathetic nerve to the SAN, causing an increase in the heart rate.

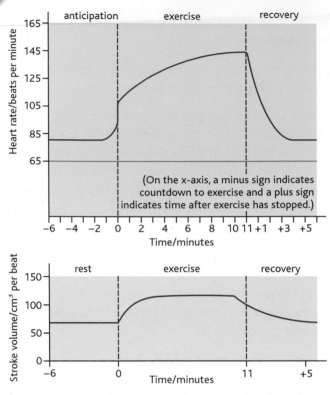

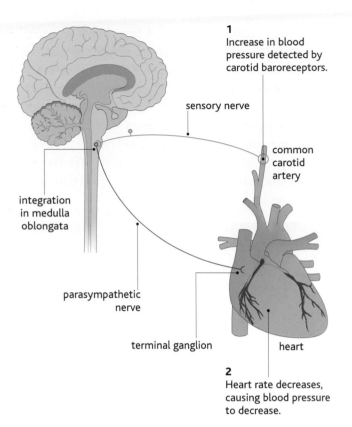

1
Increase in blood pressure detected by carotid baroreceptors.

2
Heart rate decreases, causing blood pressure to decrease.

fig. 7.3.5 The impact of exercise on the heart rate and on the cardiac volume.

The increased stretching of the heart atrial muscle as blood returns from the body also makes the muscles contract harder, increasing the volume of blood expelled at every stroke. This does not depend on the cardiovascular centre in the brain – it is a feature of cardiac muscle.

Baroreceptors (sensors that are sensitive to pressure) found in the sinuses of the carotid arteries in the neck are also important in the feedback control of the heart rate, particularly as exercise ends. As blood pressure in the arteries increases, the baroreceptors are stretched. They send nerve impulses to the cardiovascular centre which then sends impulses through the parasympathetic system to slow down the heart rate and cause a widening of the blood vessels (vasodilation). These two actions lower the blood pressure.

The reverse happens when exercise starts – the blood vessels dilate in response to the hormone adrenaline which is released with exercise, and blood pressure falls a little. This reduces the stretch of the baroreceptors and they almost stop responding. When they do not stimulate the cardiovascular control centre it immediately sends signals along the sympathetic nerve to stimulate the heart rate and increase the blood pressure again.

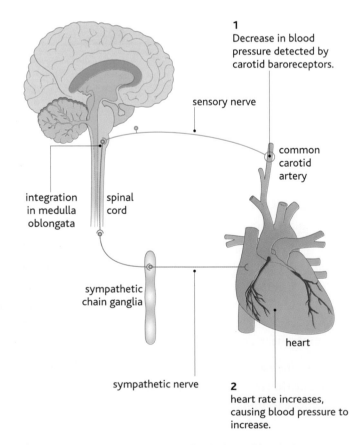

1
Decrease in blood pressure detected by carotid baroreceptors.

2
heart rate increases, causing blood pressure to increase.

fig. 7.3.6 Negative feedback system for the heart through the baroreceptors.

During exercise, impulses from the cardiovascular centre affect other effectors as well as the heart. When many impulses travel along the sympathetic nerve to the heart to speed it up, fewer impulses are sent along sympathetic nerves to many blood vessels, causing the smooth muscles lining the vessels to contract, narrowing or closing the vessels. In this way the blood flow is diverted from temporarily less important areas to provide more blood for the heart and the muscles to use. As you will see from **table 7.3.1**, the blood supply to the brain is fairly constant but the amounts of blood flowing elsewhere in the system vary considerably.

Structure	At rest		Vigorous exercise	
	$cm^3 min^{-1}$	% of total	$cm^3 min^{-1}$	% of total
Heart	190	3.3	740	3.9
Liver	1 340	23.5	590	3.1
Adrenal glands	24	0.4	24	0.1
Brain	690	12.1	740	3.9
Lung tissue	100	1.8	200	1.0
Kidneys	1 050	18.4	590	3.1
Skeletal muscles	740	13.0	12 450	65.9
Skin	310	5.4	1 850	9.8
Other parts	1 256	22.0	1 716	9.1
Total blood flow	5 700		18 900	

table 7.3.1 Redistribution of blood flow in response to exercise.

Questions

1 Draw a clear flow diagram to show the negative feedback system involving the baroreceptors which is used in the response of the heart to exercise.

2 Using data from **fig. 7.3.6**, produce a graph to show what you would expect to happen to cardiac output (dm^3 per minute) during a period of rest, followed by 10 minutes of exercise and another 10 minutes of recovery time.

3 a Using data from **table 7.3.1** draw bar charts or pie charts to show the difference in the percentage blood flow to different areas of the body at rest and during exercise.
   b Explain why these differences occur.

4 Summarise how the output of the heart is matched to the demands of the body.

Breathing rhythms 5.7.13, 5.7.14, 5.7.15

When you exercise, the muscle cells (including the heart muscle) need much more oxygen. The respiratory system has to respond and homeostasis is maintained as a result of more negative feedback systems.

Components of lung volume

As part of your AS Biology course you looked at breathing and gaseous exchange (*AS Biology* pages 112–13). To understand the way breathing is controlled in more detail, you need to begin by looking at how air flows into and out of the lungs.

A certain amount of air is always present in the respiratory system, filling up the spaces when no air is flowing. Otherwise, the volume of air drawn in and out of the respiratory system is very variable. Most of the components of the lung volume are given specific names for ease of reference.

- **Tidal volume** (V_T) is the volume of air that enters and leaves the lungs at each natural resting breath.

- **Inspiratory reserve volume** (IRV) is the volume of air that can be taken in over and above the normal inspired tidal volume. In other words, this is the extra air that you can take in when you breathe in as deeply as possible after a normal inspiration.

- **Expiratory reserve volume** (ERV) is the volume of air that can be expelled over and above the normal expired tidal volume. This is the extra air breathed out when you force the air out of your lungs as hard as possible after a normal expiration.

- **Vital capacity** (VC) is the total of the tidal volume and the inspiratory and expiratory reserves. It is the volume of air which can be breathed out by the most vigorous possible expiratory effort following the deepest possible inspiration.

- **Residual volume** (RV) is the volume of air left in the lungs after the strongest possible expiration.

- **Total lung capacity** (TLC) is the sum of the vital capacity and the residual volume.

- **Inspiratory capacity** (IC) is the volume that can be inspired from the end of a normal expiration – in other words, V_T + IRV.

The volume of air breathed in or out is called the **tidal volume**. In a normal person at rest it is about $0.5\,dm^3$ or about 15% of the vital capacity of the lungs. The rate of breathing can be expressed as the **ventilation rate**. This is a measure of the volume of air breathed in a minute:

$$\begin{array}{c}\text{ventilation rate}\\(dm^3\,min^{-1})\end{array} = \begin{array}{c}\text{tidal}\\\text{volume}\end{array} \times \begin{array}{c}\text{frequency of}\\\text{inspiration}\end{array}$$

The ventilation of the lungs needs to supply all the oxygen required by the tissues of the body whatever they are doing, and also remove all the waste carbon dioxide. The ventilation rate is affected by two things: the amount of air taken into the lungs at each breath and the number of breaths per minute. For example, the tidal volume can increase from 15% of the vital capacity to 50% during heavy exercise. The frequency of inspiration shows similar increases.

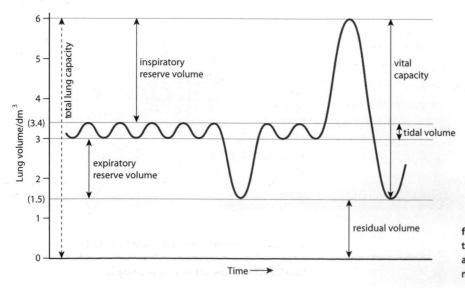

fig. 7.3.7 This diagram (based on spirometer traces) gives you an idea of average lung volumes at rest, although men and women, athletes and non-athletes can vary considerably.

Measuring the volume of inhaled or exhaled air

To find the vital capacity of a person's lungs, or to measure their inspiratory or expiratory reserves, we can use a spirometer. Spirometers come in a wide variety of shapes and sizes but they all work in the same way as a gasometer.

Some spirometers are portable and can be used during exercise outside, but many are lab-based pieces of equipment. They may be linked directly to a computer or to a simple revolving drum system (a kymograph).

The subject of the experiment breathes in and out of the airtight chamber making it move up and down, until all the oxygen is used up.

Revolving drum on which a trace is drawn out as the lid moves up and down.

Airtight chamber – in this case a Perspex lid floating on water. The chamber is filled with oxygen at the beginning of the experiment. Attached to the lid of the chamber is an arm with a pen on the end.

Canister of soda lime to remove carbon dioxide from the exhaled air. This is important because carbon dioxide levels affect the rate of breathing and therefore, if carbon dioxide was allowed to accumulate, the investigation would be affected.

fig. 7.3.8 Using a spirometer, the volume of gas inhaled and exhaled under a variety of conditions can be measured.

Control and regulation of breathing

The oxygen needs of the body can change rapidly from the relatively low levels at rest to the high levels demanded during strenuous exercise. The amount of carbon dioxide to be removed changes similarly. The ventilation rate must be able to adjust, by increasing both the tidal volume and the frequency of inspiration to keep the concentration of gases in the blood as close to the ideal level as possible. This control is the result of several feedback systems.

The basic stimulus to inhale and exhale is given by an area of the hindbrain (**medulla**) known as the **respiratory centre** (or **ventilation centre**). It involves a feedback system based on the stretching of the bronchi during breathing.

The respiratory centre contains an inspiratory centre which controls breathing in. This is often just referred to as the respiratory centre as it is the main factor in breathing control. There is also an expiratory centre which controls forced exhalation. We inhale because impulses from the respiratory centre travel along sympathetic nerves, causing the intercostal muscles and the diaphragm to contract. As the lungs inflate, stretch receptors in the walls of the bronchi send nerve impulses increasingly rapidly to the respiratory centre. Eventually these impulses inhibit the respiratory centre and it stops stimulating the breathing muscles. You stop breathing in – and as the muscles relax, you exhale. This gives a basic, deep, slow breathing rhythm, comparable to the resting rhythm of the heart.

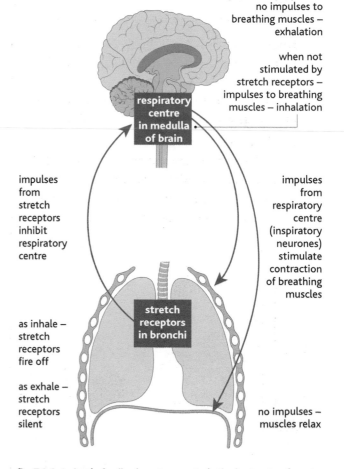

when stimulated by stretch receptors – no impulses to breathing muscles – exhalation

when not stimulated by stretch receptors – impulses to breathing muscles – inhalation

respiratory centre in medulla of brain

impulses from stretch receptors inhibit respiratory centre

impulses from respiratory centre (inspiratory neurones) stimulate contraction of breathing muscles

stretch receptors in bronchi

as inhale – stretch receptors fire off

as exhale – stretch receptors silent

no impulses – muscles relax

fig. 7.3.9 A simple feedback system controls the basic rate of breathing. The breathing muscles (intercostal muscles) are the muscles between the ribs and the diaphragm.

In addition, the conscious areas of the brain can override the respiratory centres while we are conscious. We are all capable of choosing to hold our breath (but only for so long!), take a deep breath or breathe faster – but most of the time, and always when we are unconscious, our breathing is completely under automatic control.

Breathing and homeostasis

As the demands of the body change, inputs from other receptors interact with the basic respiratory rhythm to give a finely tuned response to most situations, including stress, exercise and oxygen deprivation.

The main stimulus affecting the breathing rate is the level of carbon dioxide (not oxygen) in the blood. An increase in carbon dioxide concentration – and the subsequent fall in pH – leads to an increase in both the rate and the depth of breathing, as the diaphragm and the intercostal muscles contract harder and more frequently. A fall in carbon dioxide concentration has the opposite effect.

As soon as exercise starts, impulses from the cortex of the brain (which consciously recognises movement has begun) stimulate the respiratory centre in the medulla. This in turn stimulates the respiratory muscles and increases the rate and depth of ventilation.

Chemoreceptors sensitive to the level of carbon dioxide and the pH of the blood (in the hindbrain itself, the **carotid bodies** in the carotid arteries and the **aortic bodies** in the aortic arch) send impulses back to the main respiratory centre when carbon dioxide levels rise. Impulses are then sent out to the breathing muscles (the effectors) so the breathing rate changes in a negative feedback system which removes the extra carbon dioxide and at the same time matches the oxygen needs of the body.

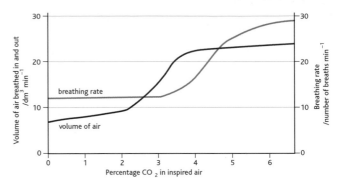

fig. 7.3.11 Graph showing the effect of carbon dioxide concentration on both the rate and depth of breathing.

The chemical sensors along with the stretch receptors in the muscles and lungs all act on the respiratory centre to maintain increased ventilation rates until the exercise is complete and the oxygen debt has been paid off.

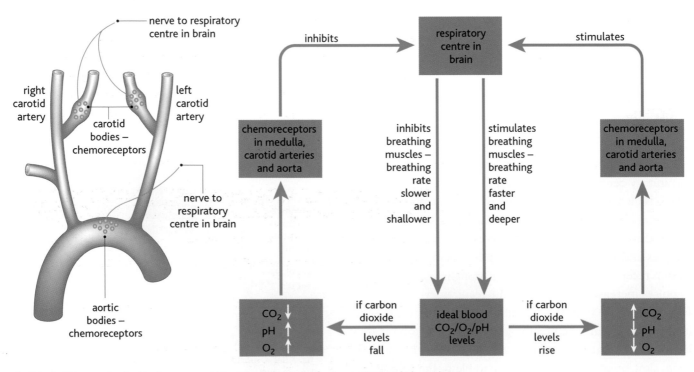

fig. 7.3.10 This negative feedback system enables your body to supply the oxygen needed – and get rid of the carbon dioxide produced – whatever you are doing.

HSW The challenge of altitude – and using children to investigate it

As you go higher above sea level both the atmospheric pressure and the oxygen concentration in the air are reduced. The highest permanent human habitations are about 5500 m above sea level.

For most people, moving to high altitude can be an unpleasant experience. The lack of oxygen can cause headaches, dizziness, breathlessness, sweating, dim vision and even unconsciousness – the symptoms of mountain sickness. The body eventually responds to the lack of oxygen by increasing the breathing rate but this removes too much carbon dioxide. As a result the normal stimulus to breathe is lost, resulting in abnormal breathing patterns.

With time, many people **acclimatise**. The ventilation of the lungs increases, extra red blood cells are formed, giving an increase in the oxygen-carrying capacity of the blood, and cardiac output goes up. However, people who move to a high altitude can suffer from altitude sickness at any time.

People born high in the mountains show a very different level of acclimatisation. They have an increased lung volume with high numbers of both alveoli and blood capillaries. The red blood cell count is so high that the blood is measurably thicker than normal. As a result, the indigenous people of mountains such as the Andes and Himalayas can carry out levels of physical work that would challenge most people at sea level!

Scientists have studied altitude sickness for many years, but in 2007 a very different study was carried out. The Smiths Medical Young Everest Study took nine British children aged from 6 to 13 on a trek to the Everest Base Camp to observe the effects of altitude and oxygen depletion on their breathing systems. They were hoping to find clues about the control of breathing in severe conditions, and

how the body copes when oxygen is in short supply. The initial finding showed that the children coped better than adults with low levels of oxygen saturation of the blood.

fig. 7.3.12 Some of the team who went to Everest to investigate the way young children cope with low oxygen levels. The results are already being used in Great Ormond Street Hospital.

Doctors are using the data collected to help develop guidance on giving oxygen to premature babies and children with breathing difficulties – because although oxygen saves lives, it can cause lung damage and blindness. A bigger study involving 100 children is now planned. Some people have expressed doubts about the ethics of using children in these investigations. Although most of the children coped well with the conditions, one child struggled. There is already a great deal of information on adults which could be used. However, the research team feel that using children gives more appropriate data for use in the treatment of other children. The children were going trekking in Nepal anyway on a family holiday, they were monitored and supported all the time and were happy to be helping other children.

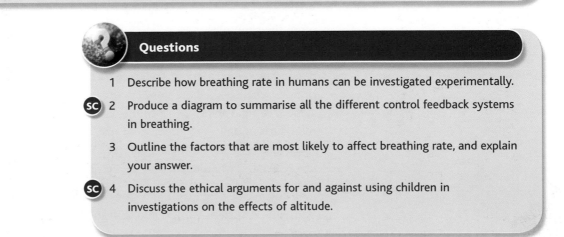

Questions

1 Describe how breathing rate in humans can be investigated experimentally.

SC 2 Produce a diagram to summarise all the different control feedback systems in breathing.

3 Outline the factors that are most likely to affect breathing rate, and explain your answer.

SC 4 Discuss the ethical arguments for and against using children in investigations on the effects of altitude.

Temperature control and exercise 5.7.16

As the muscles work hard during exercise, large amounts of heat energy are released by the exothermic reactions of aerobic respiration. In fact, the amount of heat energy produced during hard physical exercise could potentially raise the body temperature by 1 °C every 5–10 minutes. However, the chemical reactions of the body cells can take place within only a relatively narrow range of temperatures, because once temperatures rise above 40 °C most of the body enzymes are denatured (see *AS Biology* pages 86–9). Because of this sensitivity of enzymes to temperature, it is vital to control the internal body temperature.

Thermoregulation is an important aspect of homeostasis in the human body. The temperature of the human body naturally varies over the 24 hour cycle and is controlled by several feedback mechanisms.

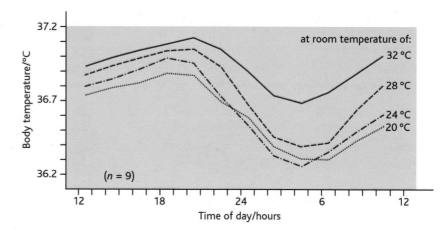

fig. 7.3.13 Human body temperature varies naturally throughout the 24 hour day – with the lowest point coming in the early hours of the morning, and the highest in the early evening.

Heat balance

When you exercise, the ability of your body to thermoregulate is severely tested. It is the core or internal temperature of the body which is important. The surface temperature fluctuates rapidly, but it is the internal temperature which is mainly relevant to enzyme activity. Living organisms are continually producing heat as a result of their metabolic reactions. When people exercise they produce considerably more heat as a result of all the respiration going on in their muscles.

People can also exchange heat with their surroundings, gaining or losing heat depending on a variety of factors. The balance between the gains and losses decides whether the core temperature of the organism rises, drops or stays the same (see **fig. 7.3.13**). Most of the ways in which people exchange heat with their surroundings are affected by size. Small children have a large surface area to volume ratio which means that they lose and gain heat more rapidly than a larger person, whether they are exercising or not.

The balance of heat losses and gains determines the core temperature. The body uses a variety of means to shift the balance and gain or lose heat as needed before, during and after exercise.

Temperature limits

Experiments carried out on human subjects in calorimeters, resting and exercising, along with observations on seriously ill patients and people who have been exposed to extreme cold, have produced a picture of the temperature tolerance of the human body. In some experiments the subject is naked so that any responses to changes in temperature are purely physiological. In other experiments the subject wears the same clothes throughout the living and exercising investigations.

fig. 7.3.14 A calorimeter is a sealed chamber where every change in temperature, oxygen use, etc. can be measured and recorded. They used to be very severe, but modern calorimeters are relatively comfortable.

As the external temperature drops, a range of thermoregulatory mechanisms conserve heat (see page 165). Below a certain point these measures are no longer sufficient. This point is known as the **low critical temperature**. If the temperature keeps on falling, the metabolic rate will increase in an attempt to produce sufficient heat to maintain the core temperature. Eventually the chemical reactions can no longer take place and the subject dies – this is the **low lethal temperature**. This is not usually a problem linked to exercise – but if someone exercises hard in cold conditions, they can get chilled very quickly once they finish exercising, as the sweat evaporates from their skin and they lose heat fast along a temperature gradient. If people are forced to exercise in cold water – for example, swimming after a shipwreck – this can also result in the temperature dropping to the point of developing hypothermia and even reaching the low lethal temperature.

A bigger problem for most people is the rise in temperature associated with exercise. This is a particular problem for anyone exercising in very hot conditions. As the external temperature rises, thermoregulating mechanisms such as sweating can keep the core temperature stable until the **high critical temperature** is reached. If the external temperature continues to increase, the metabolic rate starts to go up with the reactions doubling their rate for every 10 °C rise in temperature. Once this happens, positive feedback occurs, because the faster the metabolic rate the more heat is produced. Death usually occurs when the core temperature reaches about 42 °C – the high critical temperature – when the enzymes controlling cell reactions fail.

fig. 7.3.15 In 2006, five young American athletes between the ages of 11 and 17 years of age died of heat stroke playing American football. In the European heatwave of 2003 an estimated 19 000 people died because their bodies could not cope with the high external temperatures either because they were exercising or because they were old and their normal temperature regulating feedback systems failed.

Questions

1 Explain why the maintenance of a relatively constant internal temperature during exercise is so important.

SC 2 Suggest strengths and limitations of the human calorimeter as a research tool.

Human temperature regulation 5.7.14

Temperature control in humans is a good example of homeostasis as we regulate body temperature within a very narrow range. How is this control brought about? The main source of heat is from our metabolism, but humans are found and survive in almost every area of the world and so need effective ways of both losing and conserving heat.

We have a wide variety of physiological mechanisms allowing us to gain or lose heat as needed. The major difference between humans and other mammals with respect to heat loss is, of course, that we can manipulate our environment to help us to survive. People build houses, light fires and wear clothes to help prevent heat loss when it is cold. We make air-conditioning and build swimming pools to keep ourselves comfortable in high temperatures. However, we still maintain all our physiological adaptations for temperature regulation and they play the major role in the maintenance of our core body temperature. When it comes to exercise – and especially sports performance – we rely mainly on our bodies to regulate our core temperature.

The major homeostatic organ involved in thermoregulation is the skin. Some heat loss takes place as water evaporates from the surfaces of the mouth and nose, and this cannot be completely prevented because of their moist surfaces. However, the skin has an enormous surface area which can be modified either to conserve heat or to lose it (see **fig. 7.3.16**).

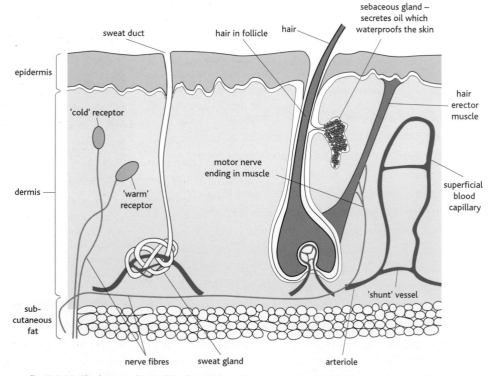

fig. 7.3.16 **The human skin and its functions – the same major structures are present in the skin of all other mammals too. Many of the features are involved in thermoregulation.**

Keeping cool during exercise

The skin is the largest single organ of your body. It covers the entire surface of the body in a waterproof layer, providing protection both against mechanical damage and from the ultraviolet radiation of the Sun. It plays a major homeostatic role in maintaining the core body temperature when you are exercising, preventing you from overheating in a number of ways.

A rich supply of capillaries runs near to the surface of the skin. Heat loss by radiation, convection and conduction to the environment takes place from the blood flowing through the skin. This heat loss is controlled via the **arterio-venous shunt**. When you are exercising, the shunt is closed, which allows more blood to flow through the capillaries at the surface of the skin. This is known as **vasodilation**. As a result the skin appears red and flushed, and more heat is lost.

When you are exercising, the erector pili muscles are relaxed and the body hairs lie flat against the body, minimising any insulating air layer that is trapped next to the skin. This has little or no impact on heat loss in human beings, because we have so little body hair, but it is important in other mammals.

The rate of sweat production in the sweat glands increases when the core temperature starts to increase. As more sweat is released onto the skin surface, heat is lost as the water evaporates. Almost $1\,dm^3$ of sweat is usually produced and lost in a day – but this can rise to $12\,dm^3$ in very hot conditions. This means it is very important to keep drinking plenty of water when you are exercising, so the tissues remain hydrated and sweat can be produced.

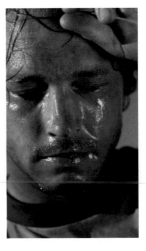

fig. 7.3.18 Sweating is a very important way in which the body cools down during exercise. If the body stops sweating, the core temperature soon starts to rise.

Subcutaneous fat acts as insulation, reducing heat loss. People who are very physically active, such as elite athletes, tend to have very little subcutaneous fat as they use up all the energy from their food. This reduces the insulation and increases the amount of heat which can be lost by conduction from the surface of the skin. Very overweight people overheat easily – a disadvantage when they start to exercise as it can put them off.

Keeping warm

Homeostatic mechanisms also act when the core temperature starts to fall. Some of the heat conservation measures are the exact opposite of the heat loss responses of the skin. So the arterio-venous shunt in the blood supply to the skin opens, reducing the blood flow through the capillaries and so reducing the heat lost from the surface of the skin. Sweat production is reduced and so heat loss by evaporation is reduced too. The erector pili muscles are contracted, pulling the hairs upright. In humans this is visible as 'goose-pimples' but has little effect on temperature regulation, but in hairy mammals it traps an insulating layer of air which helps to reduce heat loss.

In a warm environment

- vasodilation occurs

- sphincter muscles around arterioles leading to superficial capillaries are not stimulated to contract and therefore relax

- more blood can flow into these capillaries, dilating them with the pressure; less blood flows through deeper shunt vessels

- more blood flows close to the body surface

- as more blood flows close to the body surface, the temperature gradient between the body surface and the environment becomes steeper, so heat loss by conduction and radiation is increased.

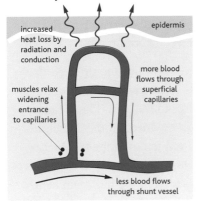

fig. 7.3.17 The superficial blood vessels play an important part in thermoregulation – here in cooling the body down.

In a cold environment

- vasoconstriction occurs

- sphincter muscles around arterioles leading to superficial capillaries contract

- this constricts the passage into these capillaries and more blood flows through deeper shunt vessels

- less blood flows close to the body surface

- as most blood is diverted further from the body surface, the temperature gradient between the body surface and the environment is less steep, so heat loss by conduction and radiation is reduced.

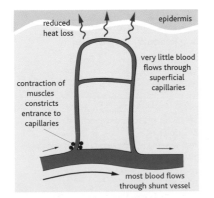

fig. 7.3.19 The superficial blood vessels play an important part in thermoregulation – here in warming the body up.

The metabolic rate of the body also speeds up, producing extra heat. This takes place particularly in the liver and the muscles. Shivering – involuntary contractions of the skeletal muscles – also helps to generate metabolic heat. The energy released is used to raise the body temperature. This is particularly important in the successful emergence of animals from hibernation and for temperature control in very young human babies. Animals living in cold areas develop thick layers of subcutaneous fat which acts as an effective insulator against heat loss.

Control of the core (blood) temperature

In a homeostatic feedback system there needs to be receptors sensitive to changes in the system. In the case of thermoregulation there are two types of receptors. Receptors in the brain directly monitor the temperature of the blood, while receptors in the skin detect changes in the external temperature. This allows for great sensitivity not only to actual changes in the core temperature but to potential changes too.

The temperature receptors in the brain are sited in the hypothalamus (see page 221). When the temperature of the blood flowing through the hypothalamus increases, the **heat loss centre** is activated and sends out impulses along motor nerves to effectors which increase the blood flow through the skin and increase sweating. The erector pili muscles are relaxed so that the hairs lie flat and any shivering stops. The metabolic rate may be reduced to lower the amount of heat generated in the body. The response is the same whether the increase in core temperature comes from internally generated heat during exercise or a fever, or external factors such as a warm room.

If the temperature of the blood flowing through the hypothalamus drops, the **heat gain centre** reacts by sending nerve impulses to the skin. These cause a reduction in the blood flow through the capillaries in the skin, along with a reduction in the production of sweat and contraction of the erector pili muscles to raise the hairs. Impulses from the heat gain centre also stimulate involuntary muscle contractions (better known as shivering) and raise the amount of heat released in metabolism. Thus the core temperature is usually maintained within very narrow limits (see **fig. 7.3.20**).

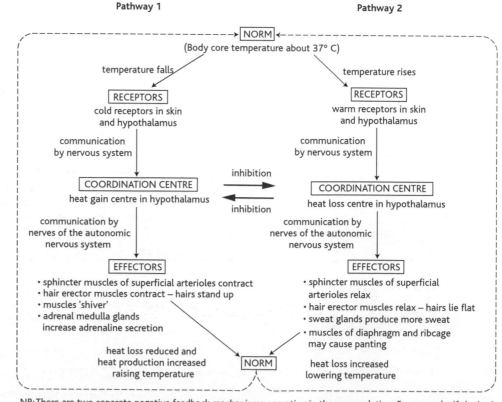

fig. 7.3.20 The hypothalamus acts as the 'thermostat' of the body. As a result of sensitive feedback mechanisms, the temperature of the body is usually controlled to within 1 °C of its normal temperature.

NB: There are two separate negative feedback mechanisms operating in thermoregulation. For example, if the body temperature rises, heat loss is increased by sweating. There is not just reliance on the fact that the hairs lie flat and that vasodilation occurs as the heat gain centre is inhibited.

Responses to the skin temperature receptors are also important in the homeostatic control of temperature. Impulses from skin receptors inform the brain if the environment is hot or cold, and the behaviour of the animal is modified accordingly. For example, as the skin heats up, an animal may seek shade, while cooling of the skin surface might give rise to increased activity to raise the amount of metabolic heat produced.

HSW Temperature control in term and premature infants

The mammalian foetus does not have to control its own body temperature – while it is in the uterus a stable temperature is maintained for it by its mother's thermoregulatory systems. Newborn babies often have problems regulating their own temperature. The surface area:volume ratio is three times greater for a baby than an adult, so there is proportionately a much larger surface over which to lose heat generated inside the body. If the skin temperature of a newborn baby drops by just 1°C, its oxygen consumption goes up 10% as the metabolism increases to produce more heat. A study in Sweden on 27 newborn infants showed how the babies struggled to maintain their core temperature – and how close contact with the mother made the process much easier than being left in a cot. Other studies have shown that measuring the difference between the core temperature and the foot temperature of a newborn baby gives a good picture of how well it is controlling its body temperature.

Babies who are born very prematurely are poorly prepared for the regulation of body temperature. They have a minimal amount of insulating subcutaneous fat. The shivering response is poorly developed and a special brown fat which full-term babies have that can be broken down just to produce heat, has not been laid down in any quantity. The skin is very thin and so the blood flows close to the surface. The skin is also extremely porous so water evaporates freely from it, causing cooling of the blood. And because of the small size of such infants, the surface area:volume ratio means that all types of heat loss occur very readily.

One of the main priorities in the care of pre-term babies is to allow as much of the energy intake as possible to be used for the growth and maturation of the body systems. Thus it is vital to minimise heat loss and prevent the expenditure of energy on attempting to keep warm. Incubators are designed to do exactly this, maintaining a constant temperature for the air surrounding the baby. The air may also be humidified to reduce cooling by the evaporative loss of water from the skin. Thin plastic and aluminium sheeting (rather like cling-film) wrapped around the baby for the first few weeks will reduce this effect still further – a simple idea which is remarkably effective.

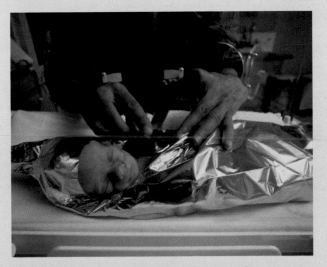

fig. 7.9.21 The temperature control mechanisms which we as adults take for granted are not ready to function in a pre-term baby. This picture shows just some of the technology needed to carry out the task artificially.

Questions

1 An athlete completes a 90 minute training programme and then drinks several glasses of water straight from the fridge. Explain what effect this would have in terms of homeostasis and temperature regulation.

2 An elderly man insists on taking his dog for a long walk even though temperatures have risen to 34°C. Explain why this is not advisable.

3 Describe the negative and positive feedback systems seen in human thermoregulation.

7.4 Health, exercise and sport

The risks of too little exercise

5.7.18

Exercising increases the fitness of your heart and the capacity of your lungs and these increases can be measured directly. Exercise also builds muscles and can be used to help control body mass. In *AS Biology* pages 52–69 you considered evidence pointing to lack of exercise as a cause of obesity and coronary heart disease (CHD). Research also suggests a strong correlation between exercise levels and type 2 diabetes (see below). However, deciding that lack of exercise is one of the factors causing these problems demands a high level of evidence.

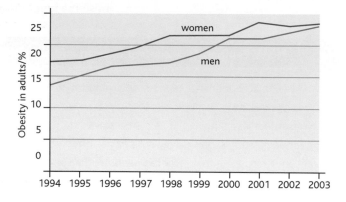

fig. 7.4.1 The prevalence of obesity among adults in the UK has increased significantly over the past 10 years. What impacts will this have on health?

HSW Correlation or causation?

As you will realise from your earlier studies, it isn't always easy to determine if a correlation actually indicates a cause. For example, lack of exercise may appear to increase the risk of obesity, CHD and diabetes. But could other factors be involved? Could it be the type of food that obese people tend to eat rather than lack of exercise which increases their risk of CHD? Does lack of exercise increase the risk of diabetes or is it the obesity which so often results from lack of exercise? These are the sort of questions which must be answered before deciding if these links are causative.

If there appears to be a strong correlation between two factors, a causal link is more likely if you can demonstrate a causal mechanism – in other words, a biological explanation for factor X causing problem Y. And if all the evidence from a wide range of sources shows the same thing it strengthens the argument for a causal link rather than simple correlation.

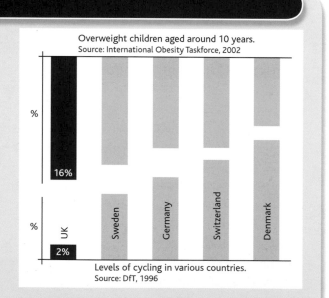

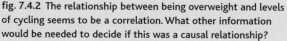

fig. 7.4.2 The relationship between being overweight and levels of cycling seems to be a correlation. What other information would be needed to decide if this was a causal relationship?

Exercise and obesity

As you saw in *AS Biology* pages 34–69, there have been a number of studies looking at the effect of exercise on obesity. Almost every study shows a strong correlation between levels of exercise in a population and obesity levels. There is also a clear causal mechanism. The food you take in supplies energy.

Exercise uses up energy. The balance between the energy you take in and the energy you expend is easier to maintain when your lifestyle includes moderate, regular exercise (at least three or four times a week), compared with a lifestyle involving no aerobic exercise. Lack of exercise tends to lead to an excess of energy taken in which the body stores as fat – resulting in obesity.

Exercise and diabetes

There are two types of diabetes. You learnt about type 1 diabetes in *AS Biology* page 180. Type 2 diabetes tends to develop later in life – often over the age of 40. The symptoms are produced either because you can no longer make enough insulin for your needs, or because your body cells no longer respond to the insulin you make, or a combination of the two. In the UK 1 in 10 people over 65 years old have the condition.

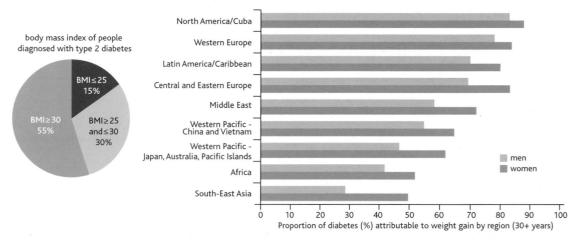

body mass index of people diagnosed with type 2 diabetes

BMI≤25 15%

BMI≥30 55%

BMI≥25 and≤30 30%

fig. 7.4.3 Analysis by the International Obesity Task Force and the WHO Global Burden of Disease research programme suggest that obesity is a major risk factor of type 2 diabetes.

fig. 7.4.4 Exercise seems to be a cheap and readily available treatment which can help prevent type 2 diabetes.

There is a correlation between low exercise levels and type 2 diabetes. Current research suggests increasing exercise levels, leading to weight loss, can prevent the development of type 2 diabetes in at-risk individuals. This suggests more clearly a causal link, although it can be difficult to separate the effect of exercise and excess weight.

In one US study on 3234 overweight people already showing early signs of type 2 diabetes, people who maintained a regular exercise programme for three years reduced their risk of developing type 2 diabetes by 58%. The trial was halted a year early because the benefits of increased exercise (and its associated weight loss) were so clear.

In 2003 the World Health Organization published a document showing that their doctors and scientists are convinced that regular physical exercise prevents many diseases, and that a lack of exercise and a sedentary lifestyle are causative of both obesity and of many linked diseases including CHD and type 2 diabetes. They state that longitudinal studies (see *AS Biology* page 56) clearly indicate that increased physical activity reduces the risk of developing type 2 diabetes regardless of body weight.

Questions

SC 1 Look at the evidence presented in the graphs on these pages. Find out as much as you can about the sources of these data. For each graph evaluate the reliability and/or usefulness of the data. Justify your conclusions as clearly as you can.

SC 2 Explain the difference between correlation and causation. Use the data on these pages, and on pages 52–69 in *AS Biology*, to assess the relationship between obesity, diabetes, heart disease and level of exercise.

The risks of too much exercise 5.7.18

Lack of exercise is linked to a number of diseases – but too much exercise can also cause health problems! Elite athletes in training and competition, and people who take normal exercise to extremes, can reach a point where they are doing themselves harm by over-exercising.

Exercise and the immune system

There is considerable evidence which shows that moderate exercise benefits the immune system, measured by the reduced number of upper respiratory tract infections (colds!). However, there is both anecdotal evidence and some scientific data to suggest a correlation between athletes in heavy training programmes and an increase in minor infections. For example in 1999 data were published showing that 13% of the runners in the Los Angeles marathon reported upper respiratory tract infections in the week after the race, compared with 2% of non-runners with comparable fitness levels. A theoretical graph hypothesising a causal link between exercise and the immune system was developed (**fig. 7.4.5**). However, it may not be that simple. There are a number of possible explanations for the observed infection rate of these intense athletes:

- The suppression of the immune system of the marathon runners after their extreme exertion.

- Thousands of people are in close proximity in the early stages of a marathon so viruses could spread easily between them.

- Athletes often travel to events using aircraft, and lots of people meet up at sporting events from football matches to marathons, so it seems likely that elite athletes have a higher risk of exposure to pathogens when they are at events where they are exercising very hard.

Scientists have carried out a number of investigations to try to discover if there is a causal relationship between levels of exercise and the state of the immune system.

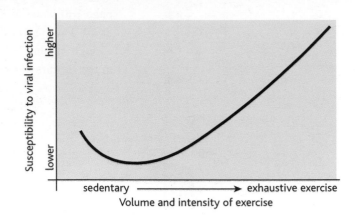
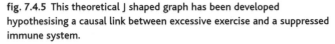

fig. 7.4.5 This theoretical J shaped graph has been developed hypothesising a causal link between excessive exercise and a suppressed immune system.

Exercise and immunity

Analysis of the blood of athletes and others has shown that moderate exercise results in a measurable increase in T killer cells. These are part of the immune system (see pages 100–103) which recognise and destroy whatever pathogen they meet. This offers a causal mechanism for the observed effect of moderate exercise on upper respiratory tract infections. However, there is also evidence that very intensive exercise lowers the numbers and activity of these T killer cells. Some studies show reductions in phagocytes, B cells and T helper cells as well. If this is the case, most of the immune response will be reduced in efficiency, offering a causal mechanism for the impact of intense exercise.

Stress hormones such as adrenaline and cortisol affect the immune system, suppressing inflammation and reducing antibody production. Intense exercise and the psychological build-up to competition can cause stress. So this could be another cause of the increase in infections in competition-level athletes. It is difficult to decide exactly how exercise affects the immune system either positively or negatively, and if it is the level of exercise or the stress that causes any adverse effect.

HSW Analysing the data

fig. 7.4.6 Most people think exercise is good for them – but is it really?

Exercise certainly seems to affect the immune system – but exactly how still isn't completely clear. It helps to consider a number of different studies. **Table 7.4.1** summarises some data published in *The Physician and Sports Medicine* June 1999 which reveals the conclusions of a number of different investigations over the past 30 years into the effect of exercise on immunity. Use the questions at the end of this spread to help you analyse these data.

Population studied	Activity type and intensity (when known)	Effects on upper respiratory tract infections (URTIs)
61 rowers, 126 non-rowers	Rowing: intense	Increased frequency and severity of infections in rowers
150, 18–65 years	Ultramarathon: intense	Increase in URTI symptoms in faster runners
8000, all ages	Swimming: moderate	Increased URTIs compared with non-swimmers
83, 60–72 years	Orienteering: intense	URTIs more frequent, lasted longer than controls
137, 11–14 years	Various sports: moderate	No effect
87 men	University sportsmen: intense	86% had URTIs over 8 weeks
199, 20–23 years	Various sports: moderate	Males no effect
36 women, 25–45 years	Running: moderate	Reduced length of infections
2311, 35–37 years	Marathon running: intense	URTIs doubled in training Faster runners 6× increase after race
530, 17–75 years	Distance running	More URTIs when running over 15 km/week
10 men	Running (3 weeks)	URTIs in three men
96 cadets	Initial training	No change in URTIs but immune function depressed
16, 60–72 years	Moderate exercise	Number of URTIs reduced
482 men	Special warfare training	High incidence URTIs
44 elderly women	Walking: moderate	Reduced number URTIs
750, 40–81 years	Running	URTIs increased when training over 70–80 km/week
34, 18–29 years	Various activities : moderate	No change in URTIs even when given cold virus

table 7.4.1 Studies on the effect of exercise on upper respiratory tract infections.

Questions

1 a Using **table 7.4.1**, select three studies which are likely to be the most valid and reliable. Explain your choices.

   b If you were asked to discard two studies, which would you choose and why?

2 a How many of these studies confirm the hypothesis that moderate exercise benefits the immune system but extreme exercise is damaging to the immune response?

   b Describe the strengths and weaknesses of the data shown in moving the model from correlation to causation.

How healthy is your heart? 5.7.18

On pages 34–69 of *AS Biology* you looked at various forms of heart disease. One aspect you considered is the effect of exercise on the risk of developing CVDs. The heart is a muscle and like all muscles, it develops with use. The tissue of a fit heart has a better blood supply and copes better with periods of anaerobic respiration than the heart of someone who never takes any exercise.

The causes of heart disease are complex. They may be linked strongly to your genetics, to your lifestyle or – for most people – a bit of both. Whatever the cause, sometimes the natural pacemaker system of the heart doesn't work properly and the heart goes into an abnormal rhythm. If doctors can pick up this abnormal rhythm, return it to normal and ideally find out the cause of the problem, then they may be able to keep you alive and well in future.

How are ECGs used to diagnose heart disease?

As you saw on pages 152–3, the electrical activity of your heart can be recorded to give an electrocardiograph (ECG). In a normal ECG the P wave represents the depolarisation of the SAN and related tissue in the atrium. The QRS complex represents the spread of excitation through the ventricles, and the T wave reflects the rapid repolarisation of the Purkyne tissue in the ventricles.

If your heart starts behaving abnormally, e.g. during a heart attack, the normal electrical activity of the heart will be disrupted, and the rhythm of the contraction of the muscles will change. These different rhythms – known as **arrhythmias** – of the heart can be detected using an ECG. Doctors can use the information from the ECG (along with information from other tests) to diagnose what is wrong with your heart – and give you the right treatment.

If part of your heart is starved of oxygen during a heart attack – in other words, it is **ischaemic** – then it cannot fill and empty normally. This gives a very typical ECG recording.

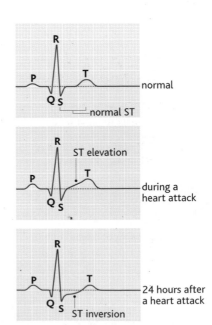

fig. 7.4.7 An ECG with ST segment elevation is a clear indicator of a heart attack: 24 hours after a heart attack, the T wave becomes inverted. Paramedics and doctors need to identify these indications quickly so that they can treat patients appropriately.

In some people arrhythmias of the heart are also caused by the atria beating too fast and ineffectively. This is called **atrial fibrillation**. Atrial fibrillation increases the risk of a clot forming, causing a stroke. It also means the heart does not pump so efficiently – but many people live relatively normal lives with atrial fibrillation by taking medication to prevent their blood from clotting too easily.

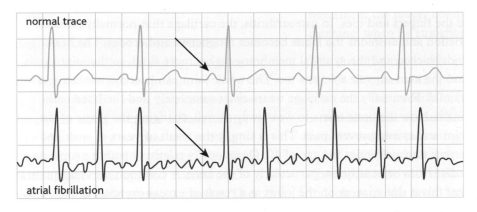

fig. 7.4.8 These ECGs show changes to the heart during atrial fibrillation. The P waves (indicated by the arrows), which show the depolarisation of the atria, are missing or very irregular, the atria contact rapidly and the ventricles beat irregularly.

Sometimes, the heart beats far too quickly, a condition known as **tachycardia**. One common cause of this symptom is stress, although this does not cause any long-term or serious problems. More severe tachycardia can also be the result of problems in the heart itself. In this case, the heart can beat so quickly that there isn't time for the ventricles to empty properly and so the muscles around the body and the brain may become starved of oxygen.

One of the biggest dangers during arrhythmias of the heart is that the ventricles will lose their rhythm and go into ventricular fibrillation. The ventricles contract erratically and weakly – the whole heart 'wobbles' and little blood is pumped out into the arteries. When this happens there is often a rapid fall in blood pressure, so the brain, the body and the heart itself are rapidly starved of blood. It often leads to a heart attack or even sudden death.

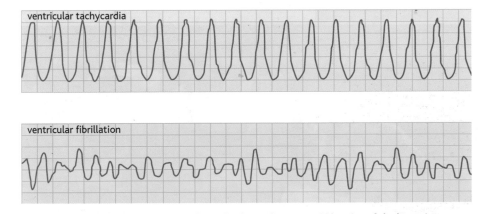

fig. 7.4.9 The ECG of the patient in tachycardia shows the very rapid beating of the heart. In ventricular fibrillation the ventricles lose their regular stimulation. They beat in a very irregular way and often only contract weakly, so the body loses its supply of oxygenated blood.

In some cases, an abnormal heart rhythm can be corrected by giving the heart a large electric shock. Ventricular fibrillation can sometimes be corrected in this way. The equipment used is known as a **defibrillator**.

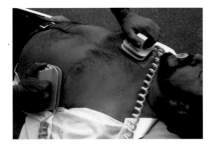

fig. 7.4.10 For many years defibrillators were only used in hospitals. Now semi-automatic defibrillators are sometimes found in pubs, restaurants and leisure centres so that they can be used to give fast, life-saving treatment to people in the community.

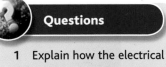

Questions

1 Explain how the electrical activity recorded in an ECG is related to the beating of the heart, and why changes in this activity lead to problems.

2 Explain the difference between atrial and ventricular fibrillation in terms of their ECGs and the effect on the patient.

Case history 3

The anterior cruciate ligament (ACL) is very important in keeping the knee joint in place. (see **fig. 7.4.11**). If it is damaged then further injuries are likely and the joint itself may even be destroyed. A 21-year-old professional footballer suddenly collapsed during a game, gripping his right knee. His knee was swollen and an MRI scan the next day showed a complete rupture of his ACL.

There are two main treatment options. The first uses rest and no surgery, while the second involves reconstructive surgery of the ACL. Research shows surgery is best for people who wish to continue in sport. After 2 weeks' rest to reduce the swelling, this footballer was operated on.

There are several different techniques to repair the ligament. Some involve using the patient's own patella or hamstring tendons. Others use an allograft (donated tissue from someone who has died). Following the operation, done using keyhole surgery, this player underwent a long and intensive physiotherapy regime to restore his knee movement and to build up his muscle power – it was successful but took 9 months!

Modern imaging technologies such as MRI and CT (computed tomography) scans have had a dramatic impact on how accurately injuries are diagnosed. For example surgeons used to open up the knee just to diagnose a problem. Today the patient simply has a 20 minute scan!

Using prostheses

Medical technology has made great strides in treating sports injuries and enabling athletes to continue to compete at the highest levels. There has also been a revolution in the development and design of artificial joints (particularly hips and knees) and limbs (prostheses). These are enabling ordinary people to escape the pain and disability resulting from arthritic damage to their joints and helping athletes with permanent disabilities to compete more effectively at all levels of sport.

For example, a knee joint which is damaged by wear and tear, arthritis or another condition can be completely replaced. Most commonly the end of the femur is replaced with a metal prosthesis, while the end of the tibia/fibula is replaced by a combination of metal

and plastic. The process can revolutionise a patient's life, freeing them from pain and restoring mobility. People with replacement joints can take moderate exercise effectively again. However, there are limitations and there can be complications. Some sports, such as skiing and horse riding, are discouraged because of the chance of falls damaging the new joints. Replacement joints, unlike real ones, wear out more quickly if you exercise a lot. The metal and plastic parts may wear loose from the bone to which they are attached. Bits wearing off the joint can cause inflammation and even cause the real bone to be reabsorbed and weakened.

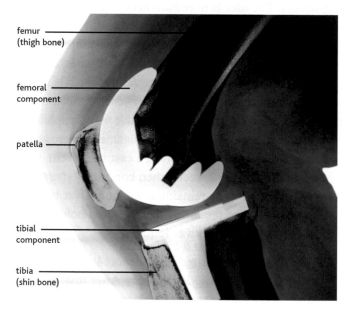

femur
(thigh bone)

femoral
component

patella

tibial
component

tibia
(shin bone)

fig. 7.4.15 Most people who have a complete knee replacement like this one can no longer compete in sport at the highest levels, although they should be able to enjoy exercise for pleasure.

Even more dramatic are some of the prosthetic limbs which have been developed for athletes in recent years. Everyday prostheses are usually designed with a combination of appearance and function in mind. Sporting prostheses are simply designed to enable disabled athletes to run as effectively as possible. Using new alloys, plastics and carbon fibres, limbs and part limbs have been developed which have revolutionised the way people with disabilities can compete. The dynamic response prosthetic foot changes shape as the body weight presses down on it, returning back to shape as it lifts off the ground and providing a similar 'spring in the step' to a functioning ankle. Jointed prosthetic feet are available which help on uneven surfaces such as in golf. Carbon fibre limbs such as the 'Cheetah prosthetic' (**fig. 7.4.16**) make no attempt to look like a human leg – but give outstanding functional performance.

HSW Medical technology and ethics

Oscar Pistorius was only 11 months old when both of his legs were amputated below the knee. He began running competitively in his teens when he discovered carbon fibre blades, prosthetics designed with athletes in mind. He won gold medals in the 100, 200 and 400 m events in the 2008 Beijing Paralympics and holds world records for disabled runners.

fig. 7.4.16 Using the latest medical technology, Oscar Pistorius and other disabled athletes can run faster than all but the most elite able-bodied runners.

In 2007 Oscar Pistorius took part in an international competition against able-bodied runners. However, this triggered considerable debate including claims that the artificial limbs gave him an advantage over able-bodied runners. Pistorius was put through rigorous tests which showed that using the 'Cheetah prosthetic' he could run at the same speed as an able-bodied athlete while using up to 30% less energy. Subsequently, the International Amateur Athletics Federation (IAAF) banned the use of such prostheses in open competition. Presumably the fear is that as technology progresses, disabled athletes might regularly be able to outrun able-bodied competitors. This is another case where science raises the questions – but society must provide the answers!

Questions

1 a Describe osteoarthritis.

SC b Compare the causes of osteoarthritis in people under 40 and over 40.

2 a Summarise the two knee injuries described in case histories 2 and 3 and how they affected the joint.

   b Explain how surgery as described for the ACL and the median meniscus allow a footballing career to continue when an artificial knee would not.

SC 3 Investigate the IAAF ban on the use of prosthetic limbs in competition. Describe the issues that it raises.

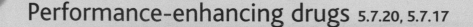

Performance-enhancing drugs 5.7.20, 5.7.17

To be the best in the world – or even the best in a club or school – athletes need to be able to supply as much oxygen as possible to their muscles, and to have the biggest and most efficient muscles they can develop. Many athletes achieve these goals by carefully planned training programmes, dedication and very hard work. But some also use drugs to enhance their performance. Many of these substances are banned.

Which substances are banned?

The World Anti-Doping Agency (WADA) is the body which oversees the battle against the use of performance-enhancing substances and techniques. Athletes and their coaches are constantly coming up with new ways to enhance performance chemically. WADA, along with the Olympic Movement and individual national athletic organisations, try to monitor all of these and decide which to ban. Some substances and techniques are banned at all times, in or out of competition, unless there is a clear medical reason for an athlete to take them. Others are only banned for use during competition. The main groups of completely banned substances are summarised below.

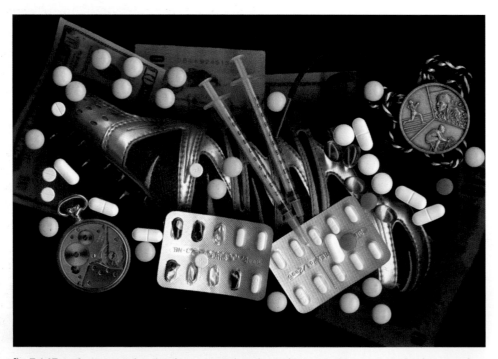

fig. 7.4.17 Performance-enhancing drugs – even those banned in competition – are not hard to come by for athletes and their coaches.

- **Anabolic steroids** – steroids often related to the male sex hormone testosterone, used for building muscle mass and performance.

- **Hormones** and their **releasing factors** – hormones that have very specific effects, e.g. erythropoietin (EPO) which stimulates the formation of red blood cells, growth hormones which affect muscle growth.

- **Beta-2 agonists** – dilate the airways, allowing more air into the lungs. Athletes with asthma are allowed to take a certain dose from their inhalers.

- **Hormone agonists** – chemicals which mask or change the action of another hormone.

- **Diuretics** – athletes have to provide urine samples for drug testing. Excess urination may eliminate traces of illegal substances before they can be tested. Diuretics stimulate excess urination, so they are illegal as well.

- **Blood doping** – athletes have blood transfusions of their own blood, removed months earlier, or donated blood, or even artificial oxygen-carrying compounds. All these techniques raise the amount of oxygen carried in the blood, enhancing performance.

- **Gene doping** – any attempt to change the genetic makeup of the cells to enhance athletic performance is banned.

Any attempt to swap samples to avoid testing, or to tamper with the samples of another athlete, is also strictly forbidden.

Other chemicals which are completely banned in competition include:

- **Stimulants** – increase the heart rate and make you more alert, e.g. caffeine, amphetamines and cocaine.

- **Narcotics** – powerful painkillers, e.g. heroin (diamorphine) and morphine, which allow athletes to ignore pain and compete harder.

Some drugs are banned only in particular sports, for example:

- **Beta blockers** – these are drugs which make the heart beat more slowly and reduce any response to adrenaline such as trembling. They are used by athletes who need a very steady hand and are banned in 17 different sports including shooting, darts, gymnastics and the helm in a sailing boat.

HSW Catching the cheats

The stakes in modern sport are high, both in prestige and in money. There is huge pressure on athletes to succeed, and some are prepared to take the risk and use banned substances to enhance their performance. The authorities in all sports are working to prevent cheating, and drugs testing is a major part of the prevention strategy. Scientists are working to develop increasingly sophisticated tests to identify traces of any banned substances, even when the athletes have attempted to hide them. The blood and urine of athletes are routinely tested at every competition. The winners of any event are always tested and a random selection of other athletes is tested as well. The authorities also target any athletes who show a sudden unexplained improvement in results. Athletes can be called for testing at any time, including when there are no competitions.

Two samples are taken of both blood and urine. The first is put through a battery of tests including mass spectrometry and DNA profiling. If any banned substances show up, the second sample can be tested to confirm the situation. In an attempt to avoid problems in the future, samples from the winners of medals at the Beijing Olympics in 2008 will be kept for up to 8 years so that as new tests become available they can be tested again.

How do drugs work?

The different types of chemicals in performance-enhancing drugs work in different ways. You are going to consider two widely used groups of drugs.

Anabolic steroids

Anabolic steroids are steroid hormones often closely related to the male sex hormone testosterone. Natural testosterone (and all these steroid hormones) can pass through the cell surface membrane. Once in the cell they bind with receptor molecules and are carried into the nucleus of the cell where they modify gene expression (see *AS Biology* pages 84–7). The hormone/receptor complex acts as a transcription factor, binding to the DNA and switching on particular genes linked to protein synthesis. This changes the RNA which is produced, which in turn affects the type and numbers of proteins and therefore enzymes produced.

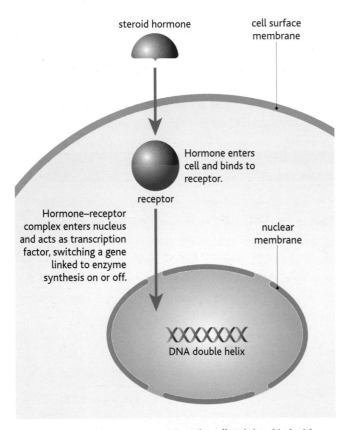

fig. 7.4.18 Steroid hormones move into the cell and then bind with a receptor to form a transcription factor. This binds to the DNA in the nucleus and switches on the gene/mRNA synthesis sequence which leads to the production of a particular protein.

The hormone stimulates protein synthesis and bigger and stronger muscles result, especially when the hormone is used alongside carefully planned exercise. However, natural testosterone is quickly broken down in the body, so a large range of synthetic testosterone-like hormones have been developed. Chemical modification has resulted in hormones with the same action as, or even better than testosterone, but with a much longer life in the body. Nadrolone is one well-known synthetic anabolic steroid which has been used by high-profile athletes. Body builders also use these illegal drugs to help build up a massively muscular and honed physique. Both men and women are known to use these drugs.

Bigger, stronger, fitter muscles might seem like a good idea, however they are obtained. But there is strong evidence that using extra anabolic steroids – and particularly the gross overuse seen in some athletes – can have severe side effects, causing lasting damage to the body. People have been known to use 10–100 times the normal levels of these drugs in their attempt to win. The drugs disrupt the normal production of hormones, so they are linked to infertility, problems in the menstrual cycle in women, a drop in sperm production in men and even impotence. They are also linked to liver damage, high blood pressure and heart attacks. Steroids can also affect and raise levels of aggression, particularly in young men.

Yet the use of steroid drugs seems to be increasing – studies in the US showed over 3 in 100 male 12th grade students (17–18 year olds) used steroids. Many want to boost sports performance, and some do it to build muscle for bodybuilding or weightlifting.

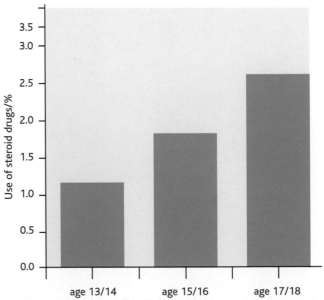

Source: *Monitoring the Future*, Institute for Social Research, University of Michigan.

fig. 7.4.19 Graph to show increasing use of steroid drugs in US high school students.

Erythropoietin

Erythropoietin is a very different type of hormone which is also taken by athletes to improve their performance. It is a peptide hormone, and like the steroids it switches genes on, acting as a DNA transcription factor. This results in the production of the enzymes needed for the synthesis of more red blood cells (erythrocytes).

Erythropoietin is made naturally in the kidneys and it stimulates the formation of erythrocytes in the red bone marrow. For some time it has been possible to make erythropoietin using DNA technology, modifying ovary cells from other species, such as hamster, to produce large quantities of the hormone. It is very useful to doctors in treating anaemia and other conditions. Athletes also use it to gain a competitive edge. The more red blood cells you have in your blood, the more oxygen you can carry to your muscles and the better you can compete. For example, a study of 15 Swedish athletes by the Stockholm Institute of Gymnastics and Sports found an improvement of nearly 10% in their aerobic performance after they had used the drug.

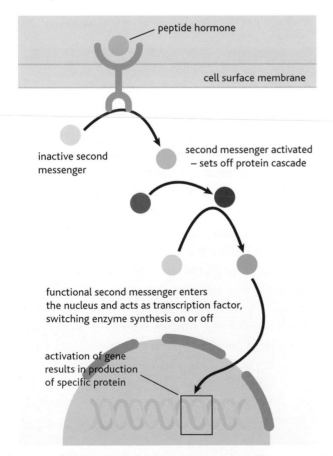

fig. 7.4.20 Peptide hormones such as erythropoietin bind to receptors in the cell membrane and trigger a protein kinase cascade which results in a transcription factor moving into the nucleus of the cell and switching on a specific gene, resulting in the production of new proteins.

Unlike steroid hormones, peptide hormones do not enter the cell. They bind to a receptor in the cell surface membrane. This membrane-bound complex activates a second messenger in the cell cytoplasm and triggers a protein kinase cascade. This usually involves the activation of several different proteins until the final product enters the nucleus and acts as a transcription factor. In the case of erythropoietin, this transcription factor switches on the genes linked to protein synthesis of the enzymes needed for the production of more red blood cells.

As erythropoietin is a naturally occurring hormone it has been very hard to isolate in tests, although the fact that it is made in animal cells has made DNA trace identification possible. However, the evidence has been challenged by some athletes, claiming samples have been contaminated. Erythropoietin is particularly popular with endurance athletes and cycling is one sport where it is thought to be very commonly used.

Although erythropoietin occurs naturally in the body, the abuse of the drug can lead to serious health problems and death. An excess of red blood cells thickens the blood and can lead to strokes and heart attacks. These are particularly common during the night when the heart rate is at its lowest. For example 18 European professional bicycle racers died in unusual circumstances between 1987 and 1991, many of them in their sleep. Young, fit athletes are not expected to die, and doctors and blood specialists think that erythropoietin may well have been implicated in many of these deaths.

Questions

1 Suggest why some drugs are banned completely and others only banned during competition.

SC 2 a Suggest why athletes might want to switch on particular genes.

   b Compare the way steroid and peptide hormones act as DNA transcription factors to switch on particular genes.

3 Look at **fig. 7.4.19** on steroid use in young Americans.

   a What more would you need to know before using this as reliable information?

   b Explain why is it inaccurate to say that the graph reflects steroid use in young Americans.

The ethics of performance-enhancing practices 5.7.20

Not all of the substances used by athletes to enhance their performance are banned. For example, creatine is found naturally in muscles as creatine phosphate. You get it directly in your diet and your body can synthesise it. But many athletes take creatine supplements, which evidence suggests may increase the creatine phosphate stores in the muscles, helping when short bursts of high-intensity exercise are needed. Some bad reactions to high levels of creatine have been reported, including kidney damage and high blood pressure. Yet creatine is not banned because it is a nutritional supplement, not a drug.

In comparison, the use of the hormone erythropoietin to increase the erythrocyte count *is* banned. So is donating and storing blood to transfuse back into your system just before competition to increase the oxygen-carrying capacity of the blood (blood doping). However, it is completely legal for an athlete to pay to train for weeks at high altitude where the body naturally increases the number of red blood cells to carry more oxygen – triggered by natural extra erythropoietin secretion! This can give a top athlete an average improvement in performance of 2–3% at sea level, enough to make the difference between winning and losing.

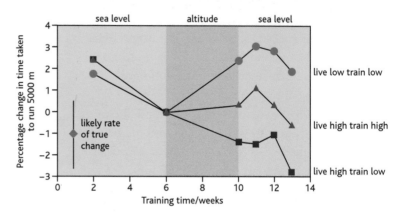

fig. 7.4.21 Graph based on a study by Levine and Stray-Gundersen on 39 runners to show the effect of different altitude training regimes on the time taken to run 5000 m.

HSW The ethics of using performance-enhancing drugs or processes

Science has developed a number of ways in which athletes can enhance their performance and gain a vital edge over their competitors. They range from specialised training programmes to performance-enhancing drugs. But where does wanting to win end and cheating begin?

Ethical absolutists take an unwavering moral position. They will have one of two possible – and completely opposite – attitudes on the use of performance-enhancing drugs in sport:

- It is never, under any circumstances, acceptable for athletes to use performance-enhancing substances.

- It is always perfectly acceptable for athletes to use any means available to them, including performance-enhancing drugs, to compete more effectively.

On the other hand ethical relativists recognise that there may be exceptions, and that not everyone will have the same standpoint. So an ethical relativist might suggest:

- It is wrong on the whole for athletes to use performance-enhancing substances but there might be some circumstances where it was acceptable.

Athletes themselves who use performance-enhancing substances take a variety of positions. Some will take banned and possibly harmful substances or use illegal techniques such as blood doping believing everything is acceptable in the pursuit of excellence. Others feel that other athletes use performance-enhancing substances, and they don't want to be disadvantaged.

If you are an absolutist, everything is clear cut. If you are a relativist, what issues will you need to consider? Many of the substances used by athletes are quite safe when used therapeutically. However, at the high doses used in training, drugs such as anabolic steroids and erythropoietin carry the risk of serious health problems and even death. Strong painkilling drugs can allow an athlete to continue with an injury, causing further and perhaps permanent damage. Even if an individual is prepared to take the risk, should society allow this as ethically acceptable? At the moment the answer is almost universally no.

Another issue arises if a practice which enhances performance is so expensive, or new, that it is beyond the reach of most competitors. So most competitors could afford anabolic steroids if they wanted to use them, but the most recent versions and least detectable versions of some drugs are beyond the incomes of most people. Is it OK to use drugs if everyone does it, but not if they are only available to a favoured few?

Athletes are currently banned from blood doping or using erythropoietin to raise their red cell count. Yet it is completely acceptable for them to pay to live at altitude for several weeks, increasing natural erythropoietin levels and so increasing their red blood cell count! The only

difference is that living at altitude for a short time does not increase the red cell count to levels which cause a health hazard. Current research is looking at setting a maximum red blood cell count or haemoglobin level which is acceptable for a competing athlete. Then it could be the red blood cell count which is measured and accepted, regardless of whether the athlete has carried out blood doping, taken erythropoietin or lived at altitude, as long as the levels are within safe limits. Absolutists find this idea unacceptable, relativists feel it is bowing to the inevitable.

At the moment society is trying to decide what is and what is not acceptable – where do you stand in the debate?

fig. 7.4.22 Spanish cyclist Maria Moreno and North Korean shooter Kim Jong-su were just two of a number of athletes found taking banned substances in the 2008 Beijing Olympics. She used erythropoietin to boost her erythrocyte levels, while he used a beta blocker which lowered his heart rate and stopped him trembling before he shot.

Questions

1 Explain what the bar on the graph in **fig 7.4.21** tells you about the reliability of the results.

2 Describe an absolutist and a relativist ethical position on the proposal to set a maximum total red blood cell count for athletes rather than measure erythropoietin levels.

Examzone: Topic 7 practice questions

1 In an investigation, small samples of tissue were removed from the leg muscles of international athletes of the same age and sex. The athletes included sprinters (100 m), middle distance runners (800 m) and long distance runners.

SDH is an enzyme involved in the reactions of the Krebs cycle. LDH is an enzyme that catalyses the conversion of pyruvate to lactate.

The results of the analysis of the muscles are shown in the table below.

Athletes	Mean percentage of slow twitch fibres	Mean SDH activity (arbitrary units)	Mean LDH activity (arbitrary units)
100 m sprinters	24	1.70	1.60
800 m runners	52	2.00	1.10
Long distance runners	70	2.25	1.00

a Explain why successful sprinters usually have a low percentage of slow twitch fibres in their leg muscles. **(2)**

b i Explain the relationship between the mean activity of SDH in the leg muscles and the distances run by the athletes. **(2)**

ii Explain the relationship between the mean activity of LDH in the leg muscles and the distances run by the athletes. **(2)**

c Describe the role of the electron transport chain of mitochondria in the synthesis of ATP. **(4)**

d Explain the fate of lactate produced by the activity of LDH in athletes such as sprinters. **(2)**

(Total 12 marks)

SC 2 Tachycardia is a heart condition in which the heart beats very rapidly, even when the patient is at rest. The diagram below shows part of two electrocardiograms (ECGs), one from a person with a normal heartbeat and one from a patient with tachycardia.

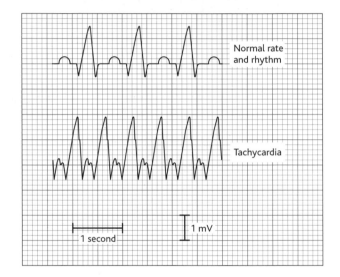

a Describe the normal electrical activity that occurs in the heart during one complete heartbeat. **(4)**

b Calculate the heart rate of the person with a normal heartbeat, using the information in the ECG. Show your working. **(2)**

c Compare the ECG of the person with a normal heartbeat with the ECG of the patient with tachycardia. **(2)**

d Suggest what effects tachycardia could have on cardiac output. Explain your answer. **(3)**

(Total 11 marks)

SC 3 Research has been carried out on the effect of amphetamines on sporting performance.
The table shows data from a study of volunteers taking part in swimming trials over a fixed distance. Each time is the average for three swimmers racing on four separate occasions.

	Average performance		
Event	After taking placebo (seconds)	After taking amphetamines seconds	Percentage (%) improvement
Freestyle	136.88	135.94	0.69
Backstroke	159.80	158.32	0.93
Breaststroke	171.87	170.22	–

a i Calculate the percentage improvement for breaststroke. Show your working. (1)

ii State **two** variables that should have been controlled in this study. (2)

iii Suggest the importance of using a placebo (inactive substance) rather than no drug being given. (1)

b Amphetamines are similar in chemical structure to certain neurotransmitters. One effect of amphetamines can be to reduce blood flow through the skin during exercise.

i Suggest how this reduction in blood flow might occur. (1)

ii Suggest the effect of reduced blood flow through the skin on body temperature regulation. (1)

iii Apart from changes in blood flow through the skin, explain how the body controls its temperature when generating heat through exercise, such as running. (3)

c Do you think that the use of amphetamines as a performance-enhancing drug should be made legal? Explain your views. (1)

(Total 10 marks)

4 The diagram below shows some of the stages in aerobic respiration.

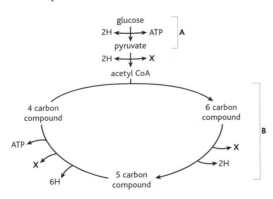

a i Name substance **X**. (1)

ii Name stages **A** and **B**. (1)

b Explain what happens to the hydrogen that is produced during stage **B**. (4)

c Explain how ATP is able to supply energy for biological processes. (1)

(Total 7 marks)

SC **5 a** Joint injuries often shorten the career of athletes. Explain the advantages of keyhole surgery on damaged joints, such as the knee, compared with traditional surgery. (2)

b Two weeks after taking part in a 56 km race, 33% of the runners developed respiratory tract infections. Those who completed the race were three times more likely to develop an infection after the race compared with a control group that did not run. Explain **one** factor that could contribute to this higher infection rate. (3)

(Total 5 marks)

6 a Cardiac muscle contracts myogenically. Explain what is meant by the term **myogenic**. (2)

b The diagram below shows structures in the heart which are concerned with the coordination of contraction.

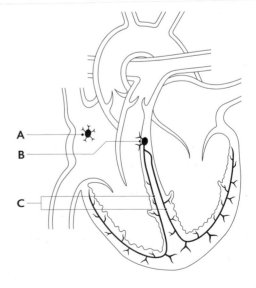

i Name parts **A**, **B** and **C**. (3)

ii Explain how the structures shown in the diagram coordinate the contraction of the heart. (3)

(Total 8 marks)

185

Topic 8 Grey matter

This topic deals with responses to the environment by plants and by animals. It then looks at the structure and function of the human nervous system, including the brain, and how the human brain develops. Drugs and their effect on the brain are discussed, as well as how our knowledge of the human genome and the production of genetically modified organisms can be used to produce new drugs.

What are the theories?

Plant growth is in response to chemical changes that affect how their cells grow and develop. In humans, electrical impulses in nerve cells are brought about by changes in ion concentrations inside and outside the nerve cells. The unique qualities of these impulses not only allow us to receive and respond to stimuli, they are also coordinated by the brain to produce more complex responses.

Communication between brain cells includes a range of chemical neurotransmitters. Imbalances in these chemicals can result in conditions such as Parkinson's disease and depression. Understanding of the human genome could make it possible to produce more targeted and effective drugs to treat conditions like these and others.

What is the evidence?

Imaging the brain using techniques such as MRI, fMRI and CT scans has greatly increased our knowledge of how the brain functions and develops. Evidence has also been gathered from other sources, including from experiments on animals such as kittens and monkeys. This has made it possible to build models that compare the contributions of nature (genes) and nurture (environment) to the development of the brain. You will have the opportunity to carry out your own investigation on habituation to a stimulus.

What are the implications?

The use of animal experiments raises moral and ethical concerns, even though they have resulted in greater understanding of the effects of the imbalances of brain chemicals and the development of drugs that act on the brain to relieve these conditions. Producing drugs that are targeted at particular groups or individuals also raises issues, including who should benefit most. And consideration of the use of genetically modified organisms for producing the drugs requires an understanding of the associated risks and benefits.

The map opposite shows you all the knowledge and skills you need to have by the end of this topic. The colour in each box shows which chapter they are covered in and the numbers refer to the Edexcel specification.

Chapter 8.1

describe how plants detect light using photoreceptors and how they respond to environmental cues (2)

compare mechanisms of coordination in plants and animals i.e. nervous and hormonal, including the role of IAA in phototropism (details of individual mammalian hormones are not required) (8)

Chapter 8.2

describe the structure and function of sensory, relay and motor neurones including the role of Schwann cells and myelination (3)

describe the structure and function of synapses, including the role of neurotransmitters, such as acetylcholine (5)

describe how the nervous systems of organisms can detect stimuli with reference to rods in the retina of mammals, the roles of rhodopsin, opsin, retinal, sodium ions, ion channels and hyperpolarisation of rod cells in forming action potentials in the optic neurones (6)

explain how the nervous systems of organisms can cause effectors to respond as exemplified by pupil dilation and contraction (7)

describe how a nerve impulse (action potential) is conducted along an axon including changes in membrane permeability to sodium and potassium ions and the role of the nodes of Ranvier (4)

◀ builds on Chapter 2.3

Chapter 8.3

locate and state the functions of the regions of the human brain's cerebral hemispheres, hypothalamus, cerebellum and medulla oblongata (9)

describe the role animal models have played in developing explanations of human brain development and function (12)

discuss whether there exists a critical 'window' for exposure to particular stimuli (11)

describe how animals, including humans, can learn by habituation (14)

discuss the moral and ethical issues relating to the use of animals in medical research from two ethical standpoints (16)

describe the role played by Hubel and Wiesel's experiments with monkeys and kittens (12)

describe how to investigate habituation to a stimulus (15)

describe the use of magnetic resonance imaging (MRI), functional magnetic resonance imaging (fMRI) and computed tomography (CT) scans in medical diagnosis and investigating brain structure and function (10)

consider the methods used to compare the contributions of nature and nurture to brain development (13)

builds on Chapter 2.3 ▼

builds on Chapter 2.4 ▼

builds on Chapter 3.2 ▼

Chapter 8.4

explain how imbalances in certain naturally occurring brain chemicals can contribute to ill health (e.g. dopamine in Parkinson's disease and serotonin in depression) and to the development of new drugs (17)

discuss how the outcomes of the Human Genome Project are being used in the development of new drugs and the social, moral and ethical issues this raises (19)

outline two ethical positions relating to whether the use of performance-enhancing substances by athletes is acceptable (20)

builds on Chapter 1.1 ▲

▲ builds on Chapter 4.2

explain the effects of drugs on synaptic transmissions, including the use of L-Dopa in the treatment of Parkinson's disease and the action of MDMA in ecstasy (18)

discuss the risks and benefits associated with the use of genetically modified organisms (21)

builds on Chapter 2.3 ▲

builds on Chapter 3.4 ▶

Responding to the environment 5.8.2

All living organisms need control systems. The complex biochemistry of a cell needs to be controlled to make sure that the right products are available at the right time. All living organisms need to grow, but only at the appropriate time and in the right places. Getting food and reproducing are also important biological driving forces. To control these processes successfully, a system of communication within the organism is needed.

Internal communication in plants

Specific chemicals released by cells in response to a stimulus can act as messages. Plants – even enormous trees – rely on chemical messages for communication between different parts, allowing them to respond to factors such as light and gravity. The chemicals move from cell to cell and also through the plant transport system.

Which stimuli affect plants?

We rarely think of plants as being sensitive because their movements are not usually easily noticed. Beyond needing light and water to survive, they are regarded as being largely insensitive.

In fact, plants respond to a variety of stimuli, most of which are environmental cues that have a direct impact on the well-being of the plant. They are sensitive to light, and not simply the presence or absence of it. Plants respond to the direction from which light comes, the intensity of the light and the length of daily exposure to it. Light affects how much they grow, the direction of growth and when they reproduce. Plants are also sensitive to gravity, to water, to temperature and in some cases to touch and to chemicals. Different parts of the same plant may react differently to the same stimulus (for example, shoots grow towards light but roots grow away from it). As well as these responses to external stimuli plants also respond to internal chemical signals. Most of the responses of plants are concerned either directly or indirectly with maximising the opportunities for photosynthesis and reproduction.

Plant responses

Plants respond to a variety of stimuli by producing or destroying chemical messages. Many of the messages are plant hormones, which play a similar role to animal hormones. They are produced in one area of the plant, are transported around the body of the plant and have their effect on cells elsewhere. Plant growth responses to environmental cues are known as **tropisms**. Animals respond to nervous and chemical messages in a variety of

fig. 8.1.1 Chemical control systems allow plants to respond to light and gravity – but some of them respond to touch as well. The slow responses of the runner bean and the fast response of a Venus fly trap are both examples of thigmotropism.

ways which include the release of further chemicals, the contraction of muscle cells and growth. The main way in which plants respond to their chemical messages is by growth. In some cases growth is stimulated while in others it is inhibited. For example, sometimes one side of a plant grows more than the other (see **fig. 8.1.1**), resulting in the bending of the shoots or roots in response to a particular stimulus. To understand how plants respond to stimuli in their environment, you need to understand exactly how they grow.

How plants grow

Growth is a permanent increase in the size of an organism or of some part of it. It is brought about by cell division, the assimilation of new material within the cells which result from the division and cell expansion which follows this assimilation (see **fig. 8.1.2**). The cell expansion is particularly noticeable in plants, where rapid enlargement can take place as a result of water taken up by osmosis before the cell wall becomes rigid. The main areas of cell division and elongation in plants are known as the meristems. These are areas which occur just behind the tip of a root or shoot. Not only are they the main areas of growth, they are also particularly sensitive to the chemical messages produced in response to a variety of stimuli. These chemical messages seem to make it easier for the cellulose walls to be stretched. When one side of a plant grows more than the other, the result is the bending of shoots or roots in response to a particular stimulus.

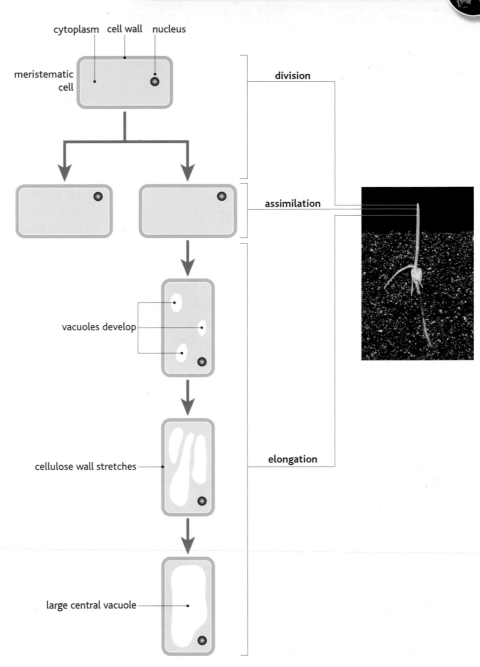

fig. 8.1.2 Plants respond to a variety of stimuli by differential growth. The growth-regulating chemicals generally seem to affect cell elongation, making it easier for the cellulose cell wall to be stretched, although they do also affect the cell division stage, increasing the number of divisions that occur.

Questions

1 List as many of the different environmental cues that elicit a response in plants as you can. For each, try to explain why it is important for the plant to respond to that stimulus.

2 Growth in animals usually stops at a certain stage. The meristems of plants, where growth occurs, remain active throughout the life of the plant. Explain why this difference is important in the way organisms respond to stimuli.

The effects of light on plants 5.8.2

Chlorophyll formation depends on light, and day length (or night length) is the environmental cue that determines changes such as bud development, flowering, fruit ripening and leaf fall. Without light, the metabolism of a plant is severely disrupted and prolonged light deprivation causes death.

Sensory systems in plants

For some time it has been known that the seeds of many plants will germinate only if they are exposed, even if very briefly, to light. Researchers in the US Department of Agriculture showed that **red light** (wavelength 580–660 nm) is most effective at stimulating germination in lettuce seeds while **far red light** (wavelength 700–730 nm) actually inhibits germination.

If the seeds are exposed to a flash of red light, they will germinate. If they are exposed to a flash of red light followed by a flash of far red light, they will not germinate. With a series of flashes of light, it is the colour of the final flash which determines whether or not the seeds will germinate (see **fig. 8.1.3**). Scientists hypothesised a plant pigment that reacts with different types of light, and in turn affects the responses of the plant. In 1960, this pigment was isolated from plants and called **phytochrome**.

Phytochrome is a blue-green pigment which exists in two interconvertible forms: P_R or P_{660} absorbs red light; P_{FR} or P_{730} absorbs far red light (see **fig. 8.1.3**). When one form of the pigment absorbs light, it is converted reversibly into the other form. The length of time it takes for one form of the pigment to be converted into the other depends on the light intensity. In low light intensity it takes minutes, but in high light intensity it takes seconds.

The conversion of P_{FR} to P_R also takes place very slowly in the dark. P_R is the more stable form of the pigment, but it is the P_{FR} which is biologically active.

red light (rapid)

$$P_R \qquad \rightleftharpoons \qquad P_{FR}$$

far red light (rapid)

or slow conversion in the dark

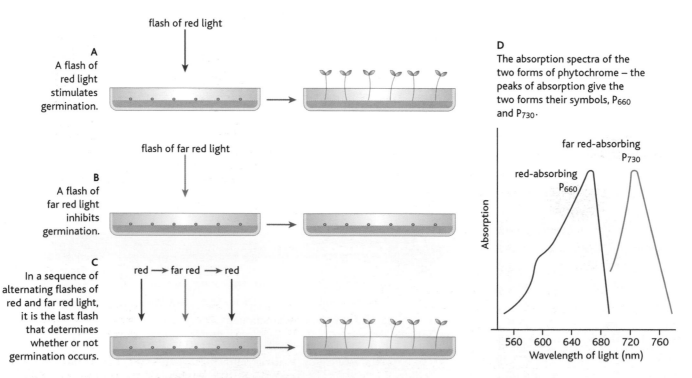

D

The absorption spectra of the two forms of phytochrome – the peaks of absorption give the two forms their symbols, P_{660} and P_{730}.

fig. 8.1.3 The idea of a phytochrome light receptor system in plants moved from an hypothesis to a well-accepted theory once the predicted light-sensitive chemical was extracted and analysed.

As normal sunlight contains more red light than far red light, the usual situation in a plant during daylight hours is for most of the phytochrome to be in the far red form. If the night period is long enough, it is all converted back into the red form. The explanation for the control of the germination of the lettuce seedlings is that it is initiated by the biologically active P_{FR}, but a flash of far red light converts it back to the inactive P_R before it has an effect.

Phytochromes enable plants to respond to environmental cues such as change in day length. In some cases phytochromes have a stimulating effect on growth in plants, in others an inhibitory effect. Exactly how phytochromes influence the responses of the plant is still not fully understood. The presence of phytochromes may stimulate the production of other growth regulators and plant hormones, bringing about the response to light.

Phytochromes and etiolation

Plants which are grown in the dark become **etiolated** – they grow rapidly, using up food reserves in an attempt to reach the light. As a result the plants end up tall and thin, with fragile stems and long internodes and small, pale, yellowish leaves as no chlorophyll is formed. Etiolation seems to be a survival mechanism. Once the plant reaches the light growth slows and the leaves turn green as chlorophyll forms. This response appears to be the result of phytochromes. In the dark, there is plenty of P_R but no P_{FR}. P_{FR} seems to inhibit the lengthening of the internodes (stem between the leaf nodes), and stimulates both the formation of chlorophyll and the expansion of the leaves. So without P_{FR}, the internodes grow but the leaves do not and no chlorophyll forms.

HSW Developing ideas of photoperiodism

In temperate regions such as the UK the period of daylight can vary from around 9 to 15 hours throughout the year. The lengths of the days and nights give important environmental cues to living organisms, directing their growth, development and behaviour. One of the most clearly affected activities is flowering, and scientists have developed models of how plants sense and respond to day length cues.

In the 1920s W.W. Garner and H.A. Allard in the US studied a particularly tall, large-leaved form of tobacco plant known as the 'Maryland Mammoth'. Most tobacco plants flower in the summer but Maryland Mammoths kept growing and eventually flowered in December. Garner and Allard realised the plants were responding to an environmental cue. The key variable appeared to be day length. With more than 14 hours of daylight, no flowers – but below 14 hours a day, the plants flowered. The **critical day length** was thus shown to be 14 hours.

Scientists found that day length appeared to be the environmental cue affecting flowering in many plants. Plants flowering when days are short and nights are long became known as **short-day plants** (SDPs), e.g. strawberries, chrysanthemums and the tobacco plant. Plants flowering with relatively long days and short nights are known as **long-day plants** (LDPs), e.g. snapdragons, cabbages and henbane. It can be very difficult to decide

whether a plant is a short- or long-day plant – the two groups merge. Other plants, such as cucumbers, tomatoes and pea plants, are unaffected by the length of the day and are known as **day-neutral plants** (DNPs).

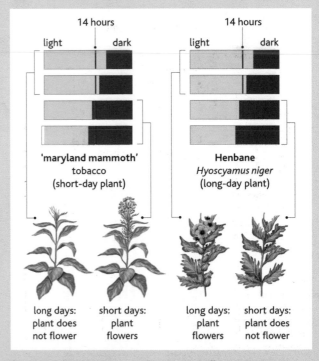

fig. 8.1.4 Following the work of Garner and Allard, scientists hypothesised that short-day plants will not flower with more than a critical amount of daylight, and long-day plants will not flower with less than a critical amount of daylight.

Different flowering patterns allow plants to take advantage of different circumstances. In temperate regions short-day plants tend to flower in spring and autumn, when the light-shading canopy of leaves either has not developed or has fallen off. They also flourish near the equator, where the days are never longer than about 12 hours. Long-day plants flower in the summer in temperate regions, and are found further from the equator where in some seasons there are very long days.

Scientists subsequently discovered that the length of the period of *darkness* is actually the environmental cue affecting flowering, not day length! It was demonstrated that if a short-day plant such as a cocklebur has the long night (period of darkness) interrupted by flashes of light, they do not flower (see **fig. 8.1.5**).

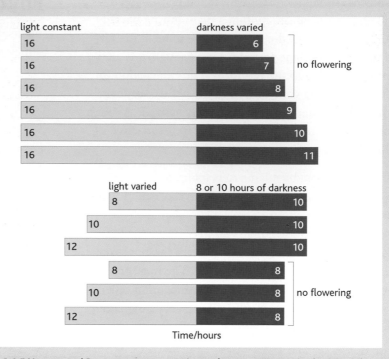

fig. 8.1.5 Hamner and Bonner gave one experimental group constant day length while the hours of darkness varied. In another, the hours of darkness were kept constant and the hours of light exposure were changed. It was darkness that affected flowering! Plants should really be long or short *night* plants – but in fact the names have been left the same!

fig. 8.1.6 The discovery that plants respond to periods of dark has made it possible in the UK to have poinsettias at Christmas when they would not naturally be flowering.

How is the length of the dark signal received?

All the research on photoperiodism points to the involvement of the phytochromes in the sensitivity of plants to the photoperiod. The changes in flowering patterns which can be brought about by disturbing the dark periods can also be affected by red or far red light alone. Red light inhibits the flowering of short-day plants, but if the red light is followed by far red light, the inhibition is lifted.

Red light leads to the formation of P_{FR}. Far red light or a long period of dark converts this back to P_R. The current hypothesis is that P_{FR} inhibits flowering, and the lack of P_{FR} allows flowering to occur. It is thought that it is the lack of P_{FR} rather than the build-up of P_R which leads to flowering. As the two forms of phytochrome are almost always present to some degree in a plant, it is the balance between them which is affected by varying periods of light and dark, and which in turn affects flowering. In long-day plants the situation is reversed, and it appears that a build-up of P_{FR} during the daylight hours stimulates flowering.

The detection of the photoperiod seems to take place in the leaves of the plant. The presence of a plant hormone known as **florigen** was hypothesised by the Russian plant physiologist Mikhail Chailakhyan in the 1930s. It was thought that florigen was made in response to the changing levels of phytochromes and carried in the plant transport system to the flower buds. The evidence included the following findings:

- If the whole plant is kept in the dark apart from one leaf which is exposed to the appropriate periods of light and dark, flowering occurs as normal. A plant kept in total darkness does not flower (see **fig. 8.1.7a**).

- Using the same experimental set-up, if the photoperiodically exposed leaf is removed immediately after the stimulus, the plant does not flower. If the leaf is left in place for a few hours, it does flower.

- If two or more plants are grafted together and only one exposed to appropriate light patterns, all the plants will flower (see **fig. 8.1.7b**).

- In some species, if a light-induced leaf from one plant is grafted onto another plant the new plant will flower.

For years no one could isolate the theoretical hormone and the florigen theory fell into disrepute. However, recently scientists have shown that when a leaf is exposed to a given amount of light and dark, a particular form of mRNA is produced in the leaf, linked with a gene associated with flowering (the FT gene or Flowering Locus T). It had been believed that a large molecule like this FTmRNA could not be florigen as it would not be able to leave the cell. Now it has been demonstrated that such molecules as this mRNA *can* move from cell to cell to the transport tissues through the plasmodesmata, and that the FTmRNA travels to the apex of the shoot, where other genes associated with flowering are activated. So FTmRNA looks as if it may well be florigen!

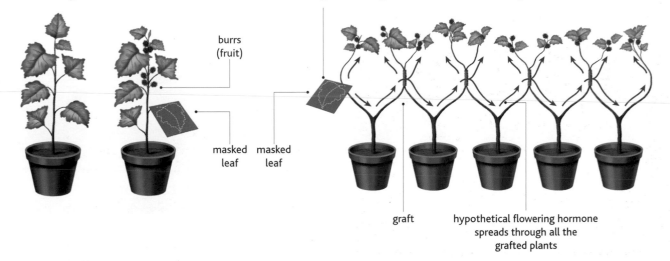

Experiment A

Cocklebur, a short-day plant, will not flower if kept under long days and short nights.

If even one leaf is masked for part of the day – thus shifting that leaf to short days and long nights – the plant will flower; note the burrs.

burrs (fruit)

masked leaf   masked leaf

Experiment B

1 Graft five cocklebur plants together and keep under long days and short nights, with most leaves removed.

2 Induce a leaf by long nights/short days.

3 If a leaf on a plant at one end of the chain is subjected to long nights, all of the plants will flower.

graft   hypothetical flowering hormone spreads through all the grafted plants

fig. 8.1.7 Evidence like this is building a clear picture of how the photoperiodic response in the leaves is transferred to the flowering regions of the plant.

Questions

SC 1 Draw up a a table to summarise the effects of red light (P_{FR} build-up) and far red light (P_R build-up) on different parts of a plant.

SC 2 How does the evidence presented support the idea of the plant hormone florigen? Take each bullet point in turn and explain its relevance.

SC 3 Produce a flowchart to show how phytochromes and florigen interact to bring about flowering in a plant.

Tropic responses in plants 5.8.2

The way in which plants respond to environmental cues is not confined to the control of their overall growth and flowering. The growth responses known as tropisms are made to a number of different stimuli. The movements of plants in response to light which comes from one direction only (**phototropism**), and to gravity (geotropism), chemicals (chemotropism) and touch (thigmotropism) also involve chemical messages.

Once a seed begins to germinate in the soil the shoot and root must keep growing if the developing plant is to survive. But growth must take place in the right direction. The shoot must grow up towards the light source for photosynthesis. The roots must grow downwards into the soil which will provide support, minerals and water for the plant. The movements of these parts of the plant take place in direct response to environmental stimuli. The direction of the response is related to the direction from which the stimulus comes.

fig. 8.1.8 Geotropism means it doesn't matter which way up a seed falls, the shoot grows up and the roots grow down!

Phototropism

If plants are grown in bright, all-round light, they grow more-or-less straight upwards. In even but low light they will also grow straight upwards, and in fact will grow faster and taller than in bright light. But if the light to which plants are exposed is brighter on one side than another or only shines from one side (**unilateral light**) then the shoots of the plant will bend towards that light and the roots, if they are at all exposed, will grow away. Shoots are said to be **positively phototropic** and roots are **negatively phototropic**. This response has an obvious survival value for a plant. It helps to ensure that the shoots receive as much all-round light as possible, allowing the maximum amount of photosynthesis to take place. Also, if the roots should emerge from the soil – as they might do after particularly heavy rain, for example – they will rapidly turn back to the soil. But how are phototropisms brought about?

To answer this satisfactorily we need to start with a model of how growth is controlled in a shoot under conditions of all-round light.

fig. 8.1.9 Phototropism in action as small seedlings grow towards light coming from one side only.

HSW What's the evidence?

Much of the evidence for and work on tropisms has been carried out using germinating seeds and very young seedlings. This is because they are easy to work with and manipulate. As they are growing rapidly any changes show up quickly and tend to affect the whole organism rather than a small part as might be the case with a mature plant. The most widely used seedlings are those of monocotyledonous plants – usually cereals such as oats and wheat. This is because the shoot, when it emerges, is a single spike with no leaves apparent. This makes manipulation and observations even easier than in dicotyledonous shoots. The newly emerged oat shoot is known as a **coleoptile**, although the more general term 'shoot' will be used in this book. These early shoots are relatively simple plant systems, so the control of the responses to light in an intact adult plant may well be more complex than our basic model allows.

HSW Building a model

A succession of research over many years has helped explain phototropism. In the nineteenth century Charles Darwin and his son Frances carried out some experiments on oat coleoptiles and showed that the phototropic response of plants to light was due to some sort of message being passed from the root tip to the growing region.

From the late 1920s onwards the Dutch plant physiologist

Frits Went showed that the control of growth in plants relied on chemical messages. He had the simple idea of attempting to block or collect any message that passed from the tip to the growing region behind it, in order to show the nature of the message.

Figure 8.1.10 gives a brief résumé of some of Went's evidence.

Experiment A

shoot grown in the dark   tip removed, growth stops   tip replaced

A shoot grown in the dark grows straight upwards. When the tip is removed, upward growth stops. If the tip is replaced, growth begins again.
Conclusion: The tip of a shoot exerts an influence on the region of the growing cells behind it.

Experiment B

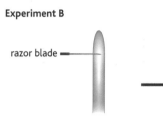

razor blade

A razor blade is inserted into the shoot just behind the tip. The shoot stops growing on the side that the blade is inserted. The shoot bends over.
Conclusion: The signal from the tip is blocked by the razor blade. The message is probably chemical, as an electrical signal would pass through the metal blade.

Experiment C

shoot grown in the dark and decapitated   tip placed on agar block   agar block replaced

The tip of a shoot growing in the dark is removed, placed on an agar block and left for several hours. The decapitated shoot does not grow. The agar block is then placed on the cut end of the shoot – normal growth resumes.
Conclusion: A chemical message is produced in the shoot tip, which diffuses into the agar block and then diffuses into the rest of the shoot, stimulating normal growth.

Experiment D

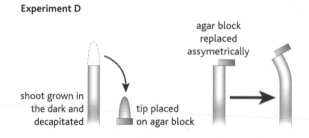

agar block replaced assymetrically

shoot grown in the dark and decapitated   tip placed on agar block

The tip of a shoot growing in the dark is removed and placed on an agar block. After several hours the block is placed asymmetrically on the decapitated shoot. The side with the agar block grows more than the other side – the shoot bends away from the stimulated side.
Went demonstrated that the amount of bending of the shoot is directly related to the amount of chemical messenger in the block, which can be used to measure or *assay* the biological activity of the messenger chemical. This is known as the *Went bioassay.*

fig. 8.1.10 Some of Went's experiments.

Questions

1 Describe how phototropisms differ from photoperiodism.

2 If a block of cocoa butter is used in experiment C instead of agar, there is no response in the decapitated shoot. Explain how this informs scientists that the message is water soluble.

SC 3 Evaluate Went's experimental procedures, listing the dependent and independent variables involved. How valid and reliable would you assess the results of this type of investigation to be?

Unilateral light and phototropisms 5.8.2, 5.8.5

The basic model of the way plants respond to light as they grow was based on shoots kept entirely in the dark or in full illumination. However, in real life plants are usually in a situation where the light from one side is stronger than the other. Experiments done on shoots illuminated from one side only (unilateral light) confirm the results from earlier experiments and add more detailed information of their own (see **fig. 8.1.11**).

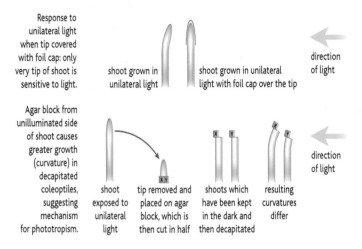

fig. 8.1.11 As a result of experiments such as these a more detailed hypothesis for the mechanism of phototropisms can be built up.

Phototropisms are the result of a chemical message made in the tip of the shoot which is transported to the growing region where it has an effect. The message is known as a plant hormone or **plant growth substance**. The growth substance involved in phototropisms is called an **auxin**. Auxins are powerful growth stimulants and are effective in extremely low concentrations. The first auxin discovered was **IAA** (**indoleacetic acid**). The term auxins is now used to cover substances including IAA which do identical jobs, referring to the whole group of chemicals. Auxins are produced commercially. Gardeners use them to help cuttings root quickly. They are also proving important in agriculture for improving the yields of crops.

How do auxins work in a plant?

Auxins seem to affect the ability of the plant cell walls to stretch (see page 189): for example, IAA is made in the tip of the shoot and diffuses back towards the zone of elongation. The molecules of IAA bind to specific receptor sites on the cell surface membranes, activating the active pumping of hydrogen ions into the cytoplasm. This changes the hydrogen ion concentration, providing

the optimum pH for the enzymes which break bonds between adjacent cellulose microfibrils (see *AS Biology* page 202) and keep the wall flexible. The cells absorb water by osmosis and the very flexible cell walls stretch and allow the cells to expand. Eventually, as the cells mature, the IAA is destroyed by enzymes, the pH of the cell walls rises and bonds form between the cellulose microfibrils. As a result the cell wall becomes more rigid – and the cell can no longer expand.

Research shows that the side of a shoot exposed to light contains less auxin than the side which is not illuminated (**fig. 8.1.13**). Light seems to cause the auxin to move laterally across the shoot, producing a greater concentration on the unilluminated side. This movement means the shoot tip acts as a photoreceptor. More hormone diffuses down to the region of cell elongation on the dark side. This stimulates cell elongation – and so growth – on the dark side, resulting in the shoot bending towards the light. Once the shoot is growing directly towards the light, the unilateral stimulus is removed. The asymmetric transport of auxin ends and the shoot grows straight towards the light. The original theory was that light destroyed the auxin. However, experiments such as those in **fig. 8.1.13** show that the levels of auxin in shoots are much the same regardless of whether they have been kept in the dark or under unilateral illumination.

Although the basic principles of tropisms have been understood for over a hundred years, this is still an area of active research. At the moment, there is no clear relationship between the phytochromes, which are such important photoreceptors in photoperiodism, and tropisms, where the movement of hormones such as IAA are involved in the responses to light. It was assumed they were quite separate processes. However, research is increasingly showing a link between the phytochromes and both phototropisms and geotropisms. For example it appears that phototropisms in a very young shoot cannot take place until the phytochromes have been activated, and that geotropisms are similarly dependent on phytochromes.

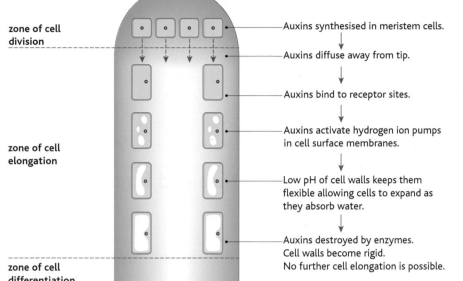

zone of cell division

zone of cell elongation

zone of cell differentiation

Auxins synthesised in meristem cells.

Auxins diffuse away from tip.

Auxins bind to receptor sites.

Auxins activate hydrogen ion pumps in cell surface membranes.

Low pH of cell walls keeps them flexible allowing cells to expand as they absorb water.

Auxins destroyed by enzymes. Cell walls become rigid. No further cell elongation is possible.

fig. 8.1.12 A summary of the role of auxins such as IAA in the growth of a plant shoot.

Questions

1 Explain in detail how IAA brings about a phototropic response in an oat coleoptile exposed to unilateral light.

2 a Explain the importance of the Went bioassay in interpreting the results of the experiment shown in **fig. 8.1.11**.

b How does this experiment confirm the current model of phototropisms?

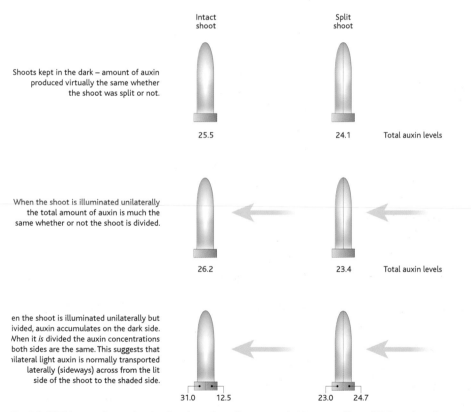

Intact shoot

Split shoot

Shoots kept in the dark – amount of auxin produced virtually the same whether the shoot was split or not.

25.5

24.1   Total auxin levels

When the shoot is illuminated unilaterally the total amount of auxin is much the same whether or not the shoot is divided.

26.2

23.4   Total auxin levels

en the shoot is illuminated unilaterally but ivided, auxin accumulates on the dark side. When it *is* divided the auxin concentrations both sides are the same. This suggests that ilateral light auxin is normally transported laterally (sideways) across from the lit side of the shoot to the shaded side.

31.0   12.5

23.0   24.7

fig. 8.1.13 This experiment involved maize coleoptiles exposed either to unilateral light or kept in the dark. The tips were removed and placed on agar blocks for several hours. The agar blocks were then placed on decapitated coleoptiles to assay the auxin concentrations.

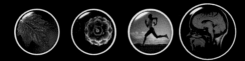

8.2 How the nervous system works

The nervous system 5.8.3, 5.8.4

On pages 188–97 you looked at the need for living organisms to have a system of control, and at the way coordination is achieved in plants using chemical communication systems. However, many animals, including humans, need a more rapid and more specifically targeted system of communication, and this is where a nervous system comes into its own.

A nervous system is made up of interconnected **neurones** (**nerve cells**) specialised for the rapid transmission of impulses throughout the organism. They carry impulses from special **receptor cells**, giving information about both the internal and the external environment. Neurones also carry impulses to specialised **effector cells**, often muscles, which then bring about the appropriate response.

The simplest nervous systems are made up of receptor cells, neurones and the nerve endings associated with the effectors (see **fig. 8.2.1**). However, many nervous systems are much more complex. As well as single receptor cells, groups of receptors have evolved to work together in **sensory organs** such as the eye and the ear. Simple nerve nets are replaced by complex nerve pathways. Some neurones only carry information from the internal or external environment into the central processing areas of the nervous system. They are known as **sensory neurones**. As animals increase in size and complexity they develop more specialised concentrations of nerve cells which form a **central nervous system** (**CNS**). This is an area where incoming information is processed, and from where impulses are sent out through **motor neurones** which carry impulses to the effector organs. In vertebrates the central nervous system consists of the brain and **spinal cord**.

Neurones are individual cells and each one has a long **nerve fibre** which carries the nerve impulse. **Nerves** are bundles of nerve fibres (**axons** or **dendrons**, see **fig. 8.2.1**). Some nerves carry only motor fibres and are known as **motor nerves**, some carry only sensory fibres and are known as **sensory nerves**, while others carry a mixture of motor and sensory fibres and are called **mixed nerves**. It is important to be very clear whether you are talking about neurones or nerves.

The structure and function of neurones

Neurones are the basic unit of a nervous system – millions of neurones that work together as an integrated whole in mammals such as ourselves. Neurones are cells specialised for the transmission of electrical signals (**impulses**). They have a cell body which contains the cell nucleus, mitochondria and other organelles, along with Nissl's granules which are prominent groups of rough endoplasmic reticulum (ER) and ribosomes needed for the synthesis of the neurotransmitter molecules. The cell body has slender finger-like processes called **dendrites** which connect to neighbouring nerve cells. The most distinctive feature of all nerve cells is the nerve fibre, which is extremely long and thin and carries the nerve impulse (see **fig. 8.2.2**). Fibres which carry impulses away from the nerve cell body are called **axons**. Fibres which transmit impulses towards the cell body (in sensory neurones) are known as **dendrons**.

Short relay or connector neurones are found in the CNS and they connect motor and sensory neurones. They are also known as bipolar neurones, because two fibres leave the same cell body.

Myelinated nerve fibres

Most vertebrate neurones are associated with another very specialised type of cell, the **Schwann cell**. The Schwann cell membrane wraps itself repeatedly around the nerve fibre forming a fatty layer known as the **myelin sheath** (see **fig. 8.2.2**). There are gaps between the Schwann cells known as the **nodes of Ranvier** (see **fig. 8.2.1**). The myelin sheath is important for two reasons – it protects the nerves from damage and speeds up the transmission of the nerve impulse.

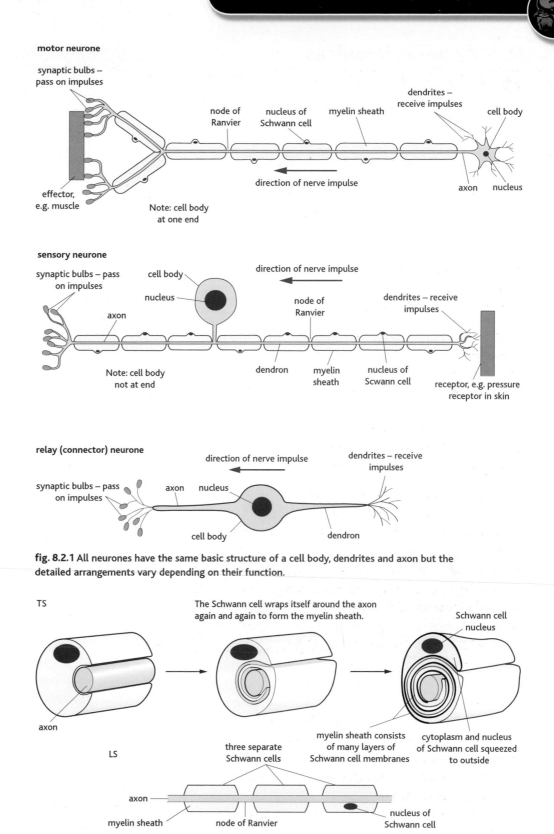

fig. 8.2.1 All neurones have the same basic structure of a cell body, dendrites and axon but the detailed arrangements vary depending on their function.

fig. 8.2.2 The myelin sheath which forms a protective, insulating layer around vertebrate nerve fibres.

Speedy nerve impulses

The role of the nerve cells is to carry electrical impulses from one area of the body to another quickly. The speed at which the impulses can be carried depends largely on two things. The first is the diameter of the nerve fibre – generally the thicker the fibre, the more rapidly impulses travel along it. The second is the presence or absence of a myelin sheath. Myelinated nerve fibres can carry impulses much faster than unmyelinated ones.

Invertebrates do not have myelin sheaths on their nerve fibres, and many of their axons and dendrons are less than 0.1 mm in diameter. As a result, many invertebrate nerve impulses travel quite slowly at around $0.5\,\mathrm{m\,s^{-1}}$. But there are times when even a relatively slow-moving invertebrate needs to react quickly to avoid danger. Many invertebrate groups have evolved a number of giant axons, which are nerve fibres with diameters of around 1 mm. These allow impulses to travel at approximately $100\,\mathrm{m\,s^{-1}}$, fast enough for most escape strategies to have a chance of success.

fig. 8.2.3 The rapid speeds at which impulses can travel through giant axons mean that invertebrates such as this squid can take violent evasive action when threatened by predators.

Vertebrates have both unmyelinated and myelinated nerves. The voluntary motor neurones that transmit impulses to voluntary muscles – for example to control movement – are all myelinated. However, the autonomic neurones that control involuntary muscles, like those of the digestive system, have some unmyelinated fibres. The effect of the myelin sheath is to speed up the transmission of a nerve impulse without the need for giant axons which take up quite a lot of space. A more versatile network of relatively small nerve fibres can carry impulses extremely rapidly, at speeds of up to $120\,\mathrm{m\,s^{-1}}$.

HSW The cause of nerve impulses

It has taken many years for our current model of nerve impulses to emerge. For example, over two centuries ago two famous scientists had a dispute over the electrical activity of the body. In 1791 Luigi Galvani discovered that the muscles in severed frogs' legs twitched when touched by brass and iron simultaneously. He thought this was the result of what he called 'animal electricity', produced by the nerves and muscles of his subjects. A few years later Alessandro Volta insisted that the effect was due to the difference in electrical potential between the two metals and nothing to do with animal electricity in the muscles at all. This dispute at the end of the eighteenth century was the starting point for a huge range of experiments in physiology, physics and physical chemistry which has led to our present-day understanding of the nature of the nerve impulse.

The current model of the nerve impulse is of a minute electrical event which is the result of charge differences between the outside and inside of the nerve fibre membrane. It is based on ion movements through specialised protein pores and by an active pumping mechanism. To look at the events of a nerve impulse it is easiest to consider a 'typical' nerve fibre – ignoring for the moment size, myelination or type.

Investigating nerve impulses

Since nerve impulses are electrical events, albeit very small ones, one of the most effective ways of investigating them has been to record and measure the electrical changes. This is done using apparatus sensitive to small electrical changes. Early work was done using a pair of recording electrodes placed on a nerve which was then given a controlled stimulus. The impulses which resulted were recorded by the electrodes and displayed on a screen.

External electrodes record the responses of entire nerves, made up of large numbers of different nerve fibres. The fibres are of varying diameter and sensitivity, and so the results of the recordings can be difficult to interpret correctly and the technique has been of limited value.

To make real progress, recordings had to be made from within individual nerve fibres. Much of the work on nerve fibres has been done using axons, because they are relatively easy to use. Sensory nerve fibres often run from a sense organ in the head directly to the brain or from individual sensory receptors in the skin to the spinal cord, making them difficult to get at. Motor axons, on the other hand, run directly to muscles, often in large motor nerves. This makes them relatively easy to access, and the effect of stimulating them can be seen immediately with the twitch of a muscle. So, much of your work on nerve impulses refers to axons – but the same events are seen in all nerve fibres.

Most axons are extremely small – around 20 μm in diameter – so making a recording from inside is not an easy procedure. About 40 years ago Alan Hodgkin and

Andrew Huxley began work on the giant unmyelinated axons of the squid which are around 1 mm in diameter. These axons allow for very rapid nerve transmission to particular muscles in situations when the squid needs to move in a hurry.

Hodgkin and Huxley used very fine glass microelectrodes inserted into the giant axon. Another electrode recorded the electrical potential from the outside. This allowed the changes which occur during the passage of an individual nerve impulse to be recorded accurately for the first time (see **fig. 8.2.4**). This technique has been refined so that now internal electrodes can be used with almost any nerve fibre.

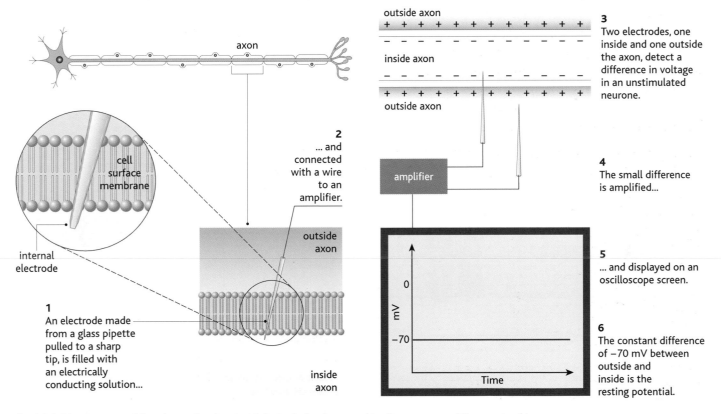

fig. 8.2.4 This apparatus, with an internal and external electrode, has been used to discover many of the secrets of how neurones work. Here you can see the resting potential of a neurone being measured – it is the potential difference across the membrane in millivolts.

Questions

1 Outline the differences between a nerve and a nerve fibre.

2 Summarise how the structure of a motor neurone is related to function.

3 The speed of transmission of a nerve impulse is in part related to the diameter of the nerve fibre. Explain why vertebrate nerve fibres always have relatively small diameters, yet the speed of the transmission of the nerve impulses is much faster than that in invertebrates.

4 Squid giant axons are widely used in neurophysiology. Explain why.

Nerve impulses 5.8.4

The concentration of sodium ions (Na$^+$), potassium ions (K$^+$) and other charged particles is different outside the axon from that inside: this is the basis of the nerve impulse.

The membrane of an axon, like any other cell surface membrane, is partially permeable. It is the difference in permeability of this membrane to positively charged sodium and potassium ions which gives it its special conducting properties. An axon is said to be 'at rest' when it is not conducting a nerve impulse. At rest, the axon membrane is relatively impermeable to sodium ions, but quite freely permeable to potassium ions (see *AS Biology* pages 104–5). It also contains a very active sodium/potassium ion pump (often referred to as the sodium pump or sodium/potassium pump) which uses ATP to move sodium ions out of the axon and

potassium ions in (see *AS Biology* pages 108–9). The effect of this is to lower the concentration of sodium ions inside the axon – they are pumped out and cannot diffuse back in again. At the same time, potassium ions are moved in, but they then diffuse out again along a concentration gradient through open potassium ion channels. Eventually the movement of positively charged potassium ions out of the cell along the concentration gradient is opposed by the electrochemical gradient. As a result, the inside of the cell is left slightly negative relative to the outside – it is **polarised**.

When you look at the events in neurones, the figures are always relative, comparing the inside of the nerve fibre to the outside solution. There is a potential difference across the membrane of around −70 mV, which is known as the **resting potential** (see **fig. 8.2.5**).

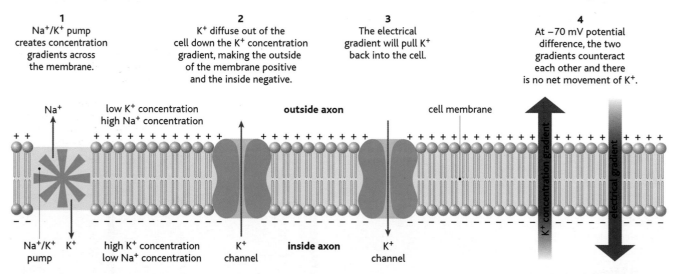

1
Na$^+$/K$^+$ pump creates concentration gradients across the membrane.

2
K$^+$ diffuse out of the cell down the K$^+$ concentration gradient, making the outside of the membrane positive and the inside negative.

3
The electrical gradient will pull K$^+$ back into the cell.

4
At −70 mV potential difference, the two gradients counteract each other and there is no net movement of K$^+$.

fig. 8.2.5 The resting potential of the axon is maintained by the sodium pump, the relative permeability of the membrane and the movement of potassium ions along concentration and electrochemical gradients.

The action potential

When an impulse travels along an axon, the key event is a change in the permeability of the cell membrane to sodium ions. This change occurs in response to a **stimulus** – for example light, sound, touch, taste or smell, in a sensory neurone, or the arrival of a neurotransmitter chemical in a motor neurone. In the experimental situation, the stimulus is usually a minute and precisely controlled electrical impulse.

When a neurone is stimulated, the axon membrane shows a sudden and dramatic increase in its

permeability to sodium ions. Specific **sodium ion channels** or **sodium gates** open up, allowing sodium ions to diffuse rapidly down their concentration and electrochemical gradients. As a result the potential difference across the membrane is briefly reversed, with the cell becoming **positive** on the inside with respect to the outside. This **depolarisation** lasts about 1 millisecond. The potential difference across the membrane at this point is about +40 mV. This is known as the **action potential**. Remember that these events happen in any nerve fibre, not just axons.

At the end of this brief depolarisation, the sodium ion channels close again and the excess sodium ions are rapidly pumped out by the sodium pump. This active transport system uses ATP. Also, the permeability of the membrane to potassium ions is temporarily increased as voltage-dependent potassium ion channels open as a result of the depolarisation. As a result potassium ions diffuse out of the axon down their concentration gradient and an electrochemical gradient, attracted by the negative charge on the outside of the membrane. As the positive sodium and potassium ions leave the cell, the inside becomes negative relative to the outside once again. It takes a few milliseconds before the resting potential is restored and the axon is ready to carry another impulse (see **fig. 8.2.6**).

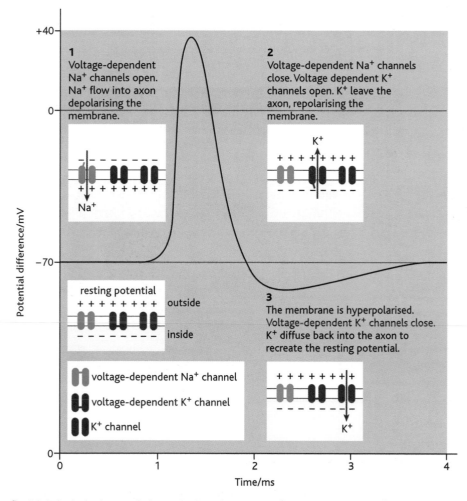

fig. 8.2.6 The ionic changes during excitation of an axon result in an action potential.

The events of the action potential can be recorded clearly using the internal/external electrode combination you have already seen. The oscilloscope trace is often referred to as the 'spike' because of its shape. It clearly shows the change in the potential difference across the membrane with the inrush of sodium ions followed by a return to the resting potential as the permeability of the membrane changes again. The **threshold** for any nerve fibre is the point at which sufficient sodium ion channels open for the rush of sodium ions into the axon to be greater than the outflow of potassium ions. Once the threshold has been reached, the action potential occurs. The size of this action potential is always the same – it is an all-or-nothing response.

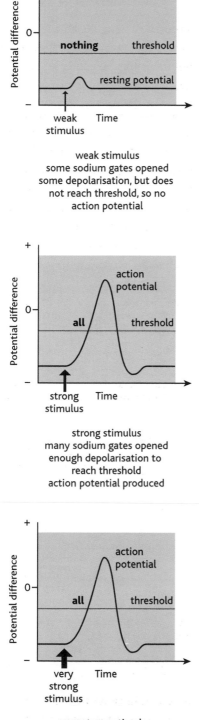

fig. 8.2.7 There are two possibilities when a neurone is stimulated: if the stimulus is *too small*, the action potential does not happen; if the stimulus is *large* enough, the action potential will happen. If the stimulus increases, the action potential stays the same.

The recovery time of an axon (known as the **refractory period**) is the time it takes for an area of the axon membrane to recover after an action potential, that is the time it takes for ionic movements to repolarise the membrane and restore the resting potential. This depends both on the sodium/potassium pump and on the membrane permeability to potassium ions. For the first millisecond or so after the action potential it is impossible to restimulate the fibre – the sodium ion channels are completely blocked and the resting potential has not been restored. This is known as the **absolute refractory period**. After this there is a period of several milliseconds when the axon may be restimulated, but it will only respond to a much stronger stimulus than before – the threshold has

effectively been raised. This is known as the **relative refractory period**. During this time the voltage-dependent potassium ion channels are still open. It is not until they are closed that the normal resting potential can be fully restored.

The refractory period is important in the functioning of the nervous system as a whole. It limits the rate at which impulses may flow along a fibre to 500–1000 each second. It also ensures that impulses flow in only one direction along nerves. Until the resting potential is restored, the part of the nerve fibre that the impulse has just left cannot conduct another impulse. This means the impulse can only continue travelling in the same direction – it cannot spread backwards as well.

HSW Building up the evidence

Some of the most convincing evidence for this model of the nerve impulse comes from work done using poisons. A metabolic poison such as dinitrophenol prevents the production of ATP. It also prevents the axon from functioning properly. But how does this confirm our model of a nerve impulse based around the active transport of sodium ions out of the axon and diffusion of potassium ions due to differential permeability?

- When an axon is treated with a metabolic poison the sodium pump stops working as ATP is used up, and the resting potential is lost at the same rate as the concentration of ATP decreases. This suggests that the ATP is being used to power the sodium pump – when it runs out, the pump no longer works.

- If the poison is washed away, the metabolism returns to normal and ATP production begins again. The resting potential is restored, suggesting that the sodium pump has started up again with the return of ATP (see **fig. 8.2.8**).

- If a poisoned axon is supplied with ATP by experimenters, the resting potential will be at least partly restored. This again confirms our model, suggesting that the poison is acting by depriving the sodium pump of energy rather than by interfering with the membrane structure and its permeability. If the latter were the case, even supplying ATP directly to the pump would have no effect because ions would move freely across the membrane and a potential difference could not be maintained.

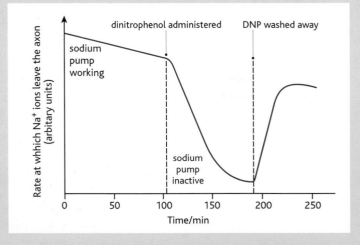

fig. 8.2.8 This graph, based on work by Hodgkin and Keynes in 1955, illustrates clearly the effect of dinitrophenol on the removal of sodium ions from the axon of a cuttlefish.

HSW The importance of internal electrodes

Our understanding of the nervous system has grown through use of both external and internal electrodes. The way the different techniques have contributed to our understanding can best be explained using a specific example.

Using external electrodes, a stimulus applied to a whole nerve gets no response until a threshold is reached. However, once over this threshold, as the strength of the stimulus increases, so does the response of the nerve until a maximum is reached. Without further knowledge, it looks as if the strength of the nerve impulse increases in response to the strength of the stimulus.

A stimulus applied to a single axon, using an internal electrode, also elicits no response until it reaches a certain threshold level. But beyond that threshold, the size of the response is always the same. However much the stimulus increases in size, the impulse in the axon is identical. This is the 'all-or-nothing law' in action – a nerve fibre either carries an impulse or it does not.

So as stimulus strength is increased, although an individual neurone either responds or it doesn't, in a whole nerve the threshold of more and more nerve fibres is reached until all of the fibres in the nerve are responding.

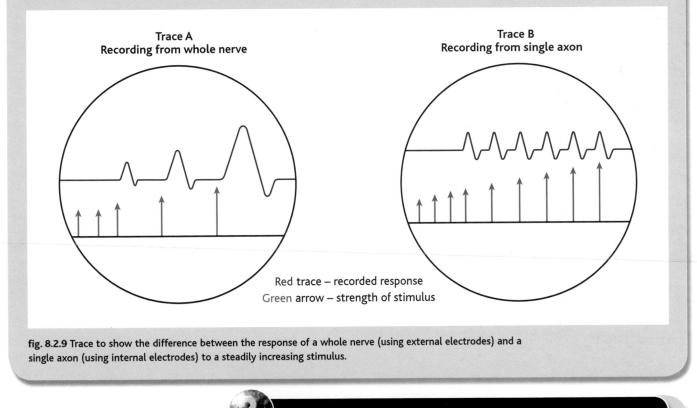

Trace A
Recording from whole nerve

Trace B
Recording from single axon

Red **trace** – recorded response
Green **arrow** – strength of stimulus

fig. 8.2.9 Trace to show the difference between the response of a whole nerve (using external electrodes) and a single axon (using internal electrodes) to a steadily increasing stimulus.

Questions

1   Describe the resting potential of a neurone and explain how it is maintained.

2   a   Describe an action potential and explain the importance of the refractory period.

    b   Explain how an action potential can be most accurately measured.

3   Explain how the graph in **fig. 8.2.8** provides evidence for the role of the sodium pump in maintaining the resting potential.

SC 4   Identify why traces A and B in **fig. 8.2.9** are so different, and explain what this tells us about the difference between nerves and neurones.

The neurones in action 5.8.5

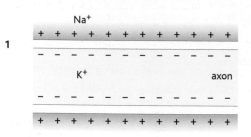

1. At resting potential there is positive charge on the outside of the membrane and negative charge on the inside, with high sodium ion concentration outside and high potasssium ion concentration inside.

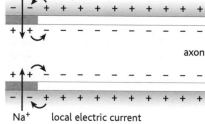

2. When stimulated, voltage-dependent sodium ion channels open, and sodium ions flow into the axon, depolarising the membrane. Localised electric currents are generated in the membrane.

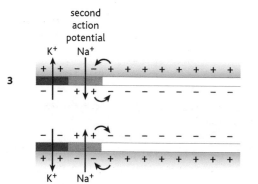

3. The potential difference in the membrane adjacent to the first action potential changes. A second action potential is initiated. At the site of the first action potential the voltage-dependent sodium ion channels close and voltage-dependent potassium ion channels open. Potassium ions leave the axon, repolarising the membrane. The membrane becomes hyperpolarised.

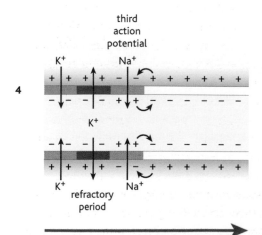

4. A third action potential is initiated by the second. In this way local electric currents cause the nerve impulse to move along the axon. At the site of the first action potential, potassium ions diffuse back into the axon, restoring the resting potential.

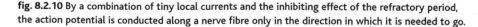

progress of the impulse

Once an action potential is set up as a response to a stimulus, it will travel the entire length of that nerve fibre, which may be many centimetres or even metres long. The movement of the nerve impulse along the fibre is the result of local currents set up by the ion movements at the action potential itself. They occur both in front of and behind the action potential. They depolarise the membrane in front of the action potential sufficiently to cause the sodium ion channels to open. The sodium ion channels behind the action potential cannot open due to the refractory period of the membrane behind the spike. In this way the impulse is continually conducted in the required direction (see **fig. 8.2.10**).

In myelinated neurones, the situation is more complex. Ions can only pass in and out of the axon freely at the nodes of Ranvier, which are about 1 mm apart. This means that action potentials can only occur at the nodes and so they appear to jump from one to the next. The effect of this is to speed up transmission as the ionic movements associated with the action potential occur much less frequently, taking less time. It is known as **saltatory conduction** from the Latin verb *saltare*, which means 'to jump'.

fig. 8.2.10 By a combination of tiny local currents and the inhibiting effect of the refractory period, the action potential is conducted along a nerve fibre only in the direction in which it is needed to go.

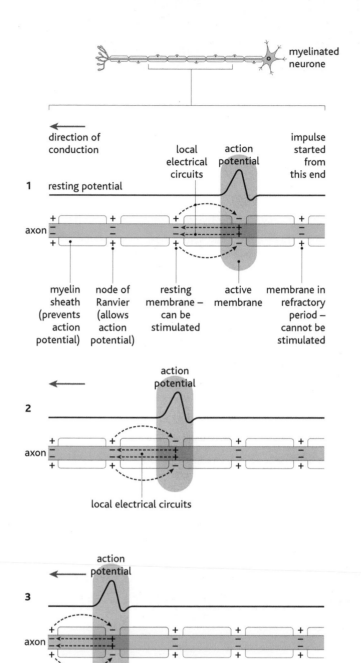

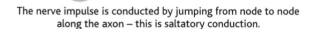

The nerve impulse is conducted by jumping from node to node along the axon – this is saltatory conduction.

fig. 8.2.11 By 'jumping' from node to node along a myelinated nerve fibre, the nerve impulses in vertebrate neurones can travel very rapidly along very narrow nerve fibres. This allows for the development of complex but compact nervous systems.

Synapses

Neurones must be able to intercommunicate. Receptors must pass their information into the sensory nerves, which in turn must relay the information to the central nervous system. Information needs to pass freely around the central nervous system and the impulses sent along the motor nerves must be communicated to the effector organs so that action can be taken.

Wherever two neurones meet they are linked by a **synapse** (see **fig. 8.2.12**). Every cell in the central nervous system is covered with **synaptic knobs** from other cells – several hundred in some cases. Neurones never actually touch their target cell, so a synapse involves a gap between two cells, a gap which the nerve impulses must somehow cross.

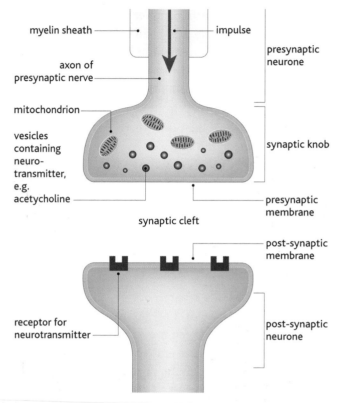

fig. 8.2.12 The structure of the synapse (based on information revealed by the electron microscope).

The functioning of synapses, rather like the contraction of muscle fibres (see pages 148–9), depends on the movement of calcium ions. The arrival of an impulse at the synaptic knob increases the permeability of the presynaptic membrane to calcium ions as **calcium ion channels** open up. Calcium ions then move into the synaptic knob down their concentration gradient. The effect of the influx of calcium ions is to cause the **synaptic vesicles** which contain a transmitter substance or **neurotransmitter** to move to the presynaptic membrane. Each vesicle contains about 3000 molecules of transmitter. Some of the vesicles fuse with the presynaptic membrane and release the transmitter substance into the **synaptic cleft**. These molecules diffuse across the gap and become attached to specific protein **receptor sites** on the post-synaptic membrane. This opens sodium ion channels in the membrane and there is an influx of sodium ions into the fibre, causing a change in the potential difference across the membrane and an **excitatory post-synaptic potential** (EPSP) to be set up. If there are sufficient of these EPSPs, the positive charge in the post-synaptic cell exceeds the threshold level, and an action potential is set up which then travels on along the post-synaptic neurone.

In some cases the neurotransmitter has the opposite effect. Different ion channels open in the membrane, allowing the inwards movement of negative ions, which makes the inside more negative than the normal resting potential. An **inhibitory post-synaptic potential** results, which makes it less likely that an action potential will occur in the post-synaptic fibre. These IPSPs play a part in the way we hear patterns of sound, for example, and they are thought to be important in the way birds learn songs.

Once the transmitter has had an effect, it is destroyed by enzymes in the synaptic cleft so that the receptors on the post-synaptic membrane are emptied and can react to a subsequent impulse.

Something similar to a synapse occurs where a motor neurone meets an effector. For example, neuromuscular junctions are found between motor neurones and muscle cells. When the transmitter is released, it stimulates a contraction in the muscle cell.

What are the transmitter substances?

One common neurotransmitter, found at the majority of synapses in humans, is **acetylcholine** (ACh). It is synthesised in the synaptic knob using ATP produced in the many mitochondria present. Nerves using acetylcholine as their transmitter are known as cholinergic nerves. Once the acetylcholine has done its job it is very rapidly hydrolysed by the enzyme cholinesterase. This makes sure that it no longer affects the post-synaptic membrane and also releases the components to be recycled. They pass back into the synaptic knob and are resynthesised into more acetylcholine.

Not all vertebrate nerves use acetylcholine as their synaptic transmitter substance. Some, particularly those of the sympathetic nervous system, produce noradrenaline in their synaptic vesicles and are known as adrenergic nerves. Dopamine is another important neurotransmitter found only in the CNS.

HSW Investigating the synapse

For many years it was suspected that transmission at the synapses was not electrical but chemical, but it was impossible to prove until the electron microscope was developed. There are several convincing strands of evidence which support the current model of the working of the synapse.

- Once the structure of the synapse had been seen using the electron microscope (see **fig. 8.2.13**), the synaptic gap could be measured. This settled the argument as to whether synaptic transmission was electrical (the nerve impulse 'jumping' across the synapse) or chemical. The gap was about 20 nm – simply too wide for an impulse the size of an action potential to jump across it.

- Electron micrographs taken after a nerve has been strongly stimulated for some time show a lack of synaptic vesicles. This reflects the observed fact that after

a period of stimulation a neurone can no longer respond (it becomes *accommodated*, see page 210). It suggests that the reason for this is that all of the transmitter substance has been used up. This supports the deduction that normal transmission across the synapse results from the release of transmitter from a small number of vesicles.

- A variety of drugs and poisons interfere with the working of synapses or neuromuscular junctions. A look at the effect of some of these substances throws light on the normal working of the system (see **table 8.2.1**). Any substance which interferes with the formation of acetylcholine, stops it being released, prevents it interacting with the post-synaptic receptors or reduces the rate at which it is broken down will in turn have a major effect on the nervous communication system of the body.

Substance	Where does it act?	What does it do?
Botulinus toxin	Affects the presynaptic membrane and stops the release of acetylcholine	Prevents transmission of impulses across synapses and so prevents the nervous system from working
Nicotine	Mimics the action of acetylcholine on post-synaptic membranes	Stimulates the nervous system
Strychnine Eserine Organophosphorus compounds used as weedkillers and insecticides Some nerve gases	Inactivate cholinesterase at the post-synaptic membrane and so prevent the breakdown of acetylcholine	Enhance and prolong the effects of acetylcholine as it is no longer destroyed. This means that nerves fire continuously, or at the slightest stimulus, and muscles are sent into tetanus.
Curare (used on arrow tips by South American Indians)	Interferes with the action of acetylcholine and stops the depolarisation of the post-synaptic membrane	Causes paralysis as the muscles can no longer be stimulated by the nerves

table 8.2.1 How drugs and poisons affect the synapses.

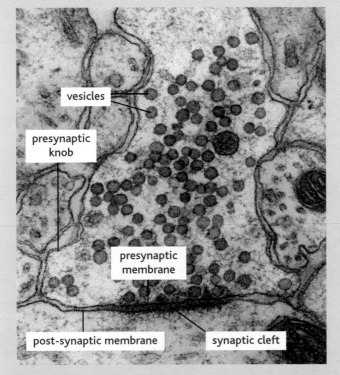

fig. 8.2.13 The evidence of the electron microscope has been vital for showing us the structure of synapses.

Electrical synapses?

With all this evidence supporting a model of chemical transmission across a synapse, it may be surprising to discover that the electron microscope also revealed the presence of electrical synapses. In vertebrates at least, they seem to play a much less important role than the chemical synapses but the evidence for their existence cannot be ignored. Electrical synapses contain many gap junctions. The presynaptic and post-synaptic membranes are only 2–3 nm (10^{-9} m) apart and membrane proteins form tiny pores linking the two cells. These pores allow the movement of ions between the two cells, and so the potential difference of the action potential can be transferred directly from one cell to another. These electrical synapses allow for the very fast transmission of impulses from one neurone to another – around 0.2 ms compared with 2 ms for a typical chemical synapse. So these synapses are used for rapid escape mechanisms in invertebrates, and rapid signalling within the CNS in vertebrates. However, they have many limitations and the chemical synapse is still regarded as the main method of communication between neurones.

Questions

1   Explain how transmission along a myelinated nerve is faster than transmission along an unmyelinated nerve.

2   Enzymes play several important roles in a synapse. Describe these roles.

3   Explain how electron micrographs and each of the substances shown in **table 8.2.1** can be used as evidence for the current model of synaptic transmission.

Interactions between neurones 5.8.3

Neurones interact in a variety of complex ways. In many cases a single nerve fibre will carry an action potential to a synapse with another cell, and transmission across that synapse will set up the next action potential. However, the situation can be much more complex than this.

Summation and facilitation

Often a single synaptic knob does not release enough transmitter substance to set up an action potential in the post-synaptic fibre. However, if two or more synaptic knobs are stimulated and release transmitter at the same time onto the same post-synaptic membrane, the effects add together and a post-synaptic action potential results. This is known as **spatial summation** (see **fig. 8.2.14**).

1
The most straightforward situation – the arrival of an impulse at one synaptic knob triggers an action potential in the post-synaptic fibre.

2
Spatial summation – action potentials need to arrive at several synapses at once to release the amount of neutotransmitter required to trigger an action potential in the post-synaptic fibre.

3
Temporal summation – one action potential arrives and, although it does not release sufficient transmitter substance itself to set up another action potential, it makes it easier for the next impulse which arrives to do so.

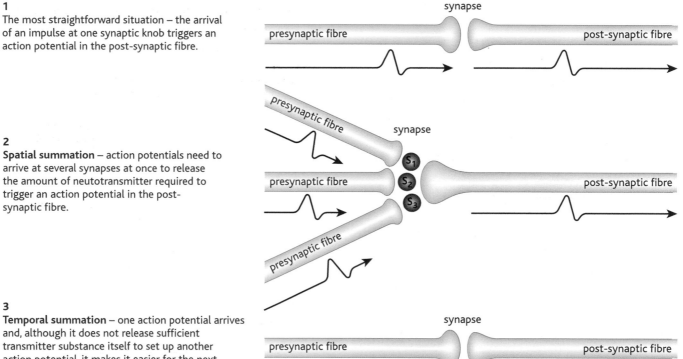

fig. 8.2.14 Different types of synaptic transmission.

In other cases, a single knob does not release enough transmitter substance from one impulse to stimulate the post-synaptic nerve fibre but if a second impulse is received from the same knob in quick succession an action potential results. This effect is known as **temporal summation** (adding over time), and it involves **facilitation**. In other words, the first impulse does not trigger a response but it makes easier (or facilitates) the passage of the next impulse (see **fig. 8.2.14**).

Accommodation

When you first put on perfume or aftershave you are very aware of the scent, but after a short time you lose that awareness. If you reapply your scent another day, you can smell it again. This reaction is the same as that of a sea anemone which, when poked with a pointer, will withdraw its tentacles. If the sea anemone is poked repeatedly, the response is lost. If left alone for a while, the sea anemone reacts when poked again. These are examples of a process known as **accommodation**.

Each time an impulse arrives at a synapse, vesicles full of neurotransmitter discharge their contents into the synaptic cleft. These vesicles can be synthesised only at a certain rate. If the synapse is used too often, all of the vesicles are discharged into the synaptic cleft and the rate of synthesis simply cannot keep up. At this point the neurones can no longer respond to the stimulus – they are said to have *accommodated* or *fatigued*. A short rest restores the response as new vesicles and transmitter molecules are made. Some synapses never fatigue, as they have an extremely rapid resynthesis rate, while others accommodate very quickly. The impact of this is seen particularly clearly in the neurones linked with the sensory organs.

What does all this mean for living animals?

The nerve fibres and synapses which we have been considering in isolation make enormously complicated systems in living animals. Individual neurones carry impulses in one direction only. The bundles of nerve fibres that make up nerves are capable of carrying vast numbers of impulses in different directions all at the same time. The nervous system as a whole gathers the available information and controls all the actions of the body, with the central nervous system collating information and sending out instructions. Synapses allow for great flexibility and intercommunications between cells and play a vital but incompletely understood role in the brain, closely linked with both learning and memory.

For simpler animals most of their nervous activity and behaviour involves reflex actions which have a minimum of input from the central nervous system. Humans also have many reflex actions, including the pupil reflex that you will study on page 218. However, we also have an extensive range of nerves which are under conscious, voluntary control. The two aspects which are crucial to an effective nervous system are a sensory system which detects stimuli, and a motor system by which effectors are made to respond.

Sensory systems

The coordinated activity of any organism does not depend purely on the passage of action potentials along nerve fibres or successful reflex arcs. There must be a continuous input of information from both the outside world and the internal environment if the animal is to be able to modify its behaviour and survive as situations change. **Sensory receptors** play a vital role in providing an animal with information about both its internal and external environment.

Simple sensory receptors are just neurones which have a dendrite that is sensitive to one particular stimulus. When the dendrite receives a stimulus, chemical events occur that result in an action potential in the nerve fibre of the neurone. This type of cell is known as a **primary receptor**. A **secondary receptor** is slightly more complicated. It consists of one or more completely specialised cells (not neurones) which are sensitive to a particular type of stimulus. These cells synapse with a normal sensory neurone which carries the impulse to the central nervous system (see **fig. 8.2.15**). The retinal cells in the retina of the eye are an example of these.

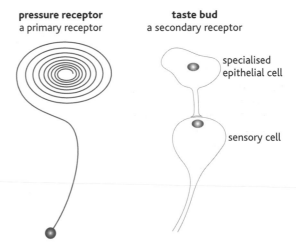

pressure receptor
a primary receptor

taste bud
a secondary receptor

specialised epithelial cell

sensory cell

fig. 8.2.15 The two main types of sensory receptors found in vertebrates.

As animals become increasingly complex, so do their sensory systems. While many sensory receptors are always found as isolated entities, in higher animals sensory receptors are increasingly found associated together in systems known as **sense organs**.

Questions

1 Define what is meant by accommodation in a neurone, and explain why it is important in the nervous system.

2 Explain how temporal and spatial summation help to make an organism more responsive to environmental cues.

How sensory receptors work 5.8.3

Sensory receptors transfer the energy of a particular stimulus – light, heat, sound, movement – into the electrochemical energy of an action potential in a sensory nerve fibre. There are various different types of receptors and a variety of ways of categorising them – these are the main ones:

- Exteroceptors respond to stimuli outside the body.

- Interoceptors respond to stimuli inside the body.

- Proprioceptors are sensitive to the relative positions of the skeleton and degrees of muscle contraction, and are very important for maintaining posture.

- Chemoreceptors are sensitive to chemical stimuli such as smell, taste and the pH levels of the blood.

- Mechanoreceptors are sensitive to mechanical stimuli such as pressure, tension, movement and gravity.

- **Photoreceptors** are sensitive to electromagnetic stimuli – for humans this is particularly visible light, while many insects are sensitive to UV light.

- Thermoreceptors respond to heat stimuli, and are particularly effective at detecting changes and differences in temperature.

fig. 8.2.16 Whatever you are doing, all of the different types of receptors in your body are sending impulses to allow you to maintain balance and homeostasis.

How do receptors work?

Just like nerve fibres, receptor cells have a resting potential which is dependent on the maintenance of an interior that is negative in relation to the outside by membrane sodium pumps. When a receptor cell receives a stimulus, sodium ions move rapidly across the cell membrane along concentration and electrochemical gradients, and this **generator current** sets up a **generator potential**. A small stimulus results in a small generator potential and a large stimulus results in a large generator potential – generator potentials *do not* obey the all-or-nothing law. If the generator potential produced is large enough to reach the threshold of the sensory neurone, an action potential will result in that neurone. If it is not, there will be no action potential – the action potential does obey the all-or-nothing law.

This process:

> stimulus → local change in permeability → generator current → generator potential → action potential

is common in one form or another to most sensory receptors.

In sensory organs such as the eye, several receptor cells will often synapse with a single sensory neurone. This means that even if the generator potential from an individual receptor cell is insufficient to set up a synapse, the potentials from several may add together or summate and trigger an action potential (see **fig. 8.2.17**). This is known as **convergence** and it is a useful adaptation for increasing the sensitivity of a sensory system to low-level stimuli. As you will see on page 215 this is an important feature of the retina cells, the light-sensitive cells of the eye.

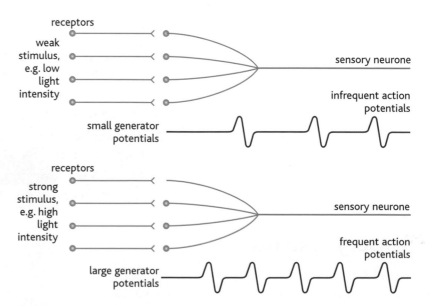

fig. 8.2.17 The interactions of receptors and sensory neurones to give high levels of sensitivity, as found in the eye and other sense organs.

When the received stimulus is weak, only a low frequency of action potentials along the sensory neurone results. But if the stimulus received by the receptors is strong, then a rapid stream of action potentials is fired along the sensory neurone. The importance of this is that, although the axon obeys the all-or-nothing law in terms of each individual action potential, a graded response is still possible, giving information about the strength of the stimulus. What this means for the eye, for example, is that we are not only aware of the difference between light and dark, but of all the varying degrees of light and shade (see **fig. 8.2.17**).

Adaptation of the receptors

The most important information carried by the sensory system is about changes in the environment that are potential problems to be dealt with by an organism. So if a receptor is exposed to a steady stimulus that continues unchanged for a period of time, the information becomes of decreasing importance to the animal unless for some reason it changes. The nervous system is adapted to cope with this situation. Instead of simply responding constantly to a steady stimulus, most receptors show a gradual decline in the generator potentials produced and so the action potentials in the sensory neurone become less frequent and may eventually stop. This is known as **adaptation**.

The mechanism by which adaptation is brought about is not fully understood, but seems to involve changes at the membrane. It may well be linked to the accommodation of the synapses in the pathway too. Some receptors adapt very rapidly, others only slowly or not at all. But in general, adaptation serves to prevent the system from carrying too many unnecessary impulses and frees the CNS from irrelevant information. Thus an unpleasant smell rapidly becomes tolerable, a hot bath feels comfortable and an irritating label in a jumper is forgotten – unless in some way the stimulus changes, when we become sensitised again.

Questions

1   **a**   Describe how a sensory receptor works.
      b   Explain how convergence increases the sensitivity of a system to low-level stimuli.

SC 2   Accommodation and adaptation have similar functions. Explain how the two processes differ and why they are important in the nervous system and for the living animal.

The human eye 5.8.6

Single sensory receptor cells are very useful and can carry vital information, even for very complex organisms. But groups of receptor cells all specialised for responding to a particular stimulus can be even more useful as they can respond in a more varied way. Relatively early in animal evolution, collections of receptors developed together to form specialised regions known as sense organs. Throughout the animal kingdom, the most common sense organs are those that respond to light, and to sound or vibration.

Sensitivity to light is found in some of the simplest living organisms. In humans it has developed far beyond a simple sensitivity to the absence or presence of light into a remarkably sophisticated optical system, allowing clear and focused vision in a wide variety of circumstances. Our eyes are sensitive to electromagnetic radiation with a wavelength between 400 and 700 nm. The ranges of other species often vary from this.

The structure of the human eye is very closely related to its function, as can be seen in **fig. 8.2.18**.

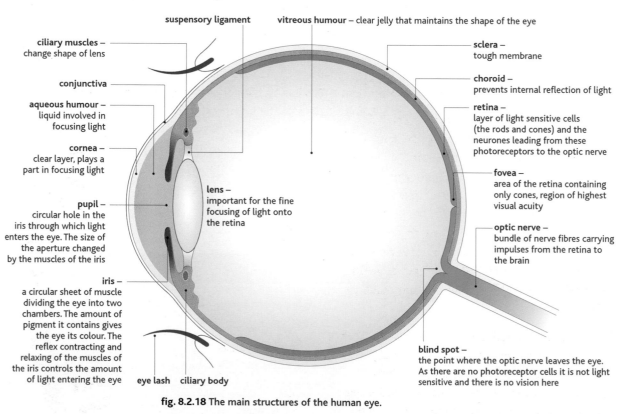

suspensory ligament

vitreous humour – clear jelly that maintains the shape of the eye

ciliary muscles – change shape of lens

sclera – tough membrane

conjunctiva

choroid – prevents internal reflection of light

aqueous humour – liquid involved in focusing light

retina – layer of light sensitive cells (the rods and cones) and the neurones leading from these photoreceptors to the optic nerve

cornea – clear layer, plays a part in focusing light

lens – important for the fine focusing of light onto the retina

fovea – area of the retina containing only cones, region of highest visual acuity

pupil – circular hole in the iris through which light enters the eye. The size of the aperture changed by the muscles of the iris

optic nerve – bundle of nerve fibres carrying impulses from the retina to the brain

iris – a circular sheet of muscle dividing the eye into two chambers. The amount of pigment it contains gives the eye its colour. The reflex contracting and relaxing of the muscles of the iris controls the amount of light entering the eye

blind spot – the point where the optic nerve leaves the eye. As there are no photoreceptor cells it is not light sensitive and there is no vision here

eye lash   **ciliary body**

fig. 8.2.18 The main structures of the human eye.

The role of the retina

Focusing is only the first step. The retina must then perceive the light and provide the information the brain needs to make sense of the image. The retina contains over a hundred million light-sensitive cells (photoreceptors), along with the neurones with which they synapse. There are two main types of photoreceptors in the retina, known as the **rods** and the **cones**. Both types are secondary exteroceptors.

You have around 120 million rods in each eye, which are spread evenly across the retina except at the fovea where there are none. They provide black and white vision only and are used mainly for seeing in low light intensities or at night. You have about 6 million cones tightly packed together in the fovea, which are used mainly for sharp vision in bright light. You are going to look mainly at the rods to see how sensory receptors work.

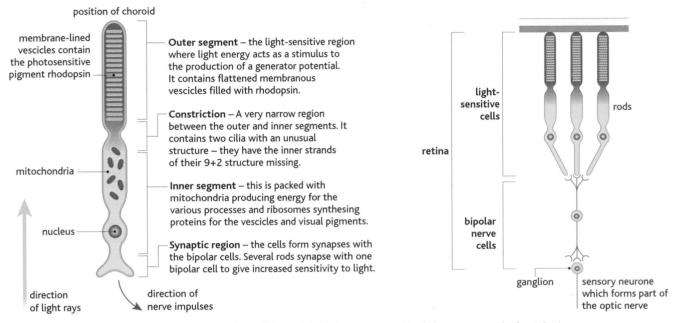

fig. 8.2.19 Rods have evolved to give great sensitivity to light, both in their structure and in their arrangement in the retina.

The rods contain a **visual pigment** called **rhodopsin** (**visual purple**). The rods are not very tightly packed together and several of them synapse with the same sensory neurone. Although this means they do not give a particularly clear picture, it does make them extremely sensitive both to low light levels and to movements in the visual field, because several small generator potentials can trigger an action potential to the CNS through the summation effect.

Note that the arrangement of the retina is 'back-to-front'. The 'outer segments' are actually next to the choroid, and the neurones are at the interior edge of the eyeball. The light has to pass through the synapses and the inner segments before reaching the outer segments containing the visual pigments. The reason for this somewhat unexpected arrangement is the origin of the retinal cells in the embryo and the way in which the eye is formed during embryonic development. This is why there is a blind spot where all the neurones pass through the layers of the eye to go into the brain.

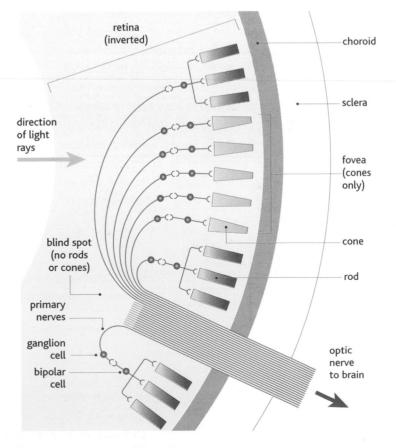

fig. 8.2.20 The structure of the retina.

How do the rods work?

The sensitivity of the rods is based on the reactions of the visual pigment rhodopsin with light. Rhodopsin is formed from two components, **opsin** and **retinal**. Opsin is a combination of lipid and protein (a lipoprotein) and retinal is a light-absorbing derivative of vitamin A. Retinal exists as two different isomers, *cis*-retinal and *trans*-retinal. In the dark, it is all in the *cis*-form. When a photon of light (the smallest unit of light energy) hits a molecule of rhodopsin, it converts the *cis*-retinal into *trans*-retinal. This changes the shape of the retinal, and puts a strain on the bonding between the opsin and retinal. As a result the rhodopsin breaks up into opsin and retinal. This breaking up of the molecule is referred to as **bleaching**.

The bleaching of the rhodopsin changes the permeability of the cell membrane of the rod to sodium ions (Na^+). The membranes of most neurones are relatively impermeable to sodium ions but rod cell membranes are normally very permeable to them. Sodium ions move into the rod cell through sodium ion channels, and the sodium pump moves them out again.

When rhodopsin is bleached by light, *trans*-retinal is formed. This triggers a cascade reaction which results in the closing of the sodium ion channels. The rod cell membrane becomes much less permeable to sodium ions and so there are fewer sodium ions in the rod cell. However, the sodium pump continues to work at the same rate, pumping sodium ions out of the cell, so the interior becomes more negative than usual. This **hyperpolarisation** is what is known as the **generator potential** in the rod. The size of the generator potential depends on the amount of light hitting the rod, and so the amount of rhodopsin bleaching that takes place. If

it is large enough to reach the threshold, or if several rods are stimulated at once, neurotransmitter substances are released into the synapse with the bipolar cell. An action potential is then set up in the bipolar cell which passes across the synapse to cause an action potential in the sensory neurone. All the sensory neurones leave the eye at the same point to form the optic nerve leading to the brain.

Once the visual pigment has been bleached, the rod cannot be stimulated again until the rhodopsin is resynthesised. It takes ATP energy produced by the many mitochondria in the inner segment to convert the *trans*-retinal back to *cis*-retinal and rejoin it to the opsin to form rhodopsin again. In normal daylight the rods are almost entirely bleached and can no longer respond to dim light – the eye is said to be **light-adapted**. After about 30 minutes in complete darkness the rhodopsin will be almost fully reformed, the eye is sensitive to dim light and is said to be **dark-adapted**. This explains why you become almost blind when you walk from a sunny garden into a house. The bright light has completely bleached the rhodopsin you need to see in the dimmer interior light. As the rhodopsin reforms in your rods, your vision returns as your eyes become dark adapted again.

The cones and colour vision

The cones work in a very similar way to rods, except that their visual pigment is known as iodopsin. There appear to be three types of iodopsin, each sensitive to one of the primary colours of light. Iodopsin needs to be hit with more light energy than rhodopsin in order to break down, and so it is not sensitive to low light intensities. But the cones provide colour vision, because the brain interprets the numbers of different types of cones stimulated as different colours. This complements the low light vision and sensitivity to movement provided by the rods.

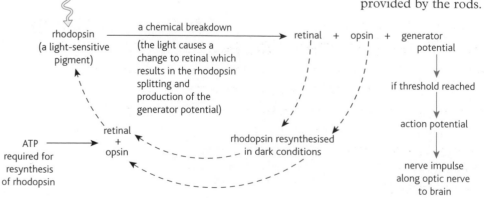

fig. 8.2.21 The reactions of rhodopsin in the light.

HSW Investigating the graded response of the rods

The rods of your eye do not give you an all-or-nothing response. You are aware of varying levels of light intensity. Yet you know that the axons which fire off potentials through the optic nerve operate on an all-or-nothing response.

Scientists have developed a model based on a graded response in the receptor cells which is amplified through a cascade system that causes the hyperpolarisation in the receptor cells. A single photon of light bleaches a single molecule of rhodopsin, but through the cascade that is set in place, several thousand sodium ion channels can be closed.

The brighter the light, the more rhodopsin is bleached and so the more sodium ion channels are closed. This gives a bigger depolarisation of the cell which lasts longer, so the cell can respond in a measurably different way to very small differences in light intensity. This can be demonstrated experimentally as in **fig. 8.2.22**. The membrane potential is recorded from the inner segment of the rod cell and associated bipolar cell. The rod cell is then stimulated with a flash of light. When the outer segment of the rod cell is exposed to light, the inner segment hyperpolarises.

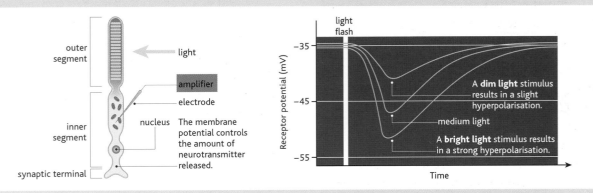

fig. 8.2.22 A practical technique for investigating the change in the membrane potentials of rod cells in response to light.

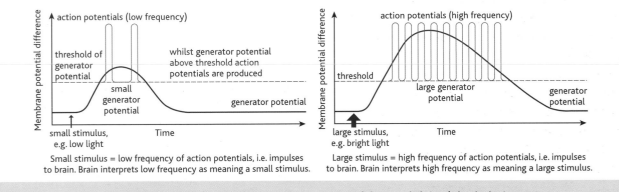

fig. 8.2.23 The graded response of the rods to light levels and the interpretation of the recorded signals by the brain.

Questions

1   a   Name the light-sensitive pigment in the rod cells and describe the effect that light has on the pigment.
    b   Explain how this change in the visual pigment is translated into a visual image in the brain.

2   Explain how the different neural connections of the rods and the cones which you can see in **fig. 8.2.20** account for the following:
    a   Rods transmit information in dimmer light than cones.
    b   Rods are more sensitive to movement than cones.
    c   Cones give a more accurate, clearer image than rods.

Coordination at work 5.8.7

Later in the book you will be looking at how the central nervous system works in animals to coordinate information and consciously control how the body responds. However, there are some responses that occur without any conscious thought. **Reflexes** are the basis of most nervous systems – fast, fixed (**unconditioned**) responses to a particular stimulus. They are controlled by the simplest type of nerve pathway in the body, known as a reflex arc. Most simple reflexes involve the spinal cord (see **fig. 8.2.25a**). An example of a cranial reflex is the control of the amount of light that enters the eye (see **fig. 8.2.25b**).

The iris as an effector

The iris is a muscular diaphragm with a hole, the pupil, in the middle. Pigments in the iris absorb light, making sure that the only way light can get into the eye is through the pupil. The amount of light that gets into your eyes is controlled by the size of the pupil. The iris has both circular and radial muscles that work antagonistically. In bright light the circular muscle is contracted and the radial muscles are relaxed, so the pupil is reduced to a narrow aperture. This reduces the amount of light entering the eye to avoid damage to the delicate rods and cones by overstimulating them. In dim light, the circular muscles relax and the radial muscles

contract, opening the pupil aperture wide so as much light as possible falls on the rods to maximise what you can see.

The size of the pupil is controlled by the muscles of the iris in the iris reflex, involving the cranial nerves of the autonomic nervous system and the brain in a cranial reflex. The muscles act as effectors, responding in a reflex action to the levels of light entering the eye through the pupil and falling on the retina. In this way the system constantly adapts to changes in light intensity.

The basic principle of the pupil reflex involves the following stages. Light may enter one or both of the eyes at the same time – the effect on the pupils is the same. Light falling on the sensory cells of the retina causes impulses to travel along neurones in the optic nerve to the brain. The brighter the light, the bigger the frequency of action potentials. This is detected in a control centre in the midbrain. The impulse then travels along two neurones to further control centres. Here the nerve impulses synapse with branches of the parasympathetic cranial nerve (the oculomotor) which transmits impulses to the iris. These stimulate the effectors (the muscles of the iris). The circular muscles contract and the radial muscles relax so the pupil constricts.

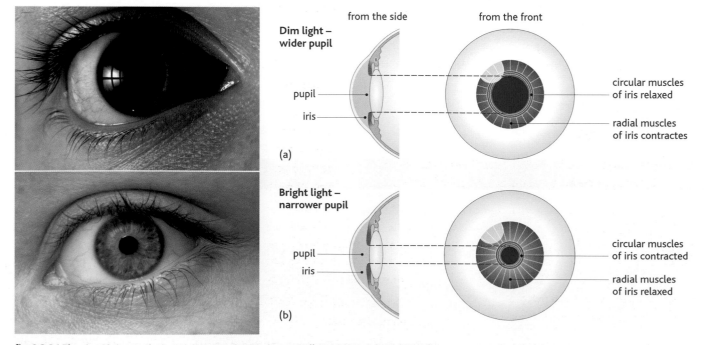

fig. 8.2.24 The size of the pupil of your eyes can change dramatically in different light conditions.

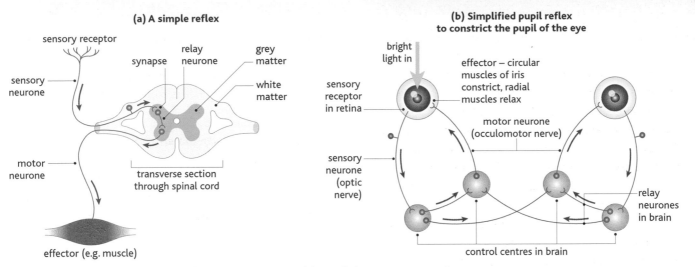

fig. 8.2.25 The reflexes that control the dilation and contraction of the pupils in your eyes are much more complex than the simple reflex arc you studied at GCSE. Diagram (a) shows a simple reflex arc involving the spinal cord; (b) shows the reflex that controls constriction of the pupil.

If the frequency of action potentials from the retina falls (when light levels drop), impulses travel from the control centres along sympathetic nerves to the iris, causing the circular muscles to relax and the radial muscles to contract and widen the pupil. This negative feedback system controls the amount of light entering the eye. The reflex response of either eye controls the dilation or constriction of the pupils of both eyes – so a bright light shone into one eye only will cause the pupils of both eyes to constrict.

The pupils respond to emotional cues as well as light. So, for example, the release of the stress hormone adrenaline causes the pupils to widen, making sure you can use all the available light to see as well as possible. Pupils also dilate when you see someone you like (or are physically attracted too) and constrict when you see someone you don't like or don't find attractive!

Comparing mechanisms of coordination

On pages 188–97 you looked at coordination in plants, which is brought about by plant hormones of different types. Some coordination in animals is also the result of hormones, such as aspects of growth and sexual maturity as well as responses to stress and the control of blood sugar levels in mammals. However, animals also have nervous systems. How do they compare?

Chemical control is relatively slow but it can be very long lasting. Hormones are carried around the body of an animal in the plasma as it moves around the circulatory system. They move into the target cells by diffusion and are picked up by receptors on cell membranes. Plant hormones also move in the transport systems of plants (the phloem) and by diffusion between cells. Chemical control is often linked to changes involving growth of an organism. It allows for long-term responses to environmental changes. However, it can also be used for day-to-day responses and is well suited to delicate control mechanisms such as negative feedback systems.

Nervous control is usually very rapid, making it an ideal form of internal communication and control for organisms that move their whole bodies about. If you need to respond quickly to environmental cues, nerve impulses give you the speed you need.

Questions

SC 1 Suggest why chemical coordination alone works for plants, while most animals use both chemical and electrical means of coordination.

SC 2 Draw up a table to compare the mechanisms of coordination in plants and animals, and state appropriate examples from pages 188–219.

3 Describe how the pupil reflex works and explain why it is important as a reflex response.

8.3 Brains and behaviour

The human brain 5.8.9

A nervous system made up of receptors, nerves and effectors will take an animal so far, but complex animals need more than this. Evolution has resulted in the **central nervous system** (**CNS**), and in particular the **brain** where information can be processed and from where instructions can be issued as required to give fully coordinated responses to a whole range of situations.

In vertebrates (including humans) the central nervous system develops as a hollow tube of nervous tissue which forms the spinal cord. This contains grey matter, made up of the neurone cell bodies, and white matter, consisting of nerve fibres. At the front or **anterior** end of a vertebrate embryo, this tube swells and to some extent folds back on itself to form a brain. The brain has three distinct areas – the forebrain, midbrain and hindbrain (**fig. 8.3.1**).

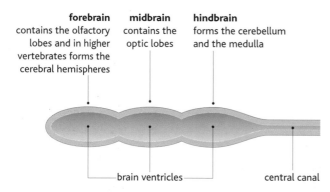

forebrain contains the olfactory lobes and in higher vertebrates forms the cerebral hemispheres

midbrain contains the optic lobes

hindbrain forms the cerebellum and the medulla

brain ventricles — central canal

fig. 8.3.1 The human brain has evolved considerably from the basic vertebrate pattern.

In some vertebrates this brain remains fairly simple, with areas very specific to particular functions such as sight or smell. In other vertebrates, including humans, the brain becomes a remarkably complex structure (**fig. 8.3.2**). The original simple arrangement of the brain into three areas is very difficult to see because a part called the **cerebral hemispheres** (also known as the **cerebral cortex**) is folded back over the entire brain. There are areas of the human brain with very specific functions concerned with the major senses

and control of basic bodily functions. There are also many regions of the brain where the precise functions and interrelationships with other areas of the brain are not clearly understood. Scientists have estimated that the human brain contains about a hundred thousand million neurones – and that each neurone synapses with up to 10 000 other neurones. That is a very complex system to try to understand!

Some of the major areas of the brain

- The cerebral hemispheres are the site of many higher functions of the brain. This is where the abilities to see, think, learn and feel emotions are sited. They are made up almost entirely of grey matter – nerve cell bodies, dendrites and synapses. The cortex is only a thin layer but it is deeply folded to give a huge surface area. The left and right cerebral hemispheres are connected by a band of axons (white matter) known as the **corpus callosum**. They are subdivided into a number of lobes which have been found to be associated with particular functions.

- The frontal lobe is associated with the higher brain functions such as emotional responses, planning ahead, reasoning and decision making. It is very much the 'conscious' area of the brain, involved with combining information from several areas of the cortex to form associations and develop ideas. It is linked with your 'personality'. The frontal lobe also contains the primary motor cortex of the brain which is involved in the control of many of the body movements. The control comes via motor neurones which pass through the hindbrain and the spinal cord carrying impulses to the muscles.

- The temporal lobe is involved with processing auditory information – in other words, sound recognition, hearing and speech. It also seems to be involved in the memory functions of the brain.

- The occipital lobe is also known as the **visual cortex**. It is concerned with processing visual information – in other words it deals with the input from the eyes and is involved in vision, shape recognition, colour vision and the sense of perspective.

- The parietal lobe has a number of varied functions. It is associated with some aspects of memory and recognition. It is also concerned with the ability to calculate, with movement and sensation, and with your ability to orientate yourself in space.

There are a number of other areas of the brain which are known to be linked to specific aspects of the way your body works. Many of these are involved in the unconscious responses of your body which maintain the processes of life.

- The **hypothalamus** coordinates the autonomic (unconscious) nervous system. It plays a major part in the thermoregulation of the body (see page 166). It monitors the chemistry of the blood and controls the hormone secretions of the pituitary gland. It also controls many basic drives – thirst, hunger, aggression and reproductive behaviour.

- The **cerebellum** coordinates smooth movements and uses information from the muscles and the ears to maintain posture and balance.

- The **medulla oblongata** (often referred to as the medulla) is the most primitive part of the brain. It contains reflex centres which control functions such as the heart rate, blood pressure, breathing rate, coughing, sneezing, swallowing, saliva production and peristalsis. It is this region which may maintain the basic life responses even when the higher areas of the brain have been effectively destroyed. **Figure 8.3.2** gives you a more detailed illustration of the various areas of the brain.

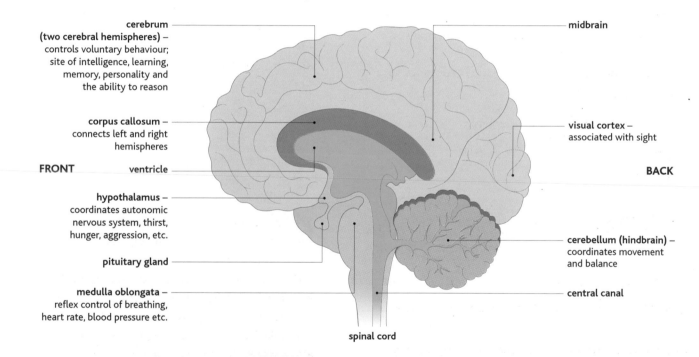

fig. 8.3.2 The brain is a remarkable organ of enormous complexity and so far our knowledge of how it works remains limited.

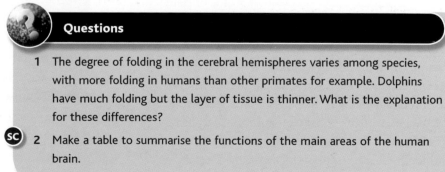

Questions

1 The degree of folding in the cerebral hemispheres varies among species, with more folding in humans than other primates for example. Dolphins have much folding but the layer of tissue is thinner. What is the explanation for these differences?

2 Make a table to summarise the functions of the main areas of the human brain.

How the human brain works 5.8.12, 5.8.16, 5.8.10

There are several hundred million nerve cells working together in the human brain. The great nerve tracts from the spinal cord cross over as they enter and leave the brain, so that the left-hand side of the brain receives information from and controls the right-hand side of the body, and vice versa. The cerebral cortex is only about 3 mm thick, and yet it controls most of the functions that make us what we are. The brain contains centres or nuclei made up of cell bodies which may have hundreds of synapses, making intercommunication between thousands and indeed millions of cells possible. You are going to look at some of the ways in which scientists investigate the brain, and then look at the models of learning and behaviour which have been developed as a result.

For many years our understanding of the human brain has been developed using evidence from two different sources: animal studies and studying human brains.

Animal studies

Many investigations have been carried out on the brains of animals. Some of the work has been related directly to the working of the human brain, although this is not always possible. Animal studies can approach the problem of understanding the brain in a number of different ways. Some experiments look at the way the brain develops normally, and what happens when obstacles are placed in the way of that development, as you will see on pages 232–3.

Another approach is to damage or remove areas of the brain of an animal and observe the effect on its behaviour. For example, the effect of removing the cerebral hemispheres from animals such as dogs and monkeys has been studied, as well as implanting electrodes to see the effect on behaviour of artificially stimulating a region of the brain.

Observations of normal behaviour and learning can also be made and (sometimes) compared with post-mortem changes in the brain. One problem with this is the human tendency to interpret animal behaviour in the light of human responses (anthropomorphism). So, for example, cats used to a caged existence, or rats which frequently explore mazes in the interests of science, are likely to be well-fed, healthy individuals

displaying normal behaviour for their species. But our natural response may be to feel sorry for them, even deciding that they look unhappy, because we are endowing them with our own human reactions to a situation.

HSW The moral and ethical dilemmas of using animals

Many people find the use of animals in brain research distasteful. Some feel that it should never be done (absolutists) and others think that there may be times when it is justified (relativists). Individual viewpoints will be affected by the **moral code**, or norm, of the society in which we live, as well as personal **ethics**, what we consider right and wrong or the best approach in that situation. For example, the strength of feeling may depend on the type of animals used. There is relatively little objection to the using sea slugs or squids, but using dogs and cats and most particularly primates is more likely to raise ethical objections.

Ethics committees decide what research can and can't be done. Their decisions are made in a relativist way, comparing the effect on the animals with the potential improvement for human life particularly for people affected by brain diseases and damage.

fig. 8.3.3 People often have strong views about the use of animals in research and even when research has been given the go-ahead by an ethics committee, not everyone agrees with their decisions.

The number of fMRI images which can be recorded each second is constantly increasing, so the ability of scientists to observe changes in brain activity as different tasks are performed is improving all the time. fMRI gives an extremely spatially accurate image of the brain. At the moment it is used mainly to investigate normal brain structure and function. For example, clear differences are visible in the activity of the brains of people with dyslexia when reading compared with the brains of normal readers. However, increasingly researchers are looking at ways of using fMRI to diagnose diseases such as the early signs of stroke damage and the onset of Alzheimer's.

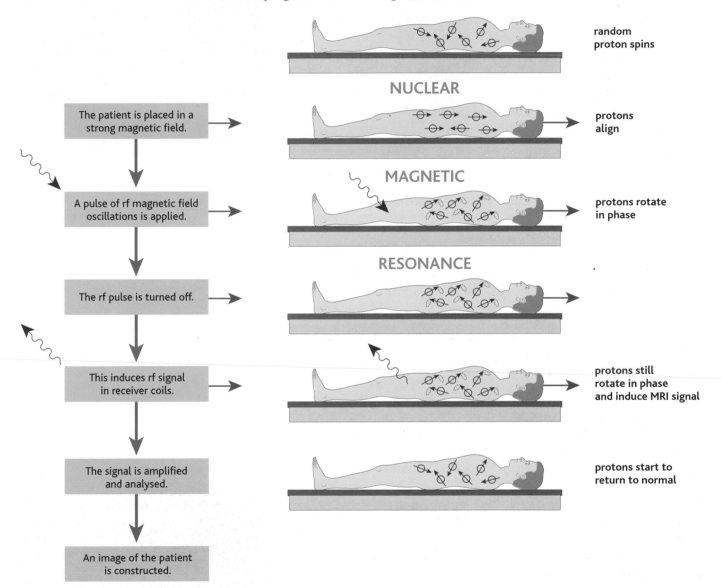

NUCLEAR

MAGNETIC

RESONANCE

The patient is placed in a strong magnetic field.

A pulse of rf magnetic field oscillations is applied.

The rf pulse is turned off.

This induces rf signal in receiver coils.

The signal is amplified and analysed.

An image of the patient is constructed.

random proton spins

protons align

protons rotate in phase

protons still rotate in phase and induce MRI signal

protons start to return to normal

fig. 8.3.7 This diagram shows you how an MRI scan is produced.

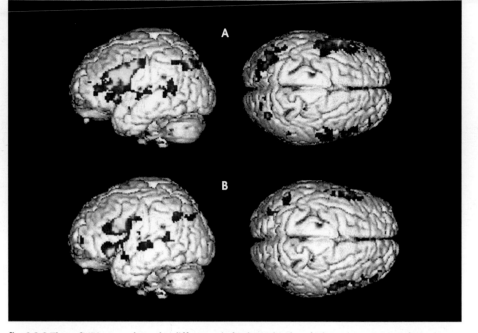

fig. 8.3.8 These fMRI scans show the difference in brain activation during a memory test between two groups of subjects, all apparently normal. However, one group (A on the image) carries an allele which is a known risk factor for Alzheimer's disease. As you can see, the brain activity is spread over a bigger area in the people with the high risk allele. Scientists think that this may show that their brains are working extra hard to compensate for minor problems which are already beginning to occur in their memory.

There are some drawbacks with fMRA, however. Like MRI, it is a noisy procedure which some people find very stressful. It has to be carried out with the patient's head remaining completely still – any movement reduces the accuracy of the image. This limits what can be tested usually to a response to images, although increasingly scientists are finding ways to allow movement in other body areas. For example, in one investigation scientists studied the brains of dancers as they moved their feet as if dancing to music. The areas which lit up were strongly linked to the speech areas of the brain.

Some neurophysiologists have queried the validity of fMRI scans. They argue that the blood flow to different areas of the brain when a subject is looking at different stimuli is a case of correlation, not causation. Further research will be needed to confirm whether or not it is a causal link. For the moment, the majority of scientists in this field are convinced that the areas shown up by this imaging technique really are the active regions of the brain involved in an activity.

HSW Improving techniques

One major drawback of current brain imaging techniques is that the individuals need to keep still. However, one relatively new brain mapping technique can be used in real time as people actively engage in real-life situations, opening up whole new areas of research. Quantified electroencephalography (qEEG) uses sensors attached to the outside of the skull to measure the activity of the brain as patients carry out different activities. It allows scientists to build up brain maps indicating which areas are used in different activities and skills. So far the main use is research into the functioning of the brain rather than diagnosis of disease and so the fact that there are no known risks for the subjects, who are volunteers, is a big advantage. The small risk associated with, for example, the X-rays used in CT scans for diagnosis, is justified by clinical need. However, research done on healthy patients should have no element of risk for them in the procedure. The major disadvantage of qEEGs is that they are not as spatially accurate in the brain as fMRI can be.

Dr David Lewis, the Director of Neuroscience in a company called MindLab International, has investigated a wide range of activities. In one case, he was asked to compare the impact of kissing with eating chocolate on brain activity in a number of young couples. Perhaps surprisingly, the chocolate stimulated many more areas of the brain than kissing did – although as Dr Lewis commented, being wired up to recording equipment possibly doesn't put you in the most romantic mood but the impact of chocolate is all down to the chemicals it contains!

In further exciting development neuroscientists are attempting to combine fMRI with qEEG to give greater accuracy to the brain maps they are producing.

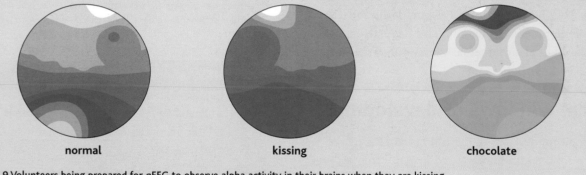

| normal | kissing | chocolate |

fig. 8.3.9 Volunteers being prepared for qEEG to observe alpha activity in their brains when they are kissing and eating chocolate. The brain maps show the impact of eating chocolate was more than twice as high as kissing, a common trend with all of the subjects – the more colours, the more activity!

Questions

1 Summarise the main imaging techniques used to investigate brain structure and function. Explain how they work, the advantages and limitations of each and give examples of their use in both understanding brain structure and function and in diagnosing disease.

SC 2 Summarise both absolutist and relativist viewpoints on the use of animal models in understanding how brains work. Explain how each group feels they have the moral high ground.

Nature and nurture in brain development 5.8.11, 5.8.13, 5.8.12

The human brain takes many years to develop fully. As early as 21 days after conception a basic neural tube has formed. By the time a baby is born this simple starting point has developed into a complex brain made up of about $100\,000\,000\,000$ (10^{10}) neurones! Once a baby is born the brain continues to grow, with the formation of new synapses and the myelination of axons rather than the formation of new neurones. A newborn baby is exposed to many new stimuli and the immature neurones move around and make the connections which will result in the mature anatomy of the brain. By 2 years old the brain is about 80% of the adult size. Scientists used to think that brain growth and development were complete by around 7 years of age. Evidence now suggests that myelination and the main structural arrangement of the brain is complete by 18, but that changes such as those involved in memory formation can continue throughout life.

The way your brain develops is in part controlled by the genes you have inherited. However, there is strong evidence from both human and animal studies that the normal development of the brain also depends on your getting the right environmental stimuli. Both nature and nurture play their parts!

Critical windows of development

One current model used to explain certain aspects of brain development in humans and in other animals is that there are critical 'windows' of development. These are periods of time during which vital neural connections are made in the brain in response to specific stimuli. In theory, if the brain does not receive these stimuli at the crucial time the pathways will not develop normally. This model has been extensively investigated using the development of the visual cortex in animals as varied as monkeys and ferrets.

Studies of the growth of the brain in animal foetuses show that the axons from the light-sensitive cells in the retina grow through to the area know as the thalamus (see **fig. 8.3.2**) where the synapses are developed in a very regular way. This results in an ordered arrangement of neurones in the visual cortex. Stained sections show that it is organised into columns of cells, known as ocular dominance columns. Neighbouring

columns of cells receive input from the same area of the retina in the left eye and the right eye. For some time scientists thought this arrangement was the result of the stimulation of the eye during a critical period after birth. However, later work has shown that this isn't the case – the columns of cells are already present in the visual cortex at birth. The existence of the columns is the result of nature – the genetics of the developing animal. They are simply modified during a later critical period.

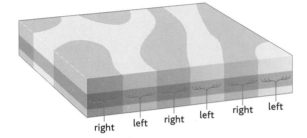

fig. 8.3.10 Justin Crowley and Lawrence Katz worked with newborn ferrets, injecting them with radioactive tracers which moved from one eye and were found in specific bands in the visual cortex, showing that the anatomical columns were in place at birth. Each coloured column is an ocular dominance column, and left and right refer to left eye and right eye.

HSW Confirming a model

J.C. Horton and D.R. Hocking worked on macaque monkeys to confirm the 'nature' hypothesis that the ocular dominance columns are in place before birth rather than developing in response to environmental cues (nurture). They delivered three foetal monkeys by Caesarean section 8 days before the end of normal gestation. This meant their eyes were at an earlier stage of development than a normal newborn monkey. The infant monkeys were kept completely in the dark throughout their lives. A radioactive tracer was injected into the right eye of each monkey 1 day after they were delivered. A week later, when they would naturally have been at full term, sections of the visual cortex were prepared and examined. They showed well-developed ocular dominance columns. This work has been confirmed in a number of other species. It has been very useful in developing our model of how the brain develops. However, there are clear ethical issues in this type of work which some people find unacceptable.

The work of Horton, Hocking and others demonstrated that the basic organisation of the visual cortex is present at birth and is therefore the result of genetic inheritance (nature). More work was needed to see if there really are any critical windows (also referred to as sensitive periods) of development in the brain when nurture (the environment) contributes to the development and can override the genetic influence.

Evidence for the effect of nurture

In the 1960s a great deal of work was done on the development of the visual cortex using kittens and monkeys. These animals were used because, unlike the flies, rats and mice used in much animal research, kittens and monkeys have visual systems which are very similar to our own. Newborn kittens and monkeys have very different visual abilities – the monkey appears visually alert and can look at specific objects while a newborn kitten is blind, with its eyes still closed permanently. Experiments suggested that in newborns the basic ability to see, and even binocular vision, is already in place.

In a series of classic experiments, David Hubel and Torsten Weisel showed that there appears to be a critical window for the development of the mature visual cortex in cats and monkeys. In the best known of these experiments they stitched shut (sutured) one or both of the eyes of infant kittens and monkeys. The age at which the animals were sutured and deprived of vision, and the length of time the eye remained closed, was varied. The effects of this early sensory deprivation on the firing of neurones in the visual cortex were then observed, sometimes many years later. Hubel

and Weisel also reared animals in the dark, and in light environments without any patterns such as vertical lines and measured the effects of these treatments on the development of the visual cortex. Some of the findings are summarised below:

- When kittens had the lid of one eye sutured shut at 1 week old (i.e. before their eyes had opened) they developed apparently normally. They could see perfectly well with their open eye. After times which varied from 1 to 3 months the closed eye was allowed to open and the other eye was stitched shut. It immediately became clear that the kittens were effectively blind in the eye that had previously been closed. They bumped into things and fell off steps and tables. Their eyes showed no physical signs of blindness, but when recordings were made in the visual cortex of these animals it was clear that very few of the cells that corresponded to the original closed eye were firing. Similar results were achieved using newborn monkeys, where the eyes were kept stitched shut for 6 months.

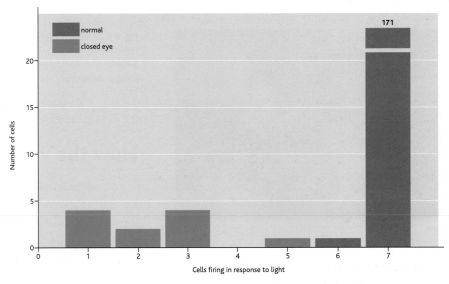

fig. 8.3.11 Results from some of the original work by Weisel and Hubel published in 1965. This shows the difference in the response of the visual cortex to light in 8–14-week-old kittens which had had their right eye closed from 1 week of age. Only 10 out of 199 cells responded to stimulation from the light-deprived eye, while the open eye responded normally.

- When the lid of one eye is closed in a cat over 4 months of age which could see normally until then, it has no effect on the vision in the eye or the recordings made in the visual cortex when the eye is eventually opened again.

- The period of susceptibility in kittens is highest between the fourth and fifth weeks after birth. Closing an eye for as little as 3–4 days during this critical period has a profound effect on the number of neurones which then fire in the linked areas of the visual cortex. A short closure at the critical time has as much effect as closing the eye from birth.

- The critical period for the development of the visual cortex in monkeys appears to be between 6 and 8 weeks after birth.

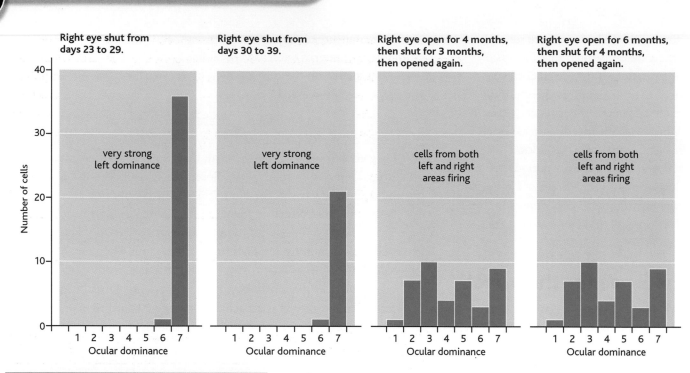

Right eye shut from days 23 to 29.

very strong left dominance

Right eye shut from days 30 to 39.

very strong left dominance

Right eye open for 4 months, then shut for 3 months, then opened again.

cells from both left and right areas firing

Right eye open for 6 months, then shut for 4 months, then opened again.

cells from both left and right areas firing

Number of cells

Ocular dominance

fig. 8.3.12 Recordings from the visual cortices of kittens from the same litter which had their eyes sutured shut at different stages of development and for different lengths of time. Using kittens from the same litter ensures genetic similarities. Ocular dominance indicates which eye is used most. As you can see, in the kittens that had one eye closed when they were very young, only the left eye registered any stimulus. In the kittens where eye closure was later, cells in both eyes fire off when they are visually stimulated.

How the visual cortex develops

The evidence shows that the columns of the cortex are there by the time an animal is born. So how do scientists explain the importance of the environmental stimulus on these columns during the critical period? All the research suggests that there is further visual development after birth. The model which best explains the observed events is as follows.

In a newborn kitten, monkey or human there is considerable overlap between the dendrites and synapses of the axons in the different columns. In the adult there is considerably less overlap. Experimental evidence from animals with one eye artificially closed suggests that the change is brought about as a result of visual experience.

Axons compete for target cells in the visual cortex. Every time an action potential passes along an axon and arrives at a target cell it releases neurotransmitter from the synapse which establishes it more firmly. If another neurone also synapses with the same target cell, but no impulses pass along it, it does not release neurotransmitter and eventually the synapses which are not firing will be weakened and destroyed. This happens throughout the nervous system to reduce the numbers of unwanted axons and synapses and to make sure that messages are carried efficiently to exactly where they are needed.

When one eye is deprived of light, none of the axons from that eye will be carrying impulses to the target cells in the visual cortex. In any area where the neurones from both eyes overlap, the synapses on the axons carrying impulses from the open eye will be very active. The synapses from the closed eye will be inactive and so they will be weakened and eventually lost. As a result, the axons and synapses from the active eye will come to dominate the cortex (see **fig. 8.3.13**).

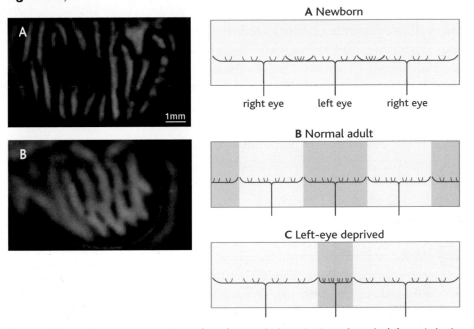

fig. 8.3.13 The white bands indicate the ocular columns which receive input from the left eye in both cases. As you can see, in a normal adult rhesus monkey the light and dark bands are equal, but in the animal which has had the right eye closed during the critical period, the bands from the seeing eye are much wider and those from the closed eye have narrowed. The second diagram shows how this comes about.

Questions

1 Describe two ethical positions on the work carried out by:
   a Crowley and Katz on infant monkeys
   b Weisel and Hubel on kittens.

2 Summarise the evidence, described here from animal experiments, for the existence of critical windows of development of sight in mammals.

3 Suggest under what circumstances scientists might collect evidence of similar critical windows of development in humans.

4 Hubel and Wiesel were awarded a Nobel Prize for their work. Why are their findings so important?

Development of the human brain 5.8.13

The development of the human brain is brought about by a combination of genetics (nature) and the environment in which it grows (nurture). To compare the contributions of nature and nurture is not easy, and to do it scientists use a combination of many different methods. These include the animal experiments you have looked at showing that in the development of the visual cortex of certain mammals (which develops under the influence of the genes) there is a critical window where environmental influences have a major effect. But we cannot just assume the same is true for human brains. Some of the research has been carried out on primates, our closest mammalian relatives, which increases the likelihood that humans will have a similar critical window when external stimuli are crucial. Experiments of the type done on kittens and monkeys would be completely unethical on human babies. So more evidence enabling us to compare the relative influence of nature and nurture is needed. This is often gathered in indirect, less invasive ways.

Individuals with damaged brains

As you saw on pages 222–7, observations on people with damaged brain areas have been vital in helping to build up a picture of the structure of the different brain areas that develop and their function. This knowledge is fundamental in understanding how the brain develops, but has not been considered of major importance in the comparison of the contributions of nature and nurture. However, studies looking at how the brain changes and develops after areas are damaged after strokes or accidents are bringing in new evidence. It was thought that the neural connections of the cortex that control voluntary movement, speech and reasoning become fixed after a certain stage. Evidence now suggests that new connections may be made which bypass the damaged area, with a different part of the brain taking over the job.

Using newborn babies

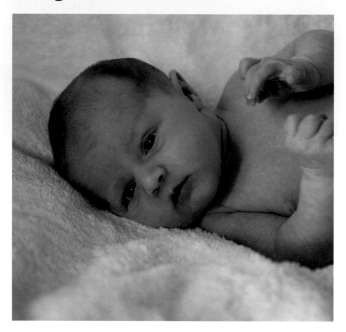

fig. 8.3.14 Studying what affects the rapid brain development of a newborn infant is a useful method of comparing the influences of nature and nurture.

The observations of doctors treating newborn babies are very useful tools for unravelling the interaction of nature and nurture in brain development. For example, babies may be born with cataracts (cloudy lenses which limit the light reaching the retina) in one or both eyes. If the cataract is removed when the child is very young, sight develops normally. But if surgery is left until the child is older, sight cannot be restored. This suggests that a critical period of development is involved, just like the young animals. Researchers looked at the outcomes of surgery carried out on babies who had a dense cataract in one eye diagnosed at between 1 and 10 days after birth. They followed up a group of 48 of these children when they were aged between 5 and 8 years old, looking at the timing of their surgery. They investigated whether the pattern of sight restored suggested that the environment (nurture) inflicted a gradual change on brain development or whether it pointed to a critical early window, pinpointed by when treatment was maximally effective.

The evidence strongly suggested that operating to remove the cataract before 6 weeks of age minimised any future sight problems.

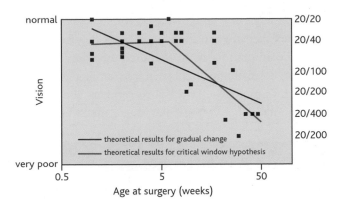

fig. 8.3.15 The research results of the effect of the timing of cataract-removal operations on subsequent levels of vision, shown as dots. They match the pattern of the critical window method better than the gradual change model. 20/20 vision is the best you can have!

This evidence points to the idea that there is a critical window of development of the visual cortex in humans, when nurture has an overriding influence on the patterns laid down by nature. This pattern reflects the development patterns seen in young monkeys and kittens, confirming the usefulness of that research.

Another study published in 2008 by Francesca Simion, Lucia Regolin and Hermann Bulf showed that babies as young as 2 days old recognise the difference between movement by a living, biological organism and non-biological movement. Using light patterns recorded from the joints and random light patterns, newborn infants showed that they could discriminate between the two different patterns of motion. They clearly preferred to look at the biological movement (it held their attention much longer) and they also looked much longer at biological displays which were the right way up rather than upside down. The biological movement presented to the infants was actually from chickens, and this type of biological movement discrimination in the brain has been seen in a number of animals including chicks, cats, pigeons, monkeys, apes and dolphins. It appears to be genetically wired into the brain – and again this makes evolutionary sense. So in this area of brain development, nature appears to be all important.

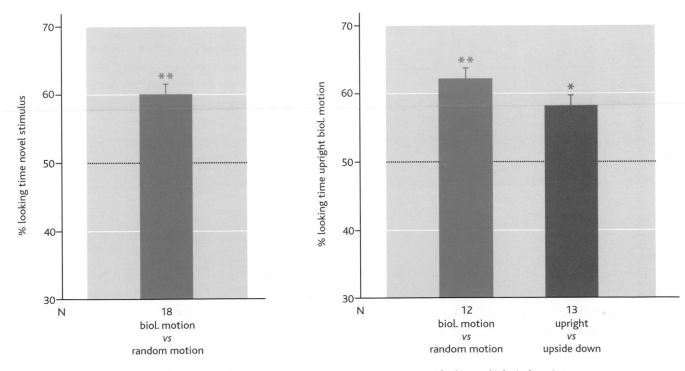

fig. 8.3.16 The results of these experiments show the percentage time that newborn babies spent looking at biological motion over random motion, and also at biological motion when it is the right way up rather than upside down. The dotted lines show the amount of time that would have been spent looking at the motion simply by choice.

Other work using the abilities of young babies suggests a genetic tendency towards face recognition (see also the twin studies below). It also suggests that there is a critical window of brain development when we learn to distinguish human faces from others. Charles Nelson in the US suggested that as babies gain experience of looking at faces one area of the cerebral cortex becomes particularly sensitive to the type of faces they see most often – i.e. human faces. At the same time they lose the ability to distinguish between less familiar types of face such as monkeys. Two UK researchers showed experimentally that younger babies are much better

HSW Studying human deprivation

Although it is impossible to carry out sensory deprivation experiments on human infants, there are times when this happens as a result of deliberate cruelty from the parents or carers. Studies carried out on severely neglected children in the US during the 1990s showed that when children are deprived of normal sensory input, their brains fail to develop properly. These children had suffered appalling neglect, with some kept in dark cupboards with virtually no human contact. The deprivation was not just of sight – it involved touch, warmth, affection, language and social interactions.

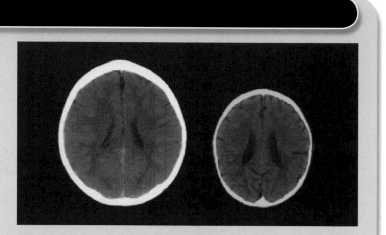

These images illustrate the negative impact of neglect on the developing brain. The CT scan on the left is from a healthy three year old child with an average head size (50th centile). The image on the right is from a three year old child following severe sensory-deprivation neglect in early childhood. The child's brain is significantly smaller than the average and has abnormal development of cortex (cortical atrophy) and other abnormalities suggesting abnormal development of the brain. From studies conducted by researchers from The Child Trauma Academy led by Bruce D. Perry, M.D., Ph.D.

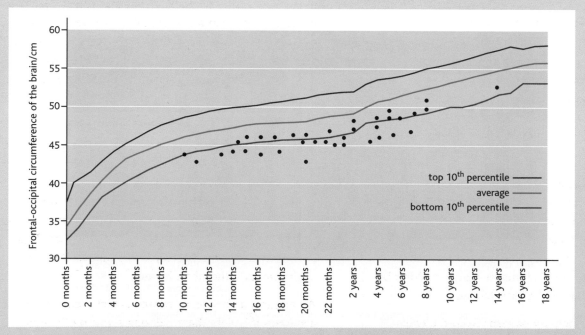

fig. 8.3.17 Data from a paper presented to the Society for Neuroscience Annual Meeting in New Orleans in 1997. The figure shows sample scans and a graph which demonstrate the effect of nurture on the overall development of the brain.

This type of evidence, while shocking, is extremely useful in comparing the contributions of nature and nurture to brain development in human beings.

than older babies at recognising the faces of different monkeys but all babies could distinguish between different human faces. There seemed to be some level of critical window around 6 months of age when the ability to recognise faces narrows down. However, familiarity can override these changes in the brain. Adults who work with monkeys and apes for example, soon learn to distinguish them easily by their faces alone. This work showed a clear interaction between nature and nurture in the development of the relevant brain areas.

Evidence from other research methods confirms that there are many ways in which environmental influences can impact on the development of the human brain – and some situations where the genetic 'hard-wiring' is there from the start and nurture has little effect.

Research methods include the use of imaging techniques, animal experiments and human observations you have met already. Other methods include twin studies which you met in *AS Biology* page 188. Twins offer researchers an almost unique tool for observing the impact of nature and nurture on development.

Twin studies and face recognition

People are social animals. Through life we need to recognise other people to make friends, support our family, find and recognise a mate, etc. But as we all know, some people are better at remembering faces than others. A great deal of research has gone into how face recognition develops in the brain, and some very recent twin studies suggest that there are strong genetic factors.

In 2007 Dr Thad Polk and his team at the University of Illinois measured activity in the visual cortex of 24 sets of fraternal and identical twins using fMRI. The twins were presented with several sets of images including houses, letters strung together and people's faces. The team used scrambled images which couldn't be recognised as a baseline measurement.

Analysis of brain activity patterns from the twins showed considerably more similarity in the brain activity of identical twins than fraternal twins when they were looking at faces or places. However, the patterns in response to words and letters showed little difference between the two types of twins. These results

suggest that there may well be a strong genetic basis for our response to faces and familiar places, but a less strong genetic link – and therefore probably a stronger environmental impact – for our word recognition. This would make evolutionary sense as we have had hundreds of thousands of years in which it has been very important to recognise other individuals as friends – or enemies – but only a very short time when letters and words have been important to most people.

Cross-cultural studies

Another approach to understanding the impact of nature and nurture on the development of the brain is to look at the way the brain develops in different cultures. One clear example of this is in depth perception. When you look at close objects, less than 30 cm away, information from both eyes falls on the visual cortex. You are effectively seeing the same object from two different angles. Within the visual cortex of your brain, the two images are effectively superimposed to give you a 3-dimensional image. However, when you look at objects which are further away, both eyes see much the same thing so you no longer have detailed stereoscopic vision. Your brain uses other visual clues from the surroundings, as well as past experience, to give you depth perception. As a result you can tell the difference between a cow standing in a field a long distance away and a toy cow on a windowsill relatively close to you. The images of the cows may be much the same size – but other clues and your life experience mean that you 'know' that one animal is big and far away, while the other is small and close to you!

The clues and cues we use to give us depth perception are largely unconscious. We only become aware of how much we depend on them when we are faced with an optical illusion which challenges us. And this is when differences between people raised in different cultures really emerge, suggesting that the brain development that gives us distance perception is the result of our environment rather than innate.

A common definition of culture is that it consists of a system of beliefs shared among a group of people. These beliefs shape the behaviour that is acceptable within the group. The experience of an individual growing up from babyhood to adulthood will depend heavily on the culture of their group – and so scientists can see if this affects the development of the brain.

For example, you may well have come across the Müller–Lyer illusion in puzzle books when you were young (see **fig. 8.3.18**). Look at it again – which of the two vertical lines, X or Y, is longer? Many people in the UK see line Y as longer – although in fact both lines are the same length. People from the Zulu culture of Africa – and other African cultural groups – rarely misjudge the length of the lines. Many scientists believe this is due to cultural differences. In the UK we live in what is sometimes known as a *carpentered world*, full of straight lines and right angles, corners and rectangular buildings. As a result we interpret lines and angles as if they belong in a rectangular room. This is the pattern laid down as our brains develop, and so we interpret the lines in that context – which makes Y look longer than X. However, the Zulu people have a *circular* rather than a carpentered culture. Their homes are circular huts and there are few straight roads or lines. So scientists believe they do not have a 'hard-wired' interpretation of this pattern of lines and so they rarely misjudge the length – they see them as they are. This model suggests that perception of distance is strongly affected by environmental experiences.

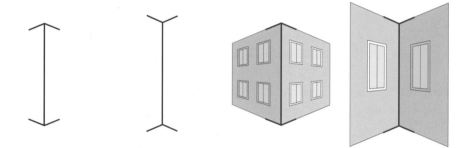

fig. 8.3.18 The Müller–Lyer illusion and the interpretation given to it by people brought up in a carpentered culture.

Other scientists, however, have proposed a different model to explain these observations. Their hypothesis is that the differences in perception are due to differing levels of retinal pigmentation, which in turn affects the ability to detect contours. People with heavier retinal pigmentation are less good at detecting contours and so less likely to be taken in by the illusion. This would explain the Zulu ability to judge the length of the lines correctly. More research is needed, although currently most evidence points to the environmental model of brain development in this area.

Other studies back up the idea of a critical window when depth perception develops. For example, in drawings there are often cues which tell you where objects can be found in relation to each other (see **fig. 8.3.19**).

fig. 8.3.19 Clues to what the boy is pointing at can be found in the picture – but how you interpret them may depend on your age or your cultural background.

In one study it was found that very young children from most cultures find it very difficult to judge distances in a picture such as **fig. 8.3.19**. They would be likely to say that the boy was pointing to the tractor rather than the cow. By the age of 11, most European children interpreted the distance cues correctly and thought the boy was pointing to the cow. However, some 11-year-old African children from particular cultures and non-literate adults whether from Europe or Africa were less likely to pick up the cues to the perspective of the picture, probably through lack of experience. These findings reinforce the model of visual depth perception as something learned as the brain develops if the right environmental clues are in place.

Questions

1 What is meant by the term 'critical window of development' in the brain? Explain how nature and nurture interact during these periods of development.

SC 2 What do you think are the ethical issues involved in using newborn babies in research into brain development?

3 Look at the data in **fig. 8.3.17**.

   a How many severely neglected children were studied?

   b How many of the neglected children studied had brains that fell on or below the bottom 10 percentile in size?

   c How would you explain this effect of severe neglect in terms of the development of the brain?

SC 4 Summarise the main methods by which the relative contributions of nature and nurture to brain development may be studied. For each one discuss the strengths and weaknesses of the method.

Learning and memory 5.8.14, 5.8.15

Another way of considering the impact of nature and nurture on the development of the brain is to look at the changes in the brain during learning, as memories are laid down. Learning is usually observed through changes in behaviour. There are two main types of behaviour, **innate** or **species-characteristic behaviour** and **learned** or **individual-characteristic behaviour**. Both can tell us a considerable amount about the brain and how it works, but there is only space for a very brief overview in this book.

Species-characteristic (innate) behaviour

Innate behaviour is a large collection of responses which are usually seen in every member of a particular species – hence species-characteristic. This type of behaviour is not learned. It is a genetically determined response to a particular stimulus, and it occurs as specific nerve pathways are laid down in the embryo from the instructions of the DNA. Innate behaviour covers an enormous range of types of response, from the simplest avoidance reflexes to highly complex courtship and territorial displays. The stimulus for a piece of innate behaviour will always elicit the same response, which has been selected over generations for its survival value (see **fig. 8.3.20**). Nature is completely dominant in the development of these neural pathways in the brain.

This type of behaviour is important in non-vertebrates which are frequently very short-lived. They do not have time to learn by trial-and-error if they are to successfully complete their life cycles. But even in vertebrates, instinctive behaviour is important both in the young, which have not had time to learn by trial-and-error, and in adults where a ready-made set of responses to a given situation leaves the higher areas of the brain free for more complex learned behaviour.

Individual-characteristic (learned) behaviour

Learned behaviour is an adaptive change in the behaviour of an individual which occurs as the result of experience. An individual learns from an experience, and modifies their behaviour accordingly. An example of learned behaviour is the reaction of a child to touching a hot oven door. The hand will be withdrawn rapidly as a result of a piece of reflex, innate behaviour. But the child will learn from the experience, and is unlikely to touch the door again deliberately. This learning will vary from child to child. Some will only need one experience of the heat to modify their behaviour. Others will try the experiment several times before the change in behaviour is made. Some individuals may not even need to touch the hot door themselves – seeing another child's reaction or being warned by an adult may be enough.

fig. 8.3.20 Innate behaviour does not need to be learned, and is usually important to the survival of the organism. Nature is dominant in the development of these pathways in the brain.

So nurture is important in the way the brain develops and learning takes place in response to the environment. But the ease with which learning takes place is at least in part purely down to genetics (nature).

- **Habituation** occurs when a stimulus is repeated many times and nothing happens – there is neither 'punishment' nor 'reward'. The animal learns to simply ignore the stimulus and make no response. It is not a simple adaptation of the sensory system (see pages 210–13) because once a response is habituated or lost it does not return unless the animal is specifically sensitised. Examples include the way birds learn to ignore a scarecrow and babies learn not to 'startle' at every sudden noise. You will be looking at habituation in more detail on pages 240–1.

- **Conditioned reflexes** are the result of animals learning to associate new stimuli with an existing unconditioned reflex, as in the case of Pavlov's dogs.

- **Trial-and-error (operant) learning** occurs when a piece of trial behaviour is either rewarded (something good happens such as food is found) or punished (something bad happens such as the animal is hurt). If the animal associates the outcome of a piece of behaviour with a reward, that behaviour is likely to be repeated. If the behaviour is associated with punishment, it is less likely to be tried again. The American psychologist B.F. Skinner did a great deal of work on this type of learning using pigeons.

- **Imprinting** is a simple and specialised sort of learning which occurs only in very young animals. At one receptive stage the young animal identifies with another organism, which is usually the parent or, if no parent is available, another large object. It will then follow this object and relate to other similar objects throughout its life.

- **Exploratory (latent) learning** takes place when an animal explores new surroundings and learns them without any immediate reward or punishment. The information may then be useful at another time.

- **Insight learning** is based on thought and reasoning. It is mainly seen in mammals, particularly primates, and is regarded as the highest sort of learning. Once a problem has been solved, the solution is then remembered.

fig. 8.3.21 A pigeon in a Skinner box soon learns to tap on the dot to get a reward of food!

Questions

1 What does innate behaviour tell us about the development of the brain?

2 How can animal behaviour be used to help compare the contributions of nature and nurture to brain development?

Habituation 5.8.14, 5.8.15

Habituation is part of the learning process in almost all animals, including human beings. It is particularly important in the development of young animals, as they learn not to react to the neutral elements in the world around them. Habituation may be relatively short term, or it may become long term so that a response is lost permanently. Memory is a crucial element of learning, and scientists think that habituation is involved in the brain development which takes place as memories are formed, when permanent changes in the synapses take place.

fig. 8.3.22 The sea-slug Aplysia has about 20 000 neurones, some of which are very large. It is a very useful experimental animal, which can be used in investigations into habituation.

Much of the work on habituation has been done on invertebrate organisms such as the nematode worm *Caenorhabditis elegans* and the giant sea slug *Aplysia*.

Aplysia breathes using a gill which is found in a cavity on the upper side of the body, with water passing through and being expelled through a siphon tube at one end. If this siphon is touched, the whole gill is withdrawn into the body cavity as a defence mechanism. However, as the sea slug, unsurprisingly, lives in the sea, the movement of the water constantly stimulates the siphon. The animal learns by habituation not to withdraw its gill every time a wave buffets it.

The mechanism of this habituation can be investigated experimentally. *Aplysia* reared in the laboratory are not habituated to waves or water movement. Eric Kandel was one of many researchers to use this animal to study the nervous system and he performed some classic experiments. He stimulated the siphon of the sea slug with a jet of water which made it withdraw its gill. The stimulation was applied repeatedly. The response of the animal became less and less until eventually water squirted at the siphon had no effect – the gill was not withdrawn at all. The animal had habituated – it had learned to ignore the stimulus. This habituation was retained over time, showing that it was not a simple case of accommodation (see page 210).

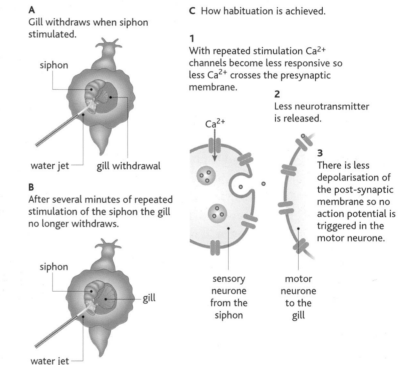

A
Gill withdraws when siphon stimulated.

siphon

water jet — gill withdrawal

B
After several minutes of repeated stimulation of the siphon the gill no longer withdraws.

siphon

gill

water jet —

C How habituation is achieved.

1
With repeated stimulation Ca²⁺ channels become less responsive so less Ca²⁺ crosses the presynaptic membrane.

2
Less neurotransmitter is released.

Ca²⁺

3
There is less depolarisation of the post-synaptic membrane so no action potential is triggered in the motor neurone.

sensory neurone from the siphon

motor neurone to the gill

fig. 8.3.23 Repeated stimulation of the siphon results in habituation – a simple form of learning as the sea slug stops responding to the stimulus.

Kandel then identified the neurones involved in the gill reflex and investigated what happened when the siphon was repeatedly stimulated. He discovered changes in the synapses (see pages 207–9). The calcium channels in the presynaptic membrane become less responsive with repeated stimulations. With fewer calcium channels open, fewer calcium ions cross into the presynaptic knob. As a result, fewer vesicles move to the presynaptic membrane, fuse and discharge their neurotransmitter. With less neurotransmitter available to bind to the post-synaptic membrane, the post-synaptic excitatory potential is not high enough to trigger an action potential – and so there is no response!

Investigating habituation

It is possible to investigate habituation in the school laboratory. Various different organisms can be used to demonstrate this simple form of learning, including worms, snails and even people!

fig. 8.3.24 Investigating habituation in the school laboratory using a giant African land snail.

Habituation in humans

Habituation is an important form of learning in humans, in both the short term and the long term. For example, if you visit someone who lives near a railway line, the first few times a train passes you will be startled or at least aware of the noise. After a few hours, you will no longer notice the trains – you have become habituated. If you don't visit again for some time, your awareness of the trains passing will be reinstated – but

you will habituate more rapidly on your second visit. Habituation is very important in the development of newborn babies who have a number of startle reflexes. These gradually become habituated as the baby grows and matures until they are lost completely. For example, the Moro reflex where a baby arches its back, and throws its arms up and out in a grasping movement if it is startled or its head is lowered suddenly, is fading fast in a normal baby within about 8 weeks of birth, allowing the baby to interact more calmly with the world around it. Modern research suggests that one of the problems for people affected by schizophrenia may be that they do not habituate as readily as other people.

The study of the brain and behaviour continues – we still have enormous amounts to discover about the workings of our own brains!

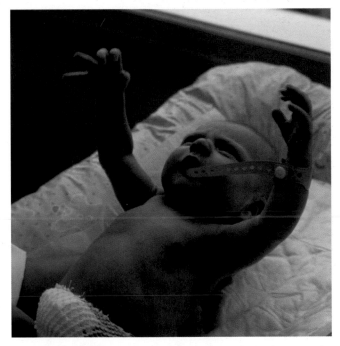

fig. 8.3.25 Habituation plays an important part in the development of a baby's brain – imagine if adults still exhibited a startle reflex like this every time there was a loud noise!

Questions

1 Sea slugs and other similar non-vertebrates can transmit nervous impulses rapidly although they do not have myelinated neurones. Why does this make them such useful experimental animals?

2 How does habituation differ from accommodation and why is this important in the development of the brain?

8.4 Brains, the genome and medicine

The chemical balance of brains 5.8.17, 5.8.18

Communication between the neurones around your body and in your brain depends on a delicate balance of naturally occurring chemicals. The brain uses a number of different neurotransmitters, some of which are found only in brain synapses (e.g. dopamine, serotonin). An imbalance in these transmitters can result in both mental and physical symptoms.

Treating diseases caused by such imbalances means getting drugs across the **blood–brain barrier**. This barrier is formed by the endothelial cells that line the capillaries of the brain which are very tightly joined together. This makes it difficult for bacteria to cross into the brain and cause infections, which is good, but it also makes it difficult to get therapeutic drugs into the brain. Drugs that affect the brain are usually active at the synapses – and there are a number of stages in synaptic transmission where they can be targeted (see **fig. 8.4.1**).

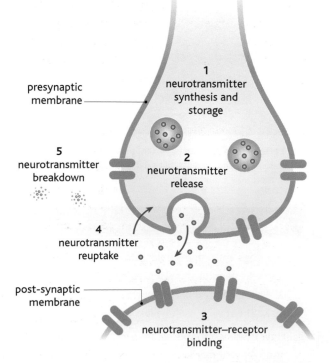

presynaptic membrane

1 neurotransmitter synthesis and storage

5 neurotransmitter breakdown

2 neurotransmitter release

4 neurotransmitter reuptake

post-synaptic membrane

3 neurotransmitter–receptor binding

fig. 8.4.1 The way the brain works depends heavily on the synapses. The five stages of synaptic transmission which are shown here can all be affected by drugs which may cure a problem, or cause one.

Parkinson's disease

Parkinson's disease involves the loss of nerve cells in an area of the midbrain known as the **substantia nigra**. In a healthy brain these cells produce the neurotransmitter dopamine, and the axons from them spread through the frontal cortex, the brain stem and the spinal cord, so they are closely involved in the control and coordination of movement. In Parkinson's disease, these dopamine-producing cells die and motor control is gradually lost. For a long time the brain compensates for the loss – most people don't show symptoms of the disease until around 80% of their dopamine-producing cells have gone.

Parkinson's disease usually develops in people over 50 years old, although it can appear in younger people. The causes are still not clear. In young-onset Parkinson's – which is very rare – there appears to be a relatively strong genetic link. However, in the most common form of Parkinson's disease, the genetic link is much weaker, and other factors are also involved. Environmental triggers may play a part and there may be a link with a number of toxins, herbicides and pesticides. Around 120 000 people in the UK are affected by the condition.

The ways individuals react to the falling levels of dopamine in Parkinson's disease vary. Common symptoms include the following:

- Tremor (shaking) which usually begins in just one hand. This is the first symptom for around 70% of affected people.

- Slowness of movements – it is hard to get started when you want to make a movement, and movements take longer to perform.

- Stiffness (rigidity) of the muscles – this can make it difficult to turn over in bed or stand up after sitting in a chair.

Other problems that arise as the disease progresses may include poor balance, difficulty in walking, problems with sleeping, depression and even difficulties with speech and breathing.

Treating the symptoms

At the moment there is no cure for Parkinson's disease. However, there are a number of drugs which can be very effective at easing or delaying the symptoms. Most of the drugs aim either to replace the natural dopamine in the brain or to allow the body to make the best use of the dopamine it still produces. Treatment can include the following:

*   **Levodopa** (**L-dopa**): dopamine cannot cross the blood–brain barrier, so it cannot be used to treat Parkinson's. However L-dopa is a precursor of dopamine which can cross the barrier and has been in use since the 1960s. Supplying the brain with L-dopa allows the remaining cells to make as much dopamine as possible. This can greatly relieve stiffness and slowness of movements. Eventually it becomes less effective as brain cells continue to die off.

*   **Dopamine agonists**: these chemicals bind to dopamine receptors in brain synapses and mimic the effect of dopamine. They are often used at the beginning of the disease when they are most effective, saving L-dopa for later.

*   **MAOB inhibitors**: in *AS Biology* page 192 you studied the enzyme monoaminoxidase A (MAOA) in the context of genetics and behaviour. Monoaminoxidase B (MAOB) is a similar enzyme which breaks down dopamine in the brain synapses. MAOB inhibitors inhibit this enzyme, reducing the destruction of what little dopamine gets made.

HSW Developing new treatments for Parkinson's disease

Research into possible new drug treatments for Parkinson's disease continues. However there are two more radical areas of research.

Gene therapy

Scientists are using knowledge gained from the results of the Human Genome Project (see *AS Biology* page 98) to help them develop gene therapies. Although Parkinson's disease is not a genetic disease, scientists are investigating the possibility of inserting healthy genes into the affected cells. There are two main approaches: adding genes to prevent the dopamine-producing cells of the midbrain from dying, and adding genes to enhance the levels of dopamine production in the remaining cells. Both approaches have produced some encouraging results. However, there are major problems in delivering the healthy genes to the cells of the midbrain, and safety must be a prime concern, so using gene therapy like this is still some years away.

Stem cell therapy

This research aims to provide a cure for Parkinson's disease rather than a therapy to relieve the symptoms. Scientists are hoping to use embryonic stem cells to replace the failing dopamine-producing cells in the brains of Parkinson's sufferers (*AS Biology* page 180). Current research using mouse models is very promising, but the ethical issues of using embryonic cells remain. There is also the risk in using stem cells that uncontrolled growth and therefore cancer may result. As scientists learn how to stimulate embryonic stem cells to become dopamine-producing cells in the laboratory, it will also provide them with a valuable tool for developing further and possibly more effective drug therapies.

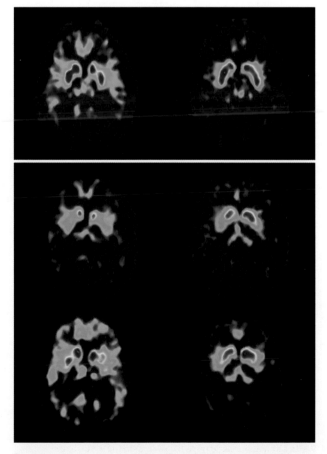

fig. 8.4.2 MRI scans to show the effect of L-dopa treatment. The scans are of a normal brain and then the brain of a Parkinson's sufferer pre- and post-treatment.

Depression

fig. 8.4.3 Depression makes people feel unbearably sad and distant from the people who love them. It drains them of all energy and enthusiasm and can cause tiredness and loss of appetite. It causes both physical and mental symptoms.

Everyone feels fed up or down from time to time, and people often say they are feeling a bit depressed. However, this is *not* true depression which is a serious illness that affects many people during their lives. The causes of depression are complex and are not fully understood. However, one cause may be problems with the neurotransmitter **serotonin** in the brain.

Serotonin is the synaptic transmitter in a group of cells in the brain stem which have axons that spread throughout the brain into the cortex, the cerebellum and the spinal cord. They have a widespread influence, and low levels of serotonin result in fewer nerve impulses travelling around the brain so overall brain activity is suppressed. It has been shown that the serotonin pathways are often abnormal in people suffering from depression. Sometimes depression is triggered as a result of external factors such as work or relationship stress or bereavement. At others it seems to be purely the result of chemical changes in the brain. Serotonin is not the only neurotransmitter implicated in depression. Dopamine and noradrenalin may also play a role in the condition for some people.

HSW Genetics and depression

As a result of research including the Human Genome Project (see *AS Biology* pages 98–9, and pages 248–51), scientists have discovered a gene (5-HTT) which appears to be linked to the production of serotonin in the brain. Evidence suggests that people with the 'short' form of this gene are more likely to suffer depression after stressful life events than people with the 'long' allele. The 20% of the population who are homozygous for the short form seem most likely to experience depression after difficult times in their lives. Heterozygotes appear to have an intermediate risk and those homozygous for the long form have a very low risk of depression. The gene codes for a reuptake protein that enables serotonin to be taken back into the presynaptic membrane after release into the synapse. Although this serotonin reuptake protein is produced whichever form of the gene is inherited, the long form of the gene means more of it is produced. People who have homozygote long forms produce more reuptake proteins than heterozygotes who produce more than homozygous short forms. The data in **fig. 8.4.4** come from an Australian study published in the *British Journal of Psychiatry* in 2006. The study was of a group of students over a 25-year period. The group was relatively small (127 members) but the information collected was detailed and the results support other larger studies.

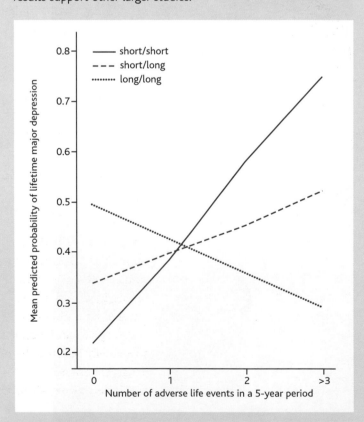

fig. 8.4.4 Effect of number of adverse life events during a 5-year period on mean predicted probability of major depression.

Building a hypothesis

There are some problems when it comes to using this evidence to develop a hypothesis for the causes of depression. The evidence suggests that the more selective serotonin reuptake proteins there are in the presynaptic membrane, the less likely you are to suffer from depression after stressful life events. The role of these proteins is to remove serotonin from the synaptic cleft. This, in turn, limits the stimulation of the post-synaptic membrane without breaking down and destroying the serotonin. Scientists are not sure why a larger number of these proteins reduce the risk of stress-related depression.

The most successful treatment for depression is the use of SSRIs (see below) which block these reuptake proteins and raise the levels of serotonin in the synapse, increasing the levels of post-synaptic action potentials. So the working of the therapeutic drugs does not seem to match the apparent role of the reuptake proteins. There is still a lot of research to be done before we fully understand the biochemical basis of depression and how it may be treated and avoided.

Treating depression

Treatment for depression includes 'talking therapies', which can help a patient come to terms with adverse life events, and the use of drugs. Many of these drugs are linked to the serotonin synapse systems and other neurotransmitters. Some of the best-known antidepressant drugs are the SSRIs (selective serotonin reuptake inhibitors). These drugs inhibit the reuptake proteins in the presynaptic membrane, so that more serotonin remains in the synaptic cleft, more impulses travel along the post-synaptic axon and the result is relief of symptoms such as a lifting of the mood and an improved ability to sleep.

Other treatments also involve neurotransmitters. **Tricyclic antidepressants (TCAs)** work by increasing the levels of serotonin and noradrenalin in the brain, while **monoaminoxidase inhibitors** (like the MAOB used in treating Parkinson's disease) inhibit the enzymes which usually cause the breakdown of neurotransmitters in the synapses of the brain.

Illegal drugs and the brain

Drugs such as L-dopa and SSRIs can have a clear and measurable effect on the way your brain works. These drugs are therapeutic and legal. Other drugs are enjoyable and legal, such as the caffeine from coffee, tea, colas or energy drinks. Caffeine crosses the blood–brain barrier and affects the brain in a number of ways which include slowing down the rate of dopamine reabsorption at dopamine synapses. But there are some drugs which are used specifically because they have an impact on the way the brain works. These drugs are often illegal. One which is widely used is **ecstasy (MDMA or 3,4-methylenedioxy-*N*-methylamphetamine)**.

fig. 8.4.5 Ecstasy tablets – illegal drugs which have a marked effect on the working of the serotonin synapses in the brain.

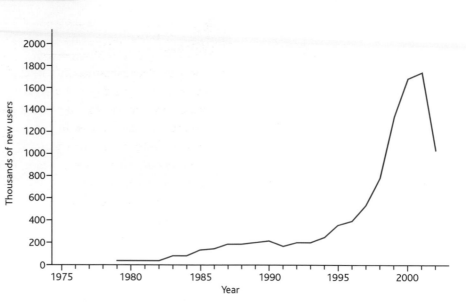

fig. 8.4.6 Ecstasy use increased dramatically through the 1990s, although few of the people using it understood the biological basis of the effect the chemical had on their brains.

Ecstasy has a marked effect on the brain. It acts as a stimulant, increasing the heart rate, rather like amphetamine, and also as a psychotropic drug which alters the way a person 'sees' the world. So the short-term effects of the drug are to change the mood, making people feel happy, sociable, full of energy, warm and empathetic. The drug brings about these changes by affecting the serotonin synapses of the brain.

Serotonin has a major effect on the way the brain works. Depression seems to be the result of too little serotonin in some way. Ecstasy blocks the serotonin reuptake transport system so that the synapses are completely flooded with serotonin, which cannot be returned to the presynaptic knob. There is also some evidence that the drug makes the transport system work in reverse, so that all of the serotonin in the presynaptic knob is moved out into the synapse which affects the post-synaptic membrane and floods the brain with impulses. Ecstasy may also affect the dopamine systems, with the high levels of serotonin stimulating the release of more dopamine, adding to the pleasure sensation, but there is some debate among scientists about whether this is really the case.

Using ecstasy causes physical changes, such as increased heart rate, and can cause problems in the body's thermoregulatory system. There may be no desire to drink which can lead to hyperthermia (overheating) with raised blood pressure and irregular heartbeat. In a small number of cases this can lead to death. Ecstasy can also affect the hypothalamus so that it secretes more antidiuretic hormone, which is normally secreted when the body needs to conserve water. This effectively stops the kidneys from producing urine and can lead to problems if someone keeps drinking water in an attempt to stay hydrated and cool down. They retain so much water that osmosis destroys their cells. This is what killed Leah Betts in 1995.

HSW Long-term brain damage from ecstasy

There are clear indications that the use of ecstasy can cause long-term damage to the brain. Scientific evidence appears to show that ecstasy can cause permanent damage to the serotonin neurones. Classic research using scans of the brain of non-drug users and long-term ecstasy users showed that the serotonin-linked areas of the ecstasy users have a greatly reduced ability to bind with the serotonin in normal conditions.

fig. 8.4.7 The difference in the serotonin uptake in the brain between a non-drug user (top) and someone who has used ecstasy regularly (bottom) looks very clear in scans like these. However, some scientists claim that this difference is an artefact of the scanning process.

A Dutch study published by the *British Journal of Psychiatry* in 2008 used MRI scans and other brain imaging techniques to show that long-term ecstasy use appears to cause both damage to, and loss of, serotonin axons in the thalamus and lower than normal levels of serotonin in the cerebral cortex. The study used 71 individuals with a broad variation in drug use.

Some studies, however, have found no adverse effects from long-term drug use. A team at the University of East London found ecstasy users outperformed non-drug users at some tests. Some of the very influential early research was carried out on squirrel monkeys, and there are arguments that monkey brains are in many ways different from human brains. Because the drugs are illegal, some scientists have suggested there is a bias towards research which shows adverse effects. However, ecstasy is now being investigated for possible therapeutic use.

Questions

1 Explain how a drug affecting each of the five stages of neurotransmission would have an effect on how nerve impulses are transmitted and what this might mean in the body.

2 Explain the difference between dopamine and serotonin synapses and their roles in the body.

3 Compare the action of the drugs L-dopa and ecstasy on the brain and their impact on human health.

 4 Describe the working hypothesis which explains the results of **fig. 8.4.4**. How does the evidence on the effectiveness of SSSRIs in treating depression undermine this hypothesis? Suggest further investigations which might help to clarify the situation in the brain during depression.

The human genome and medicine 5.8.19

The Human Genome Project set out to identify all of the genes in the human chromosomes and to sequence the 3 billion base pairs which make up the human DNA (*AS Biology* pages 98–9). It was an international project and the DNA samples came from a group of volunteers. Samples were then chosen anonymously and at random for analysis.

The project also had specific aims about the storage and analysis of all the data involved, with the ideal that all of the information about the genome should be freely available to scientists everywhere. Consideration of the ethical, legal and social issues, which are inevitably raised when such personal genetic information is unravelled, was also part of the brief. The Human Genome Project demonstrated that every individual has at least 99.9% of their DNA in common!

Following on from this initial work another massive international project was set up in 2008. The 1000 Genomes Project will analyse and compare the DNA of at least a thousand people from around the word, seeking to provide as much information as possible on biomedically relevant variations. And as before, the information will be made freely available to scientists around the globe.

Pharmacogenomics

The ability to find and manufacture a medicine which has the right effect in the right place is of vital importance in the fight against disease. Think of the impact of antibiotics – many infectious bacterial diseases that were life-threatening 70 years ago are treated easily with a course of antibiotics today.

New medicines are currently developed from existing chemicals, often those extracted from plants (*AS Biology* page 222). However, increasingly detailed knowledge of the human genome has opened up a number of new and potentially exciting advances in different areas of drug development. Each individual – apart from identical twins – is genetically unique. Until now, drugs have been produced to suit the majority of people. In the future it may be possible

to tailor drugs to suit both individuals and particular ethnic groups with susceptibilities to specific diseases. This could help the drugs work more efficiently, in lower doses, with fewer side effects. The new science of **pharmacogenomics** has been developed to link pharmaceutical expertise with knowledge of the human genome.

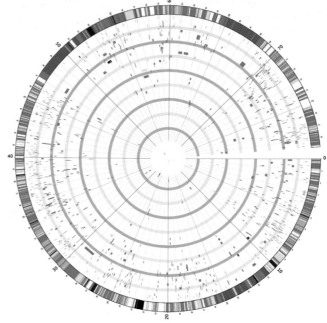

fig. 8.4.8 This is one representation of just a small part of the complex information resulting from the Human Genome Project. Pharmacogenomics aims to take information like this and use it to make more effective medicines for us all.

Genetic factors have a marked effect on the efficiency of some drugs. For example, when a relatively new group of pain relievers called kappa-opioids was first tested, the drugs did not seem as effective as the more commonly used opioids such as morphine and codeine. The initial tests were done mainly on men. However, later research has shown that they are very effective painkillers for women! The genetic makeup of the patient makes all the difference to the way the drug works. Pale-skinned, red-haired women are more responsive to common painkillers than anyone else and ibuprofen has little or no effect on pain relief in women during the second half of their menstrual cycle. More detailed knowledge of our individual genetics could have enormous benefits in terms of drug development.

Scientists expect that pharmacogenomics will also produce much more powerful drugs because the medicines they design can be exactly targeted to specific diseases or to changes in the proteins or genetic material of the cells. Knowing the fine details of the human genome make it easier to produce medicines that affect pathogens or cancer cells but do not damage healthy body cells.

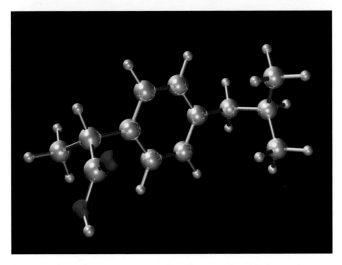

fig. 8.4.9 Ibuprofen – a common pain reliever and anti-inflammatory drug that is less effective for women at some stages of their menstrual cycle.

Using the Human Genome Project to find genome targets for particular diseases could make it possible to isolate a suitable drug candidate more rapidly. Advances such as these could be of enormous benefit, making it possible to treat more diseases, and to treat them more effectively.

Choosing the right drug

The outcomes of the Human Genome Project have the potential to save the NHS a great deal of money by making it much easier to prescribe the right drug for a patient at the right dosage. This has important implications. A study carried out in two large hospitals in Merseyside in 2004 looked at the causes of the admissions of 18 820 hospital patients. The research team found that 1225 admissions were due to adverse drug reactions – 6.5% of all the admissions – and the median stay in hospital was 8 days. More than 20 people in this study died as a result of an adverse drug reaction – around 1000 lose their lives in this way every year in the UK. Based on this research, the average cost to the NHS each year of adverse drug reactions is around £466 million pounds, using 4% of the total

bed capacity. And that doesn't take into account the impact of these problems, which can lead to permanent damage to organs such as the kidneys, on the individuals and their families in terms of lost earnings and quality of life. Access to a patient's genome could help doctors prescribe medication which will work with rather than against their patients' cells, reducing the chance of adverse reactions.

fig. 8.4.10 There are many different types of drugs for hundreds of different conditions, all made for anyone who needs them. In future you may well have tailor-made drugs just for you – and no risk of an adverse reaction.

Choosing the right dosage

Currently drug dosage usually depends on the age or weight of a person. Genetic information about individuals could allow doctors to understand just how rapidly a patient's body will respond to and excrete a particular medicine. Many people could have much lower doses of medicines, while those who need it could be given higher doses.

One of the few examples of where pharmacogenomics is being used now is in screening patients for drugs trials. It has been discovered that the cytochrome P450 gene codes for certain liver enzymes that break down many different types of drugs so they can be eliminated from the body. Variants of the gene mean some people have less active or even inactive forms of these enzymes, so they are particularly vulnerable to a drug overdose. Before anyone is accepted as part of a clinical trial for a new medicine, they are given genetic tests to see which form of cytochrome P450 genes they have to ensure it is as safe as possible for them to take part in the trial.

fig. 8.4.11 It will be society which will ultimately decide if pharmacogenetics becomes mainstream. That decision will be based on the understanding – or misunderstanding – of science, ethics and economics by individuals.

A number of issues will have an impact on how far and how quickly the new science of pharmacogenomics goes. Many of these issues have social, moral and ethical implications as well as scientific ones – which makes them all the harder to resolve. Below are some of these issues for you to consider:

- Identifying genes which affect the response to a particular drug is currently difficult, time consuming and expensive. There are a lot of drugs – and more to be discovered. There may be more than one gene involved in the way the human body responds to any particular drug. The interactions of genotypes and drugs are very complex. Is the potential benefit worth the financial investment society needs to make? But if we have the ability to do this, is it moral or ethical not to try?

- There are some tough economics to consider. At the moment the big pharmaceutical companies develop one or two drugs to treat any particular disease which are effective for most people. This 'one size fits all' approach has so far worked reasonably well. What if 75% of the population can be treated successfully with one drug, but five different drugs would be needed to provide the remaining 25% of the population with effective treatment? An absolutist standpoint would be that if appropriate drugs for an individual can be made available, they should be, regardless. A relativist position would be that costs and benefits have to be weighed in the balance, and the money used to develop a drug to treat a small number of people could be more effectively used elsewhere. Eventually society will decide – and economics are bound to be part of that decision-making process.

fig. 8.4.12 Pharmaceutical companies are businesses. It takes millions of pounds and years of research to develop one new drug (*AS Biology* pages 222–7), and the economics of pharmacogenomics just might not work.

- It may well be possible to tell people a particular drug won't work for their particular genetic makeup before alternatives are available. Is it ethical to leave people with certain genetic variations with no treatment available to them? But is it moral or ethical to give them a drug knowing it will have no effect?

- There are huge financial implications in training doctors and pharmacists to recognise all the possible drug permutations, and keeping them up to date. This has big financial implications for society – but deciding not to do it would be an ethical minefield.

- To have medical treatments tailored to the exact genetic profile of an individual means everyone will need to have their genome analysed and stored. However, there has been considerable opposition to a DNA database for use in fighting crime or overcoming immigration issues. For pharmacogenomics to have any future a DNA database becomes vital – but once it is in place it would surely be used in criminal investigations too. Society needs to have the ethical debate to decide if this is the route they want to follow *before* too great an investment is made in the science of pharmacogenomics. The potential benefits are enormous – but there are potential hazards as well.

fig. 8.4.13 Some people see a DNA database as an infringement of their civil liberties – but it is vital for pharmacogenomics to work.

HSW A 'heart disease' gene and pharmacogenomics

In early 2000 an international team of scientists published a paper revealing evidence of a genetic mutation that greatly increases the risk of an individual developing heart disease. Across the world, around 1 person in 100 carries this mutation, but on the Indian sub-continent that figure rises to 1 in 25 people. The mutation affects the formation of a specific heart protein. The mutation doesn't usually cause problems until people reach middle age – the bodies of younger people deal with the rogue protein and destroy it. As people get older this mechanism stops working and levels of the mutated protein build up. This begins to affect the way the heart functions until the risk of developing heart disease is seven times higher than for an unaffected individual. Scientists suggest this means that heart problems are almost inevitable for people with the mutation. People have no idea that they carry the mutation at the stage when they are having children, so there is no selection pressure to prevent it being passed on.

At the moment, nothing can be done to overcome the impact of this mutation. But pharmacogenomics may well be the route to a solution. By working with the faulty genes it may be possible to devise a treatment that will neutralise the rogue protein as people get older. With suitable tests, treatment could begin as the body's own breakdown mechanism begins to fail. Alternatively, a drug might be developed that blocks the production of the protein by interacting with the transcription process of the faulty gene. No one yet knows how this potential health timebomb is going to be successfully tackled but it certainly seems likely that pharmacogenomics will play a part. And because so many people are affected, it will certainly be worth pharmaceutical companies investing the time and money needed to develop a pharmacogenomically active drug.

fig. 8.4.14 The WHO have projected that by 2010, 60% of heart disease in the world will be found in India.

Questions

1 The science of pharmacogenetics depends on the outcomes of the Human Genome Project. Why?

2 What are the main potential benefits of pharmacogenomics?

SC 3 Summarise the main social, moral and ethical issues that are raised by pharmacogenomics. Describe at least two different positions that can be taken with respect to each point you raise.

SC 4 Using this resource and others, investigate and describe two new medical treatments that depend on pharmacogenomics for their development.

Drugs from genetically modified organisms 5.8.20, 5.8.21

Pharmacogenomics is an area of drug development and medical treatment that still has a long way to go before it is in regular use. In *AS Biology* pages 122–5 you discovered how organisms can be genetically modified by the insertion of a desired gene. Our growing knowledge of the human genome is already being used in the development of genetically modified organisms to produce medicines and vaccines to treat human conditions, but this science too is still in its infancy.

Microorganisms – the genetic engineer's friend

Microorganisms are the most commonly used organisms in genetic modification for a number of reasons. They are relatively easy and cheap to culture, and because they reproduce so rapidly a transferred gene is copied very rapidly when the microorganisms are allowed to replicate in ideal conditions. It is very important to be able to tell which bacteria contain the desired, recombinant piece of DNA. As one bacterium looks very like another, scientists transfer special marker genes along with the desired DNA that make it easy to pick out those microorganisms in which a successful transformation has taken place. These markers are often characteristics such as antibiotic resistance. The bacteria identified by the markers (see **fig. 8.4.15**) can then be cultured on a large scale in industrial fermenters, and the proteins which they make harvested. One major perceived risk of these microorganisms is that if they spread into the environment they carry genes for antibiotic resistance with them.

There is an ever-growing number of chemicals made by genetically engineered organisms. They include antibiotics such as penicillin, hormones such as growth hormone and enzymes.

fig. 8.4.15 Plating cultures of bacteria on agar containing the relevant antibiotics makes it possible to identify the genetically modified microorganisms containing the marked, genetically engineered plasmid, because they are the only ones that are able to survive.

Microorganisms and human insulin

As you saw in *AS Biology* page 180, people with type 1 diabetes cannot make the insulin needed for their bodies to work properly. Everyone with type 1 diabetes and some people who have type 2 diabetes (see page 169) need regular injections of insulin to keep them healthy.

The source of insulin for people with diabetes used to be the pancreases of slaughtered pigs, sheep and cattle. Although the insulin from these animals is similar to human insulin, it is not quite the same. This caused problems for some patients because their immune systems reacted to the foreign antigens on the animal insulin. Also the supply of insulin was not always reliable, because it depended on how many animals were slaughtered.

So biotechnology was used to develop a way of manufacturing human insulin using microorganisms. The process was difficult because the insulin molecule is made up of two polypeptide chains. To tackle this problem, scientists in the 1980s managed to introduce a synthesised gene for each chain into different bacteria, which were then cultured in huge numbers. The mixture from the giant fermenters needs **downstream processing** – the microorganisms and the desired end products have to be separated from the rest of the mixture. This produces two pure protein chains which are then oxidised to join them together. The resulting chemical, often referred to as humulin, appears to function exactly like human insulin. Its purity is guaranteed, making it easier to calculate doses accurately. It has been a great advantage for the majority of people with diabetes. Even more recently, a synthetic gene has been developed that mimics the normal human gene for insulin and allows proinsulin

to be made by just one type of engineered bacteria. At the end of the process, enzymes convert proinsulin to insulin.

Using microorganisms in this way removes the problems of uncertain supply and provides a constant, convenient and pure source of a human hormone. This is a clear example of the way genetic engineering and the new biotechnology have had a positive effect in human medicine.

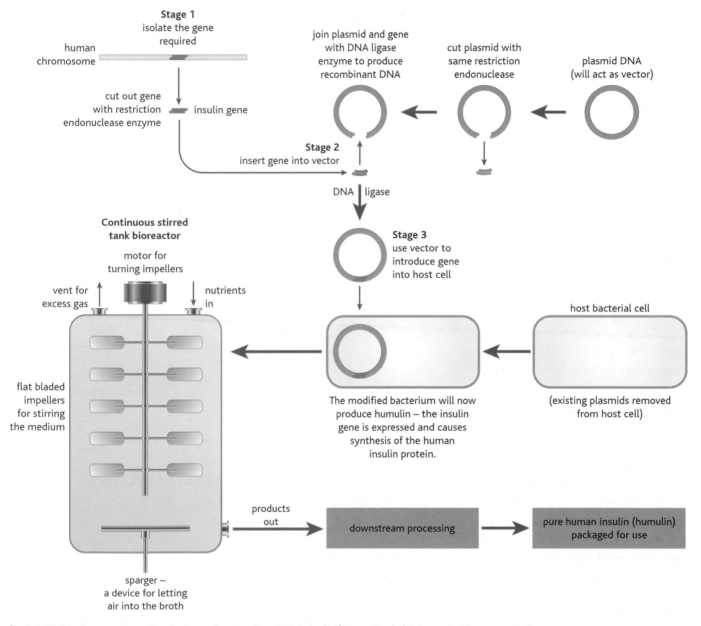

fig. 8.4.16 This diagram summaries the type of process by which humulin (human insulin) is harvested from genetically modified bacteria. The production of any drugs from genetically modified microorganisms is similar to this process.

For most parents, the birth of a baby is followed by years of pleasure and amazement at the way their offspring grow. But some children grow so slowly that it needs to be investigated. They may lack **growth hormone** (GH) or **somatotrophin**, the hormone secreted by the pituitary gland which stimulates growth.

For many years the problem was overcome by giving children regular injections of pituitary extract, made from pituitary glands taken from human cadavers. The extract was expensive and always in short supply. Genetic engineering has solved the problem of supply. The hormone can now be produced in commercial amounts by genetically modified microorganisms.

However, the solution came too late for some unfortunate children. Lack of care in the extraction of the pituitary glands led to contamination of the drug by brain tissue from individuals who had died as a result of the very rare Creutzfeldt–Jakob disease, a fatal brain disease that has been linked to BSE (bovine spongiform encephalopathy, or 'mad cow disease') in cattle. Sadly, some people were treated with contaminated pituitary extract before the new hormone was produced by genetically modified microorganisms, and they died of the disease. People sometimes express concern about the risks of using genetically modified organisms in medicines or food. It is wise to remember that risks can come from a wide variety of sources, and that genetically modified organisms can also reduce some of these risks.

Banana vaccines?

Genetically modified microorganisms have been fantastically successful at making certain human proteins such as insulin. However, prokaryotes simply do not possess the biochemistry to make some of the more complex human proteins, and so work has moved on to introduce desirable human genes into eukaryotic cells including yeast, and more recently plants and even mammals.

There are hopes that transgenic plants may become an important weapon in the worldwide fight against disease. Vaccination is a tried and tested way of eliminating serious diseases. However, the challenge in

less economically developed countries is that vaccines can be relatively expensive and so the countries cannot afford them. They usually require storing in a fridge and there may be cultural and practical difficulties with both getting to healthcare workers and allowing them to vaccinate children. Nevertheless, if plants or plant products such as bananas, potatoes or carrots can be genetically modified to carry vaccines to human diseases such as infant diarrhoea or hepatitis B, then many of these problems are solved in one go. The plants can be grown by the communities that need them, they are relatively cheap, there is no need for cool storage and there is no need for trained healthcare workers to be available for the children to be protected from deadly diseases. Trials are already in place in the US and China and bananas are emerging as a prime candidate as plant medicines, particularly for hepatitis B vaccines.

fig. 8.4.17 With around 350 million people already infected with hepatitis B worldwide, bananas could be the future of vaccination – a great alternative to a hypodermic needle in many different ways!

Making transgenic plants

Introducing genes from one type of plant into another, or even from an animal into a plant, is usually achieved using the bacterium *Agrobacterium tumefaciens*. *A. tumefaciens* causes tumours in plants which are known as crown galls. It contains a plasmid called the Ti plasmid which transfers bacterial genetic information directly into the plant DNA. It is this which normally causes abnormal growth of the plant cells, but modified plasmids can be used to carry beneficial genes into the plant genome. Then, by the process of plant cloning (*AS Biology* page 170), the modified transgenic cells can be used to produce whole new transgenic plants.

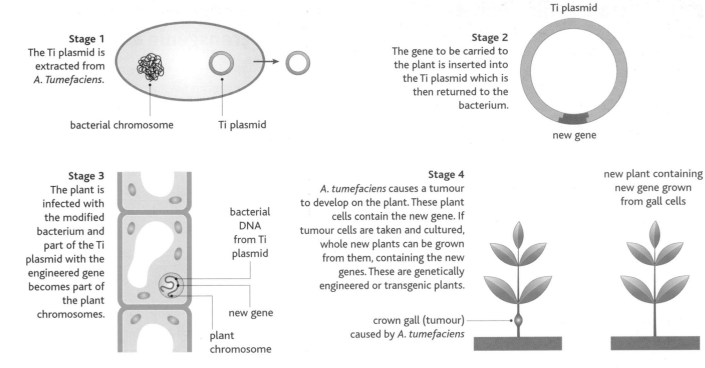

Stage 1
The Ti plasmid is extracted from *A. Tumefaciens.*

bacterial chromosome Ti plasmid

Stage 2
The gene to be carried to the plant is inserted into the Ti plasmid which is then returned to the bacterium.

Ti plasmid

new gene

Stage 3
The plant is infected with the modified bacterium and part of the Ti plasmid with the engineered gene becomes part of the plant chromosomes.

bacterial DNA from Ti plasmid

new gene

plant chromosome

Stage 4
A. tumefaciens causes a tumour to develop on the plant. These plant cells contain the new gene. If tumour cells are taken and cultured, whole new plants can be grown from them, containing the new genes. These are genetically engineered or transgenic plants.

new plant containing new gene grown from gall cells

crown gall (tumour) caused by *A. tumefaciens*

fig. 8.4.18 This is the method by which transgenic plants are created.

HSW Choices for society

There are some concerns that using transgenic plants poses risks for the environment. Just as in genetically modified bacteria, scientists usually include marker genes in genetically modified plants to make it easy to identify them. These marker genes may include alleles which ensure the plant is infertile, so that the plants cannot reproduce and fresh supplies of transgenic plants have to be bought each time they are needed. This is more of a concern where food crops are involved than where plants are being modified to use as medicines, but some of the same issues arise. Also, if some of the transgenic traits got into the wild population there might be issues of immunity developing to certain treatments. Some people worry about taking in alien DNA in genetically modified food plants. They forget that we eat many different types of DNA every day – and when the genetically modified food contains vital medicines, for many people the risk/benefit balance shifts dramatically.

At the moment the use of transgenic plants in medicine is relatively new and unknown – so concerns about risks in the general population are at a low level. Perhaps if the technology becomes more widely used, or the media coverage becomes negative, worries will grow!

Genetically modified animals

It is very difficult to transfer new DNA into eukaryotic cells but there have already been some notable successes. Some of the most exciting and recent research involving genetic engineering has been the work on inserting human genes into the tissues of sheep and cattle to produce transgenic animals. In 1991 the first transgenic sheep was born, a ewe called Tracey who produced the human protein alpha-1-antitrypsin (AAT) in her milk. This protein is missing in people who suffer from a genetic condition that affects their livers and lungs, causing emphysema to develop at a very early age. The production of proteins using **transgenic animals** involves the introduction of a copy of a human gene which codes for the desired protein into the genetic material of an egg of a different animal species. As well as the gene for the specific protein there is also a promoter sequence which makes sure the gene will be expressed in the mammary gland of the lactating female. The fertilised and transgenic embryo is then replaced inside a surrogate mother, is born and grows to maturity. When the animal is mature and produces milk, that milk is harvested, purified and the human protein extracted.

Making transgenic animals

There are a number of techniques for getting new DNA into mammalian cells, which are being tried with varying degrees of success. Whatever technique is used it must get the new DNA through the cell membrane and into the cytoplasm – or nucleus – where it can be accepted and incorporated into the host cell DNA. The methods include the following:

- **Microinjection** (DNA injection) where DNA is injected into a cell through a very fine micropipette. This is manipulated using a micromanipulator, because the steadiest hand would tremble enough to destroy the cell. The method is rather hit and miss – many cells have to be injected before one takes up the DNA successfully, but it is the method that has resulted in many of the best known transgenic animals – for example, Tracey.

- **Microprojectiles** – DNA is shot into the cell at high speed carried on minute gold or tungsten pellets. Some cells survive this treatment and accept the DNA.

- A harmless virus can be engineered to carry a desirable gene and then used to infect the animal's cells, carrying the DNA with it.

- **Liposome wrapping** – the gene to be inserted is wrapped in liposomes (spheres formed from a lipid bilayer). These fuse with the cell membrane and can pass through it to deliver the DNA into the cytoplasm.

So far transgenic sheep, cows, pigs, rabbits and mice have been produced, all capable of producing human proteins in their milk. Using large animals such as cows and sheep, large volumes of milk – and therefore human proteins – can be achieved, and the animals can be increased by breeding or cloning.

fig. 8.4.19 The pharmaceutical factory of tomorrow? Transgenic animals could be the way ahead for the treatment of a number of serious and debilitating human illnesses.

Examples of drugs from transgenic animals

More than 20 different human proteins have been produced so far from transgenic animals, and some of them are already in therapeutic use or are being trialled.

- Factor VII and Factor IX are both important components of the human blood clotting cascade which can be missing in haemophilia and other blood clotting diseases. These factors are being harvested from transgenic milk.

- Alpha-1-antitrypsin is the protein produced by Tracey. The milk of such transgenic sheep contains up to 35 g of human protein in every litre, a very high yield. The milk is very expensive – it costs several thousand pounds per litre. Trials are underway on treatment using the transgenic protein and the idea is that as the numbers of transgenic animals increase, the price will eventually come down. However, there have been major problems with developing these products commercially. Most of the transgenic sheep were destroyed when the company that produced them hit financial difficulties.

- Activated protein C for treating deep vein thrombosis and modified milk for people with lactose and other intolerances are also being tested.

As we unravel the mysteries of the human genome in ever more detail, we should come to know the genetic sequence of every chemical in our body. If many of our faulty molecules can be made for us by transgenic animals, the impact on future health and medicine could be enormous.

HSW Ethical issues

There are many benefits to using genetically modified organisms to produce drugs both for humans and for animals. However, there are some aspects of this work which are controversial and raise a number of ethical issues. As with genetically modified food, there are concerns about the safety of these products both for the humans that use them and for the animals that are used to produce them. Environmental concerns about gene transfer to wild species are also very much present.

Another area of real concern is the fact that this type of technology will be the property of just a few companies in developed countries. The new advances may be largely biased towards the needs of the richer countries – although the work on plant-based vaccines tends to negate that fear.

Some people have strong objections to the use of animals and other organisms in this way and feel that genetic modification violates the rights of the organism modified.

These are just some of the areas of concern which have been raised and discussed – there are others. However, there are many people who feel that the enormous benefits these developments may bring in medical treatments far outweigh any risks or ethical stumbling blocks which may arise.

fig. 8.4.20 One of the big concerns about genetically modified crops is that the organisms used to produce the drugs or food will interbreed with wild organisms and cause untold damage to the environment.

Questions

1 Produce a flow diagram to explain the process by which a drug is made using a genetically modified bacterium.

SC 2 Identify two ethical positions on the use of genetically modified bacteria in the production of drugs.

3 a Compare the production of a drug from a genetically modified plant with that from a genetically modified microorganism.

   b What are the risks and benefits of using genetically modified plants to produce vaccines?

SC 4 Investigate the use of genetically modified animals to produce human medicines. Select one drug and evaluate the success of this process so far.

SC 5 Discuss the risks and benefits associated with the use of genetically modified organisms (other than the transgenic animals described in your answer to question 4) in the production of drugs and for other purposes, using examples from this text and from your own research.

1   The diagram below shows one type of mammalian neurone.

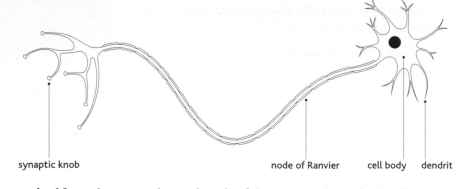

synaptic knob   node of Ranvier   cell body   dendrit

   a   i   Name the type and state the role of the neurone shown in the diagram.

                                                                              (2)

       ii   Describe the direction in which an impulse would travel.   **(1)**

   b   State precisely where in the central nervous system the cell body of this type
          of neurone is found and explain the importance of the dendrites.   **(2)**

   c   Describe the node of Ranvier and explain its importance in the neurone.**(3)**

                                                                   (Total 8 marks)

SC 2   Give an account of the role of pigments in the detection of light by flowering
           plants and animals.   **(Total 10 marks)**

   3   The graph below shows the effect of light intensity on the area of the pupil in
       the human eye.

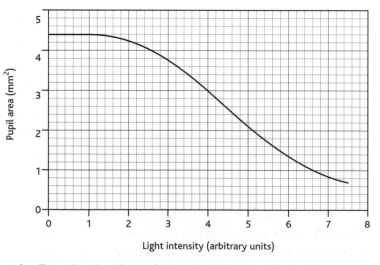

   a   i   Describe the effect of changing light intensity on the area of the pupil.

                                                                              (1)

       ii   Explain how the muscles in the eye bring about this change.   **(2)**

b Change in area of the pupil is controlled by a reflex action.

   i In this pupil reflex, name the receptor and the effector. **(1)**

   ii Explain why the pupil reflex still occurs in an unconscious person. **(1)**

c Atropine is used to dilate the pupil to allow the eye to be examined more easily.

Atropine inhibits the activity of acetylcholine. Suggest how atropine causes this inhibition. **(2)**

d The diagram shows a light-sensitive cell from the eye. The activity of the cell in the **dark** is shown.

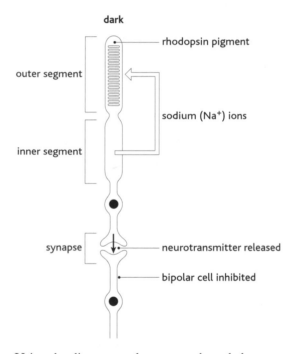

dark

rhodopsin pigment

outer segment

sodium (Na⁺) ions

inner segment

synapse — neurotransmitter released

bipolar cell inhibited

Using the diagram and your own knowledge, explain how light causes the depolarisation of the bipolar cell. **(5)**

(Total 12 marks)

4 There is much debate about the reasons for variation in human characteristics. One source of evidence in this 'nature and nurture' debate is provided by studies of identical (monozygotic or MZ) twins.

In one study, which involved 69 pairs of identical twins, 50 pairs of the twins had been brought up together since birth and 19 pairs of the twins had been brought up apart since birth. The height, body mass and intelligence (IQ) of each twin was measured and the difference between each pair was determined for each characteristic.

The table below shows the mean differences between the pairs of twins.

Characteristic	Mean difference	
	50 pairs of identical twins brought up together	19 pairs of identical twins brought up apart
Height (cm)	1.7	1.8
Body mass (kg)	1.9	4.5
Intelligence (IQ)	3.1	6.0

a Explain what these figures suggest about the effects of nature and nurture on these three characteristics. **(3)**

b Suggest **two** reasons why the conclusions drawn from the data above should be treated with caution. **(2)**

(Total 5 marks)

5 Parkinson's disease leads to the gradual loss of balance and movement, often with muscle tremors. This disease is believed to be caused by a lack of the neurotransmitter dopamine in parts of the brain. The disease can be treated with the drug L-dopa.

a Explain why the lack of dopamine leads to the symptoms of Parkinson's disease. **(2)**

b Suggest why L-dopa, rather than dopamine, is used for the treatment of patients with Parkinson's disease. **(1)**

c Multiple sclerosis is a disease that causes patches of inflammation in the brain. State the name of an imaging technique and describe how the images could be used to establish which parts of the brain have been damaged in a patient with multiple sclerosis. **(3)**

(Total 6 marks)

Index